Collect **British** Stamps

A Stanley Gibbons checklist
of the stamps of Great Britain

Collect **British** *Stamps*

61st Edition
2010

Stanley Gibbons Limited
London and Ringwood

By Appointment to Her Majesty The Queen
Stanley Gibbons Ltd, London
Philatelists

Published by Stanley Gibbons Ltd
Editorial, Publications Sales Offices
and Distribution Centre:
7 Parkside, Christchurch Road, Ringwood,
Hants BH24 3SH

© Stanley Gibbons Ltd 2010

British Library Cataloguing in
Publication Data.
A catalogue record for this book is available
from the British Library.

Errors and omissions excepted. The colour
reproduction of stamps is only as accurate as
the printing process will allow.

ISBN-10: 0-85259-736-6
ISBN-13: 978-0-85259-736-1

Item No. R0289-10

Printed by Piggott Black Bear, Cambridge

Contents

The 2010 Edition

Over **FOUR Million** copies of *Collect British Stamps* have been sold to date! From the famous Penny Black of 1840 to the absorbing new issues of today, stamps of Great Britain are extremely popular with collectors young and old. *Collect British Stamps* has been one of our flagship publications since the First Edition of this checklist in September 1967. This 61st edition has been redesigned inside and out, and includes all recent issues up to and including Christmas 2009. Prices have been reviewed and revised to reflect today's market.

Collect British Stamps appears in the autumn of each year: for a more detailed listing, the *Great Britain Concise Catalogue* is published in the spring incorporating many additional features and is ideal for the collector who needs more information about GB stamps. An at-a-glance guide to the Stanley Gibbons' Catalogues can be found on page xliii.

Scope. Collect British Stamps comprises:

◆ All stamps with different watermark (wmk) or perforation (perf).

◆ Visible plate numbers on the Victorian issues.

◆ Graphite-lined and phosphor issues, including variations in the numbers of phosphor bands.

◆ First Day Covers for Definitives from 1936, Regionals and all Special Issues.

◆ Presentation, Gift and Souvenir Packs.

◆ Post Office Yearbooks.

◆ Regional issues and War Occupation stamps of Guernsey and Jersey.

◆ Postage Due and Official Stamps.

◆ Post Office Picture Cards (PHQ cards).

◆ Commemorative gutter pairs and 'Traffic Light' gutter pairs listed as mint sets.

◆ Royal Mail Postage Labels priced as sets and on P.O. First Day Cover.

Stamps of the independent postal administrations of Guernsey, Isle of Man and Jersey are contained in *Collect Channel Islands and Isle of Man Stamps*.

Layout

Stamps are set out chronologically by date of issue. In the catalogue lists the first numeral is the Stanley Gibbons catalogue number; the black (boldface) numeral alongside is the type number referring to the respective illustration. A blank in this column implies that the number immediately above is repeated. The denomination and colour of the stamp are then shown. Before February 1971 British currency was:

£1 = 20s   One pound = twenty shillings and

1s = 12d   One shilling = twelve pence.

Upon decimalisation this became:

£1 = 100p   One pound = one hundred (new) pence.

The catalogue list then shows two price columns. The left-hand is for unused stamps and the right-hand for used. Corresponding small boxes are provided in which collectors may wish to check off the items in their collection. Our method of indicating prices is: Numerals for pence, e.g. 10 denotes 10p (10 pence). Numerals for pounds and pence, e.g. 4·25 denotes £4·25 (4 pounds and 25 pence). For £100 and above, prices are in whole pounds and so include the £ sign and omit the zeros for pence.

Colour illustrations

The colour illustrations of stamps are intended as a guide only; they may differ in shade from the originals.

Size of illustrations

To comply with Post Office regulations stamp illustrations are three-quarters linear size. Separate illustrations of surcharges, overprints and watermarks are actual size.

Prices

Prices quoted in this catalogue are our selling prices at the time the book went to press. They are for stamps in fine condition; in issues where condition varies we may ask more for the superb and less for the sub-standard. The unused prices for stamps of Queen Victoria to King George V are for lightly hinged examples. Unused prices for King Edward VIII to Queen Elizabeth II are for unmounted mint (though when not available unmounted, mounted stamps are often supplied at a lower price). Prices for used stamps refer to fine postally used copies. All prices are subject to change without prior notice and we give no guarantee to supply all stamps priced, since it is not possible to keep every catalogued item in stock. Individual low value stamps sold at 399, Strand are liable to an additional handling charge. Commemorative issues may only be available in complete sets.

In the price columns:

† = Does not exist.

(—) or blank = Exists, or may exist, but price cannot be quoted.

* = Not normally issued (the so-called 'Abnormals' of 1862–80).

Perforations

The 'perforation' is the number of holes in a length of 2 cm, as measured by the Gibbons Instanta gauge. The stamp is viewed against a dark background with the transparent gauge put on top of it. Perforations are quoted to the nearest half. Stamps without perforation are termed 'imperforate'. From 1992 certain stamps occur with a large elliptical (oval) hole inserted in each line of vertical perforations. The £10 definitive, No. 1658, is unique in having two such holes in the horizontal perforations.

Elliptical perforations

Se-tenant combinations

Se-tenant means 'joined together'. Some sets include stamps of different design arranged se-tenant as blocks or strips and these are often collected unsevered as issued. Where such combinations exist the stamps are priced both mint and used, as singles or complete sets. The set price refers to the unsevered combination plus singles of any other values in the set.

First day covers

Prices for first day covers are for complete sets used on plain covers (Nos. 430/8, 453/60, 462/78b, 485/90, and 503/12) or on special covers (Nos. 461, 479/84, 491/502 and 513 onwards), the stamps of which are cancelled with ordinary operational postmarks (1924–1962) or by the standard 'First Day of Issue' postmarks (1963 onwards). The British Post Office did not provide 'First Day' treatment for every definitive issued after 1963. Where the stamps in a set were issued on different days, prices are for a cover from each day.

Presentation Packs

Special packs comprising slip-in cards with printed information inside a protective covering, were introduced for the 1964 Shakespeare issue. Collectors packs, containing commemoratives from the preceding twelve months, were issued from 1967. Some packs with text in German from 1968–69, exist as does a Japanese version of the pack for Nos. 916/17. Yearbooks, hardbound and illustrated in colour within a slip cover, joined the product range in 1984.

PHQ cards

Since 1973 the Post Office has produced a series of picture cards, which can be sent through the post as postcards. Each card shows an enlarged colour reproduction of a current British stamp, either of one or more values from a set or of all values. Cards are priced here in fine mint condition for sets complete as issued. The Post Office gives each card a 'PHQ' serial number, hence the term. The cards are usually on sale

shortly before the date of issue of the stamps, but there is no officially designated 'first day'. Used prices are for cards franked with the stamp depicted, on the obverse or reverse; the stamp being cancelled with an official postmark for first day of issue. For 1973–76 issues cards with stamps on the obverse are worth about 25% more than the prices quoted.

Gutter pair

Gutter pairs

Almost all modern Great Britain commemoratives are produced in sheets containing two panes of stamps separated by a blank horizontal or vertical margin known as a gutter. This feature first made its appearance on some supplies of the 1972 Royal Silver Wedding 3p, and marked the introduction of Harrison & Sons' new 'Jumelle' stamp-printing press. There are advantages for both the printer and the Post Office in such a layout which has now been used for almost all commemorative issues since 1974. The term 'gutter pair' is used for a pair of stamps separated by part of the blank gutter margin. We do not list gutter pairs for self-adhesive stamps since, although the production format is the same, the stamps are separated by die-cutting.

Most printers include some form of colour check device on the sheet margins, in addition to the cylinder or plate numbers. Harrison & Sons used round 'dabs' or spots of colour, resembling traffic lights. For the period from the 1972 Royal Silver Wedding until the end of 1979 these colour dabs appeared in the gutter margin. Gutter pairs showing these 'traffic lights' are worth considerably more than the normal version. From the 2004 Entente Cordiale set, Walsall reintroduced traffic lights in the gutters of certain sets. Where these extend over more than one section of gutter margin on any stamp they are priced as blocks rather than pairs.

Traffic light gutter pair

Catalogue numbers used

This checklist uses the same catalogue numbers as other current Stanley Gibbons catalogues.

Latest issue date for stamps recorded in this edition is 3 November 2009.

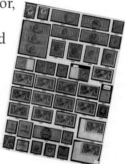
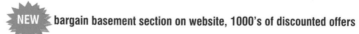

Commemorative Design Index

Stanley Gibbons information

399 Strand

Our world famous stamp shop is a collector's paradise, with all of our latest catalogues, albums and accessories and, of course, our unrivalled stockholding of postage stamps.
www.stanleygibbons.com
shop@stanleygibbons.co.uk
+44 (0)20 7836 8444

Specialist Stamp Sales

For the collector that appreciates the value of collecting the highest quality examples, Stanley Gibbons is the only choice. Our extensive range is unrivalled in terms of quality and quantity, with specialist stamps available from all over the world.
www.stanleygibbons.com/stamps
shop@stanleygibbons.co.uk
+44 (0)20 7836 8444

Stanley Gibbons Auctions and Valuations

Sell your collection or individual rare items through our prestigious public auctions or our regular postal auctions and benefit from the excellent prices being realised at auction currently. We also provide an unparalleled valuation service.
www.stanleygibbons.com/auctions
auctions@stanleygibbons.co.uk
+44 (0)20 7836 8444

Stanley Gibbons Publications

The world's first stamp catalogue was printed by Stanley Gibbons in 1865 and we haven't looked back since! Our catalogues are trusted worldwide as the industry standard and we print countless titles each year. We also publish consumer and trade magazines, Gibbons Stamp Monthly and Philatelic Exporter to bring you news, views and insights into all things philatelic. Never miss an issue by subscribing today and benefit from exclusive subscriber offers each month.
www.stanleygibbons.com/shop
orders@stanleygibbons.co.uk
+44 (0)1425 472 363

Stanley Gibbons Investments

The Stanley Gibbons Investment Department offers a unique range of investment propositions that have consistently outperformed more traditional forms of investment, from guaranteed minimum return products with unlimited upside to portfolios made up of the world's rarest stamps and autographs.
www.stanleygibbons.com/investment
investment@stanleygibbons.co.uk
+44 (0)1481 708 270

Fraser's Autographs

Autographs, manuscripts and memorabilia from Henry VIII to current day. We have over 60,000 items in stock, including movie stars, musicians, sport stars, historical figures and royalty. Fraser's is the UK's market leading autograph dealer and has been dealing in high quality autographed material since 1978.
www.frasersautographs.com
sales@frasersautographs.co.uk
+44 (0)20 7557 4404

stanleygibbons.com

Our website offers the complete philatelic service. Whether you are looking to buy stamps, invest, read news articles, browse our online stamp catalogue or find new issues, you are just one click away from anything you desire in the world of stamp collecting at stanleygibbons.com. Happy browsing!
www.stanleygibbons.com

Collecting Stamps – the Basics

It seems reasonable to assume, since you are reading this, that you already collect British stamps – but of course there are many ways of building on any collection and, if you are relatively new to it, I hope that the following will be of some guidance.

Traditionally, stamp collectors were introduced to the hobby with a quantity of world stamps, some still on envelopes and cards, which were then sorted and mounted in an album. In due course, many would decide to concentrate on a single country or group of countries and "specialisation" would begin, based on the experience built up as a "world collector".

More recently, an alternative route has become prevalent, in which, often as a gift, collection may be built on a "standing order" from a philatelic bureau, with stamps or covers arriving automatically, as they are issued, to be mounted in an album or stockbook. Albums are conveniently designed to meet the needs of this type of collection, with an illustrated space in which to mount every stamp.

This type of collection has much to recommend it – but one big disadvantage – it will be exactly the same as thousands of others, built up in the same way.

For this reason, many collectors are now returning to the delights of general collecting while maintaining their existing collections, and finding that the fun they had as children is very easy to recapture!

If you came to the hobby via "the standing order" route and would like to start a second "general collection", here are a few tips and suggestions.

Obtaining your stamps

Children were encouraged to buy – or persuade their parents to buy – the largest packet of stamps they could, as just sorting them into countries would prove enormously useful and interesting. Unfortunately large packets of world stamps are not as easy to obtain as they used to be, but you can still buy existing collections of all sorts at stamp fairs, shops or at auction, prices to suit every pocket. Just sorting and remounting such a collection will prove tremendously exciting.

Sooner or later, of course, you will identify gaps in your collection that you want to fill. It is useful to keep a note of these in a book that you can take with you when you visit a stamp shop or stamp fair – no one can remember everything and it is always annoying to discover that you have just bought a stamp you didn't need!

It is vitally important of course that you keep your "wants" book up-to-date and cross out items as you acquire them.

As well as visiting stamp fairs, you can check out the advertisements in the press; establish a good relationship with a dealer you like and, he will be happy to receive a "wants list" from you. He will then supply you with any items

on it he has currently in stock and keep a record of anything else so that he can send it on to you if he gets one. All such items are usually "on approval", so that if you have found them somewhere else, you are not obliged to purchase them.

More expensive items can be purchased at auction. Many of the larger auction houses do not like to sell items of lower value and therefore, in the main, offer more expensive single stamps and covers or complete collections and accumulations.

Other auctions offer single items of lower value and these can be a great way of picking up items you need. Stanley Gibbons Postbid auctions fall into this category, but there are many others and, once again, it is good to identify an auction house which regularly offers the type of material you are looking for and provides a reliable service.

Another method of buying stamps is "kiloware". These are stamps sold by weight and generally assumed to be "unsorted" i.e. no one has been through them before and picked the good ones out. Many collectors enjoy this approach to stamp collecting and they will tell you of the wonderful "finds" they have made – but inevitably you will be left with a vast majority of stamps that you do not want because they duplicate items already in your collection. Charity shops will always be happy to receive them – and they will eventually finish up in someone else's "genuinely unsorted kiloware" – so once again, if this is your kind of collecting, establish a good relationship with a reliable supplier.

"Kiloware" is generally supplied in the form of stamps on paper, torn or cut from envelopes – so this is probably a good point at which to discuss one of the real basics of stamp collecting – soaking stamps off paper.

It is helpful to carry out some rudimentary sorting before you start. Soaking stamps is quite a time-consuming process, so you do not want to waste time on stamps you don't need or don't want, maybe because they are damaged.

Once you have sorted out the stamps you want to soak off, pour some clean water (warm but *not* hot) into a bowl; then float each stamp (face uppermost) on the surface of the water. You can float as many stamps at one time as you have room for.

Leave the stamps for 15 minutes or so to give the water time to soak the gum that is sticking the stamp to the paper. Most stamps can then be gently peeled away. If they do not come away easily do not try to tear them off the paper. Leave them for another five minutes or so and try again.

Providing your hands are clean it's better to handle the stamps with your fingers when peeling off the envelope paper. The paper of stamps is weakened when it is damp and picking them up with tweezers may damage them.

When you have peeled the stamps off the envelope there will probably be some damp gum still on the back of them. Use a soft brush dipped in water to remove this, a paint brush is ideal. Alternatively let the stamp float on the water for a few minutes – the gum will dissolve away. However, do not immerse the stamp in water. For most stamps this would be safe enough but for some it would be dangerous as the ink may run.

Then shake off any excess water and place the stamps face upwards on a sheet of clean kitchen paper towel. This is why it is so important to clean all the gum off. If you do not, your stamps will stick to the paper and you will have to float them off all over again. When all the stamps are laid out cover them with more paper towel then make a kind of sandwich by putting a few sheets of ordinary paper on top.

Place a heavy book on this sandwich. This will flatten the stamps as they dry. After half an hour open up the sandwich and carefully remove the stamps. Spread them out on another piece of clean paper and leave to dry in the air for a little while. When completely dry they are ready for mounting in your album.

Or you can just lay the stamps face down on paper towel and allow them to dry out in the air. If you use this method do not try to speed up the drying by putting the stamps in the sun or close to a hot radiator as they will curl up and you may damage them when you flatten them out to put them in your album.

There are two things which you must be very careful about when floating stamps. Firstly, many old stamps were printed in special inks which run, change colour, or even disappear completely in water. Fewer modern stamps are affected in this way but even so it is best to be safe, so avoid letting water get on the surface of the stamp when you are floating-off. Be careful when floating stamps to keep separate stamps affixed to white and coloured envelopes. Take out any stamp which are stuck to bits of coloured paper and float these separately. Floating can easily make the ink run and so damage your stamps by staining them with unwanted colours.

These days, many countries produce "self-adhesive" stamps and these may not come away from their backing paper at all. If you believe that a stamp may be "self-adhesive', it would be better to leave it on the paper, carefully trimming round it with scissors, making sure you do not cut into the stamp.

Finally, always think twice before tearing a stamp off an envelope. Most old stamps and some modern ones too, if they have interesting postmarks, will be more valuable if left on

the envelope. If in doubt always try to ask a more experienced collector's advice.

Choosing an Album and Mounting your stamps

These are two different topics but really need to be considered together, as the way you mount your stamps will depend on the album you choose and your choice of album may depend on the way you wish to mount your stamps. Here are some of the options:

Printed Albums

You may be used to an album printed with a space for every stamp, and these may be obtained for larger groups of countries, such as the Stanley Gibbons New Imperial Album, with spaces for all Commonwealth and Empire stamps up to 1936. If this is the sort of collection you hope to build they are fine albums – but as they have a space for every stamp, filling one would be a time-consuming and expensive business!

New Imperial album

Blank albums

These are made up of blank pages, printed with a faint "quadrille" (tiny squares) which help you lay your stamps out neatly. These give you freedom to lay your collection out as you wish, leaving spaces for stamps you are hoping to obtain, or a neat display of the stamps you have. The former option may mean that you have a lot of gaps on the page, the latter may mean fairly regular rearrangement of your collection – the choice is yours.

Blank albums come in a wide range of prices and binding types, from inexpensive ring binders, through traditional "springbacks" to high quality "peg-fitting" types. Again, the choice is yours.

Stockbooks

In the past, collectors used stockbooks to hold duplicates and stamps awaiting mounting in the main album, but due to their convenience and cost, many collectors are now using stockbooks to house their main collections.

They certainly make it easy to "mount" your stamps – you just slip them into the strips on the pages and you can move them around easily to accommodate new acquisitions too! You can even write notes regarding different stamps or sets and slip those into the strips.

Stock albums

These are loose-leaf stockbooks, which have the added benefit of being able to insert extra pages in the book. Also, because the strips come in a number of formats, they look better than a stockbook layout which is a bit restricting and does not show larger items, such as covers, blocks and miniature sheets, very well.

Mounting your stamps

Before we come on to cover albums, let's return to the matter of mounting your stamps. If you have chosen either the stockbook or stock album option, this is not really an issue as you can just slip your stamps into the strips on the page. If you have opted for a printed or blank album, on the other hand, the question of mounting is important.

The traditional stamp hinge is generally the preferred option for used stamps. Instructions for their use are generally given on the packet, so I will not repeat them here, but I must stress that the key points are to *lightly* moisten the hinge before attaching it to the stamp or album page and *not to try to remove it* until it's dry or you may damage the page – or even more important, the stamp.

For unused stamps that have been previously mounted, stamp hinges are also perfectly acceptable, but for stamps which still have "full original gum" and show no evidence of having been previously hinged, most collectors now favour "hingeless mounts", which allow you to attach the stamp to the page without disturbing the gum (keeping the stamp "unmounted").

For most of the most frequently encountered stamp sizes, cut-to-size mounts are available for immediate use. Less common sizes will have to be cut from bigger strips, but even large blocks and miniature sheets cab be mounted in this way.

Although hingeless mounts are gummed, ready for use, many collectors prefer to use hinges to attach them to the album page as this makes them easier to move around when new stamps are added.

Covers

Many collectors like to include covers in their collections – either "first day" or "souvenir" covers or simply envelopes that show examples of the stamps in use. This is especially desirable of early covers, which might show unusual postmarks or other features.

Universal album

Covers can be mounted on blank pages using gummed photograph corners, but may also be accommodated in purpose-built cover albums. There are even albums, such as the Stanley Gibbons Universal, which are designed to hold stamp and cover pages together (and booklet pages too!).

What else?

So, that's covered the choice of album and the mounting of stamps: What else do you need? This comes under two headings: equipment and information.

Information

You can manage without background information, but it would be a bit like setting out on a journey to somewhere you've never been without a map.

The first thing is a catalogue to tell you what exists and will help you to identify what you have. The Stanley Gibbons catalogue range includes something for every collector from the beginner to the specialist. The features of each title are given elsewhere in this checklist (see page xliii).

Beyond that there are specialist handbooks on just about everything, but many are printed in quite small numbers and, once sold, are unlikely to be reprinted. However, specialist dealers and auction houses can be a useful source of out-of-print literature.

You should also try to keep up with what is going on in the philatelic world and, again, Stanley Gibbons is able to help, via its monthly magazine, *Gibbons Stamp Monthly*, recently described as "the best magazine for stamp collectors published anywhere". For a free sample copy and subscription details, please write to Stanley Gibbons Publications, *(the address is at the front of this checklist).*

Of course, as with everything else, much information may also be found on the internet and you will almost certainly find it worth joining the local society in your area, other stamp collectors are always happy to help a newcomer.

Equipment

Again, what you need in the way of equipment will depend largely on what you are collecting, the degree of specialisation you intend to achieve and the type of album you use.

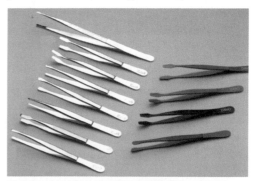

We have already discussed albums and stamp mounts, the only other item every stamp collector must have is a pair of tweezers. All stamps should be handled with tweezers; they ensure that the natural oils in our fingers do not get on to the stamps and, after a bit of practice, they are easier to use than fingers as well. They come in different lengths, with different points and made from different materials (generally stainless steel or gold-plated). Find a style that suits you and stick with it.

From then on the equipment you need is up to you. Most collectors like to have a magnifying glass so they can look at their stamps more closely. Again, they come in a wide range, from the fairly basic, offering 2 or 3× magnification, to pocket microscopes giving 30× magnification, and a digital microscope that you can attach to your computer for really detailed examination of your stamps. If this appeals to you, a demonstration of its use can be found on the Stanley Gibbons website – look for the Zoom Digital Microscope.

Another useful type of magnifier is one that incorporateS a millimetre scale – ideal for measuring overprints and other features.

Even a quick look in any catalogue will show that differences in perforation, watermark and colour can make an enormous difference to the price of a stamp. So most collectors like to have the necessary equipment to measure perforations, view watermarks and identify colours and shades.

Fortunately, as far as perforations are concerned, the perforation gauge used by most of the world's top collectors and dealers is accessible to all – it's the Stanley Gibbons Instanta – which measures perforations to a decimal point and is easy to use. There is an electronic perforation measurer which is even easier to use – but it is a bit more expensive than the Instanta.

Watermark detectors also come in a variety of types and a wide range of prices, all of which are effective in their different ways. If you are collecting older stamps, watermarks are generally clearer and can be identified simply by placing the stamps face down on a dark background or watermark tray and, if necessary, adding a few drops of lighter fluid or watermark fluid. The Morley Bright products are an excellent alternative if you do not like using fluids, which many collectors do not.

More modern stamps, especially mint ones are more difficult to sort and for these one of the electric watermark detectors will probably be the answer. The Stanley Gibbons Detectamark and other similar products take a bit of practice to get used to, but are very effective. Their drawback is that they can only handle single stamps and cannot accommodate blocks or sheets. If you are able to, visit a shop where you can see the different products demonstrated and make your choice.

Happily, the standard colour guide for stamp collectors, the Stanley Gibbons colour key, is another relatively inexpensive item which will provide years of use. It features 200 different colours and will allow you to tell the difference between "mauve", "purple", "lilac" and "violet" with ease.

Finally and especially if you are collecting the modern stamps of Great Britain at a more specialised level, you will probably want an ultraviolet lamp to identify different papers and phosphor types. Again, these come in a range of designs at different prices, so it is useful to seek the advice of an experienced collector before deciding on the one to buy. If you collect Great Britain stamps, you really need a "short wave" lamp to identify different phosphors, but some lamps incorporate both "long" and "short" wave bulbs, which give them wider potential use.

A lamp with a "hood" is generally to be recommended, firstly because direct exposure to prolonged ultraviolet light is damaging to the eyes, so you should avoid lamps which cause you to see the bulb itself while you are using it. Also, such lamps are more effective in the dark, so anything which shields the stamp being examined from other light sources, including daylight, will improve the effectiveness of the lamp. Ideally, you should use an ultraviolet lamp in a completely darkened room – but this is not practical at a stamp fair!

Philatelic accessories of all types are available from Stanley Gibbons Publications in Ringwood or at the SG shop in London. The current product guide is available on request. Alternatively, a host of useful information can be found here: www.stanleygibbons.com

Stanley Gibbons Numbers

When Stanley Gibbons published his first stamp catalogue in 1865 the stamps in it were simply listed by country and description. It was not long, however, before there were just too many stamps to be listed in this way and in order to simplify the way in which stamps could be ordered by customers, each was given its unique and individual number.

Nowadays, as each stamp is added to the catalogue in the supplement published in *Gibbons Stamp Monthly,* it is assigned its number; sets being listed according to the date on which they were issued and then by face value within that set. If several stamps of the same value belong to one set, usually issued in the form of a sheet or sheetlet, the numbering starts at the top left-hand stamp and runs down to the stamp at bottom right.

Long definitive series are listed together for the convenience of collectors so this often involves adding new numbers to an existing series. It can also happen that a stamp or set of stamps are discovered which were unknown at the time of issue – these also have to be inserted in their correct chronological sequence.

Easy identification

The Stanley Gibbons number appears in the left-hand column of the stamp listing and should not be confused with the bold number that often appears to its right and refers to its illustration. So, by using the country name and catalogue number, every stamp can be easily identified and, rather than having to order Great Britain 1924 10d. turquoise-blue on Block Cypher watermarked paper, all you have to do is order a Great Britain SG428 and state whether you want it used or unused.

In order to render them immediately identifiable, certain types of stamps are given a prefix to their catalogue number thus a number prefixed with a "D" is a postage due stamp, while an "O" means it's an official stamp. Some countries' stamps also have a prefix to allow them to be easily identified. Thus, in this catalogue, Scotland stamp numbers are prefixed with an "S" and those for Wales with a "W".

Changes

Once a number has been assigned it is not changed unless absolutely necessary. The reason, for this is that collectors often maintain their 'wants lists' using SG numbers, while auction houses around the world quote them in their descriptions, as do books and articles in the philatelic press.

Expertising bodies, including the expert committee of the Royal Philatelic Society London and the British Philatelic Association also quote SG numbers in their certificates, which generally identify scarcer or more valuable stamps, so regular changing of those numbers would render such certificates out-of-date.

Nevertheless, sometimes complete sections of the catalogue, occasionally even complete countries, have to be reoganised, and under such circumstances renumbering does take place – but this is infrequent.

Usually, new stamps added into the middle of listings have a letter suffix. This can occur in two forms. If the stamp is listable in its own right the suffix forms a part of the "main" number in the left-hand column of the listing. Thus, when the Wilding 4½d. and 5d. values with phosphor bands appeared, in 1961 and 1967 respectively, but the 4d. and 6d., both issued in 1960, had already been given the numbers 616 and 617, the 4½d. became 616a and the 5d. was listed as 616b.

Varieties of such "main" stamps, such as errors, booklet panes and watermark varieties are given letter suffixes in a different way, so that the phosphor version of the 1963 6d. Paris Postal Conference stamp (SG 636) has a "p" suffix which appears in the listing itself, to differentiate it from the normal, non-phosphor stamp – so to order one, all you need to ask for is SG 636p.

Sometimes, of course, so many stamps are subsequently added to a listing that the use of suffix letters would just become too complicated and, so far as Great Britain is concerned, this has happened with the decimal Machin series, which are prefixed "X" for the conventionally perforated series, first issued in 1971, and "Y" for the series with elliptical perforations at each side, first issued in 1993.

Adding new numbers

Thus when new stamps are added to such series – and several are appearing each year – adding new numbers does not have to mean changing those of subsequently issued commemorative issues.

Within the "Y" series, new "main" values are initially added with a suffix letter, so the numbers of previously issued stamps do not have to be adjusted with each new catalogue, but every four or five years the complete listing is updated to eliminate the suffix letters and maintain a "clean" listing of numbers. When ordering stamps from these series it is as well to mention which edition of the catalogue you are using as, if your dealer is using a different one, you may not receive what you expect!

> The Stanley Gibbons numbering system represents an easy-to-use and universally recognised system of stamp identification.

Collectors all over the world use it to keep their collections in order and dealers sort and classify their stocks by it, so its use makes life easier for everyone.

Stanley Gibbons numbers are fully protected by copyright and, while their use is encouraged, they may not be reproduced without the prior permission of Stanley Gibbons Limited.

The Stanley Gibbons Guide to Stamp Pricing

Catalogue editor and lifelong collector, Hugh Jefferies, offers a few tips.

It is a common fallacy that the prices in this catalogue show what a stamp is 'worth', should you wish to sell it.

They are, instead, the price at which Stanley Gibbons will sell a fine example of the stamp in question, but that price includes a lot of other factors, as well as the inherent 'value' of the stamp itself. There are costs in running any business and these are built into the price of any stamp shown in the catalogue, although the proportion of the price that relates to the stamp and that which relates to 'business overheads' will vary from stamp to stamp.

What is true is that the prices shown in this catalogue represent an accurate 'guide' to the value of the stamps listed in it. Stanley Gibbons are now the only major philatelic publisher whose stamp catalogue is also their price list. Naturally, if the prices are set too high, no one will buy our stamps, if they are too low, we will have difficulty replacing our stocks. It is therefore vitally important to the future of the company that the prices in this catalogue are set as accurately as possible. As a result, a great deal of care is taken over those prices – which is why they are held in such authority by collectors, dealers and stamp auction houses throughout the world.

A very accurate picture

Each year, every price in our annual catalogues is checked and amended if necessary, having regard to the prices being achieved at auction as well as the demands of our customers at 399 Strand and orders coming in via the post, email and our website. Prices are held, increased or reduced according to those factors, giving a very accurate picture of the state of the market for each and every stamp.

Can stamps be purchased for less than the prices quoted in this catalogue? Of course they can. Stanley Gibbons themselves will frequently have stamps in stock at prices lower than 'full catalogue'. Every business offers discounts and makes 'special offers' from time to time and Stanley Gibbons is no different. That apart, however, it should always be remembered that the prices quoted in this catalogue are for stamps in fine condition. Stamps with minor defects, heavy postmarks, slight fading and other flaws will frequently be offered at lower prices, both by Stanley Gibbons and by other dealers and auction houses.

Checking condition

It is very important that, when you are thinking of buying a stamp for your collection, you carefully consider the condition of the item in question. Does it match up to the Stanley Gibbons definition of 'Fine'? If it doesn't, is the price at which it is being offered too high? If you believe that the price is higher that it should be, leave it alone – or if you are really desperate, haggle for a better deal.

The knowledge as to what is 'fine' and therefore worthy of 'full catalogue' is one that you will gain with experience and will vary from stamp to stamp. Any stamp less than 100 years old should really be perfect in every way, but one can be more forgiving with older issues.

Briefly, here are a few of the things to consider.

- **Gum** – for unused stamps issued after 1936 prices are for unmounted mint – stamps never previously hinged. Modern stamps with hinge marks should be substantially discounted. For earlier stamps, heavy mounts and multiple hinges will also detract from the value, while unused stamps with the gum removed are worth considerably less.

- **Margins** – for imperforate stamps these should be clear on all sides – the design should not be cut into or even touching the edge of the stamp.

- **Perforations** – check that these are complete, that none are missing or short, especially at the stamp corners. Ideally the margin between the stamp design and the perforations should be even and well balanced – known as 'well centred'.

- **Paper** – Check that there are no tears or thins to the paper – on the front as well as the back – and that there are no bends or creases. Again, the greater the damage the further away from 'full catalogue' the stamp is worth.

- **Postmarks** – these should be clear, clean and should not disfigure the stamp. The prices for all British stamps issued after 1880 assume used stamps to be cancelled with a clean, clear circular datestamp. Heavy parcel, wavy line or slogan cancellations reduce stamp values significantly. On the other hand, very lightly cancelled stamps should sometimes be viewed with suspicion. There needs to be enough of the postmark showing to prove that the stamp has really been used!

If the above notes seem complicated, don't worry. You will soon become adept at viewing every stamp in the light of its condition and deciding what proportion of catalogue you are prepared to pay. If you are not certain, ask the dealer for a guarantee that he will refund your money if you're not happy with your purchase. All good dealers will be happy to provide this.

So, buy carefully – but, above all, have fun!

> It should always be remembered that the prices quoted in this catalogue are for stamps in fine condition.

HOW MUCH?

YOUR PRICE IS OUR PRICE!

Buying at auction means buying at source.
It's where dealers buy to re-sell later at a profit.

Auctions are open to everyone, yourself included. Singles, sets, covers, complete collections – everything, worldwide, all periods, mint and used. Lots from £1-£1000's. Never again pay more than you want to!

Our full colour catalogues are free and all purchases are covered by our 'Return for any reason' full and immediate refund guarantee.

What have you got to lose?

Tip – your bid isn't **WHAT** you'll pay; it's the **MOST** you'll pay.
Simply bid no more than the cheapest offer elsewhere, and you cannot lose!

Reply today and we'll give you £100* off.
And **NO BUYERS PREMIUM****
* 5 credit notes for £20, each valid when £50 or more spent in any one sale New customers only

APEX PHILATELIC AUCTIONS

11 Adelphi Terrace, London WC2N 6BJ

Contact Rick Warren or Tim Francis on:
Tel: +44 (0) 1342 833413 Fax: +44 (0) 1342 833892
email: sales@apexstamps.com

See us on-line at www.apexstamps.com

A Noble Investments (UK) PLC Company

Name_____

Address _____
_____
_____

e-mail:_____

Please send me your next 5 auction catalogues free of charge and my £100 introductory vouchers
** *On Postbid Sales*

(CBS10)

An exciting year ahead

It's going to be an incredible year for stamp collecting in the British Isles. Throughout 2010 the Festival of Stamps is going to spread the good news about our hobby across the entire nation. The principal theme behind much that is happening is the centenary of the Accession of King George V, known as "The Collector King" because of his immense enthusiasm for stamps.

George V 1924 Wembley Exhibition
This design was submitted by Harold Nelson, and was shown to the King on 19 February 1924. It was approved subject to amendment.

Inspiration for this celebration is that London will host, as it does every ten years, an international stamp exhibition. London 2010 will be held in London's Islington on 8 to 15 May. Dealers and exhibits from around the world will fill the entire Business Design Centre, including a special area for Royal Mail. Admission is free except on the opening day (8 May) when admission will cost £10, although accompanied children will be admitted free. Budding young collectors will find plenty to keep them busy in a special activity area being organised by the National Youth Stamp Group.

For more dealers, on 5 and 6 May there will also be Philatex Extra in the Lawrence Hall of The Royal Horticultural Society (close to Victoria Street in London). While in London on 6 May, why not visit the Royal Philatelic Society London at 41 Devonshire Place, and enjoy the displays from the other Royal Societies overseas.

A very special exhibition, titled "Empire Mail: George V and the GPO", with material, much previously unseen publicly, from The British Postal Museum & Archive (BPMA) and the Royal Philatelic Collection, can be viewed at Guildhall Art Gallery, in the heart of the City of London, from 7 May to 25 July.

Events across the year

However, the year's activities do not start in May. From the beginning of the year the British Library will be showing significant items in its very special exhibition "The British Library Philatelic Rarities". Much of this material can only be seen at the British Library. The permanent 1,000 frame "Philatelic Exhibition" will be refreshed with new or not recently exhibited material from the British Library's world class collections. It will also be running a programme of educational talks.

The Bath Postal Museum will include an exhibition on the postal aspects of the reign of King George V, including the British Empire Exhibition; it will be open from 1 February to 30 October.

From 1 April to 14 November, at the British Museum, there will be an exhibition on "Impressions of Africa" as seen on stamps, medals and money, as no fewer than seventeen African countries celebrate the 50th anniversary of their independence in 2010.

Starting in May, and running for a year, the BPMA will be showing many of its philatelic treasures in an exhibition at its home at Freeling House in Phoenix Place (close to Mount Pleasant) in London.

Other venues where there will be displays of stamps include: the Wimbledon Lawn Tennis Museum; Museum of London Docklands; Crewe Heritage Centre; Colne Valley Postal History Museum (at Halstead in Essex); Bletchley Park; Aberdeen Maritime Museum; Museum of World Rugby at Twickenham; Marylebone Cricket Club Museum at Lord's cricket ground; The National Football Museum at Preston.

Societies involved nationwide

The Association of British Philatelic Societies, working with the BPMA, is arranging events hosted by area Federations throughout the year. These will include:

Thames Valley at Thatcham on 27 March;

Scottish Congress at Perth on 16 and 17 April;

Midland at Knowle, Solihull on 24 April;

South Wales at Port Talbot on 22 May;

Essex at Colchester on 5 June;

Yorkshire at Pudsey, Leeds on 12 June;

Wessex at Plymouth on 3 July;

Kent at Tonbridge on 10 July;

East Midlands at Cambridge on 21 August;

Middlesex at Amersham on 4 September;

Surrey at Croydon on 11 September;

North-East at Newcastle-upon-Tyne on 24 to 26 September;

Sussex at Ardingly on 9 October;

Hampshire at Wickham on 16 October;

Cornwall at Liskeard on 24 October;

North-West at Bolton on 30 October.

Make sure you don't miss events near you in this exciting year. For more details, visit the website: www.london2010.org.uk.

Adhesive A gummed stamp

Albino A design impression without colour

Aniline A fugitive (water soluble) ink or dye

Bisect Part of a stamp that has been cut in two for separate use; usually during a shortage of stamps

Blind perforation A perforation which has not been punched out

Block A group of four or more unseparated stamps

Bogus A spurious, pretend stamp

Booklet A small book containing 'panes' of stamps

Booklet pane A leaf or page of stamps from a booklet

Cachet A commemorative marking, usually applied by rubber stamp

Cancellation Any authorised defacing mark on a stamp

Centre The position of a stamp design within its perforations, e.g. 'well-centred' or 'off-centre'

Chalk-surfaced paper Stamp paper coated with a chalky solution for security purposes. Attempted removal of the postmark damages the surface of the stamp

Charity stamp One bearing a premium or surcharge for charitable purposes

Classic A country's early stamp issues, mostly up to about 1875; a choice stamp

Coil stamp One from a roll of stamps used in vending machines

Coil join A tab uniting two sections of a roll of stamps

Commemorative A stamp issued to mark a special anniversary or event

Country stamp See Regional

Cover A postally used envelope, letter-sheet or wrapper

Cylinder number Letters/numerals in sheet margins identifying printing cylinders. Normally collected in 'Cylinder block' of six stamps. Also see 'Plate number'

Die An engraved plate for impressing design etc. on softer metal

Doctor blade A steel blade which removes surplus ink from the printing cylinder in the press – faulty wiping by this blade will cause a 'Doctor blade' flaw

Embossing A form of printing in relief, now rarely used

Error A mistake in stamp design, printing or production

Essay A trial stamp design, sometimes differing from the

issued stamps

Face value The denomination of a stamp, expressed on its face

Fake A genuine stamp doctored in some way to deceive collectors

First Day Cover A cover bearing stamps postmarked on their day of issue

Flaw A fortuitous blemish on a stamp; a printing fault

Forgery A fraudulent copy of a genuine postage stamp, overprint or postmark

Frama stamps See Machine label

Graphite lines Black vertical lines printed on the back of GB definitives, 1957–1959, for use with automatic letter-sorting equipment. Also see 'Phosphor' stamps

Greetings stamp Stamp intended for use on birthday or other greetings mail

Gum Mucilage on the back of adhesive stamps. Not 'glue'

Gutter The narrow space between stamps in the sheet permitting perforation

Gutter margin The blank margins dividing a sheet of stamps into panes

Handstamp A postmark or overprint applied by hand

Imperforate Stamps printed and issued without perforations, deliberately or in error

Imprint The name of the printer or issuing authority inscribed on the stamps or in the sheet margins

Imprinted stamps Stamps other than adhesives, printed direct on postal stationery items (postcards, envelopes, etc)

Jubilee line Coloured line found in the sheet margin of British stamps

'Local' A stamp with geographical limits of postal use and validity. These are not normally listed in the Stanley Gibbons catalogues

'Machin' The name given to GB definitives, first issued in 1967, bearing the Queen's head designed by Arnold Machin

Machine label Postage stamp produced by a micro-processor machine after the insertion of coins of the required value, popularly known as Frama stamps

Maltese cross Name given to the cross-shaped cancellation used on the first British stamps

Margin The unprinted edging surrounding or dividing a sheet of stamps. See also 'Gutter margin'

Maximum card A picture postcard bearing a stamp and cancellation relevant to the picture on the card

Miniature sheet A small sheet of one or several stamps, usually with decorative margins, issued as a souvenir for collectors

Mint A stamp in its original pristine state, with full gum (if so issued), when it is said to have its 'original gum' ('O.G.'). 'Unmounted mint' stamps have not been hinged. Also see 'Unused'

Mulready Envelopes and letter sheets issued by Britain in 1840 with a pictorial motif designed by William Mulready

Non Value Indicator stamp (NVI) A stamp which bears no monetary inscription, but shows the class of postage (1st, 2nd) instead

Obsolete A stamp no longer sold by a post office though it may still be valid for postage

Overprint A printed addition to a stamp. Also see 'Surcharge'

Pair Two unseparated stamps, joined as originally issued

Pane A formation or group of stamps within the sheet. Also see 'Booklet pane'

Perforations Holes punched between stamps in sheets to enable easy separation

Personalised stamp Stamp with an attached non-postal label bearing an image taken from a personal photograph

Phosphor stamps Stamps overprinted or coated with phosphorescent materials recognised by high technology letter sorting machinery

Plate number Letters/numerals in sheet margins identifying printing plates. Also see 'Cylinder number'

Postmark Any mark, such as a cancellation, connected with the postal service and found on items transmitted by post

Presentation pack A philatelic souvenir containing a set of stamps and descriptive text

Prestige booklet Stamp booklet devoted to a particular subject or event and containing special panes of stamps with descriptive text printed alongside

Proof A trial impression taken from an original die or printing plate

Regional Name given by collectors to stamps issued by Royal Mail (who term them Country stamps) for use in England, Scotland, Wales or Northern Ireland. Issues were also made for Guensey and Jersey (until 1969) and the Isle of Man (until 1973)

Seahorse Name given to the high value definitive stamps of King George V

Self-adhesive Gummed stamps (with protective backing) which do not require moistening

Se-tenant Stamps of different design or face value that are joined together

Specimen Sample stamp usually with 'specimen' overprinted or perforated on it

Strip Three or more stamps joined in a row

Tête-bêche A stamp inverted in relation to the adjoining stamp in a pair

Traffic lights Collectors' term for the colour check dots found in sheet margins

Unused An uncancelled stamp, not necessarily 'mint'

Used A stamp which has been postally used and appropriately postmarked

Used abroad Stamps of one country used and postmarked in another

Used on piece Stamp kept on part of the original cover to preserve the complete postmark

Variety A stamp differing in some detail from the normal issue

Watermark A distinctive device or emblem in stamps, formed by 'thinning' of the paper during production. A watermark is normally viewed through the front of the stamp

'Wilding' The name given to British definitive stamps, first issued in 1952, bearing the Queen's head from a photographic portrait by Dorothy Wilding

Wing margin Wide margin on one side of a stamp caused by central perforation of the sheet gutter margin

For other and fuller definitions, see the Stanley Gibbons book *Philatelic Terms Illustrated* by James Mackay.

Machins

The Machin definitive series is one of the longest running in the world, being now in its 43rd year, and has probably been the subject of more detailed study during its time of issue than any other stamp series, ever.

Arnold Machin: the designer

Certainly, it is a subject with enormous appeal. Its sheer simplicity has made it virtually impossible to replace, subsequent efforts to come up with a new design having failed to match it.

The first Machin 4d.

On the other hand, while the design may have remained essentially unchanged, the world has changed a great deal and these changes have had a profound impact on the Machin. For a start there have been financial changes; when the stamps were first issued they were denominated in pounds, shillings and pence; in 1971 the series was reissued in decimal currency. When that happened the cost of sending a 1st class letter was 3p – now it is 39p, the rate of inflation ensuring that new values have to be added to the series in order to cover the most frequently used postage rates.

Technological changes

The period has also been one of enormous technological change, both insofar as stamp production and the handling of the post are concerned. In 1967, and for many years thereafter, production methods remained pretty much unchanged from those of the 1940s. Stamps were printed by photogravure, a painstaking and time consuming method of production in the hands of just one printer, Harrison and Sons of High Wycombe. In the late 1970s the Post Office became concerned that it might be risky to rely on one supplier

and had a supply of the 8p stamp printed in Enschedé in the Netherlands. No British printer could be found to print definitives in photogravure so lithographic printers, John Waddington, The House of Questa and, later, Walsall were added to the list of suppliers, adding further interest to the series. Early litho printings did not match the quality of the photogravure stamps, but improvement came with time and the old photography-based method of production of gravure printing cylinders was replaced by computer-generated ones, improving the quality of the end product while reducing its cost. Each of these changes of printer and print and production methods can be identified.

At the same time as stamp production techniques were advancing so was the handling of mail, with greater mechanisation being the target as labour costs rose. Automatic letter sorting had begun in earnest in the late 1950s, but really took off in the sixties and was in full swing by the time the first Machins appeared. Phosphor bands were printed on the front of the stamps which could be 'read' by a machine so that the letters could be 'faced' in such a way that envelopes could be stacked ready for automatic cancelling machines. At the same time, because second class stamps had a single phosphor band, while other values had two; second class mail could be identified by machine and separated for less urgent handling.

As technology advanced during the 1970s and eighties, new methods of phosphor application were tested, with phosphor being incorporated in the paper coating ("phosphorised paper") or printed, either under or over the design ("all over phosphor"). For a time only second class stamps and some booklet stamps had phosphor bands, the others all being on phosphorised paper, but now bands are once again the norm.

Technological change has also affected the way in which stamps are sold to the public. In 1967 they were only sold from post offices, although one could obtain stamps in coils and booklets from slot-machines.

Wider availability

Customer demand for greater availability and convenience has led to the most frequently used stamps being produced with self-adhesive gum and booklets of self-adhesive stamps being available from a wide range of retail outlets – not just post offices.

The first self-adhesive

The problem of increasing postage rates was countered by the issue of stamps without a specific face value, showing just "1st" or "2nd", for first and second class mail. These would be purchased at the prevailing first and second class rates but could still be used, even after postage rates had increased.

More recently, we have seen the return of coil stamps, dispensed by Post & Go machines inside some post offices. These stamps incorporate the familiar Machin head and are therefore being included in Machin collections.

Environmental concerns have also had an impact on the Machin. In order to enhance the stamps' appearance and to improve the effectiveness of the stamp sorting process, fluorescent papers were introduced during the early decimal period, with collectors being able to detect varying degrees of fluorescence with the aid of an ultraviolet lamp. More recently, however the use of fluors in stamp paper production has ceased, although the ultraviolet lamp remains a key piece of equipment for the Machin collector who wishes to identify different phosphor types.

Design changes

Although the Machin design has remained basically unchanged over the years, there have been a few tweaks to it. It is sometimes forgotten that, when the Pounds, Shillings and Pence stamps first appeared back in the sixties, three stamps, the 7d., 8d. and 9d. had the value on the right-hand side of The Queen's head but with decimalisation the value was placed in the lower left corner as standard.

7d. value at right

The high values have always been given special treatment – all that has changed is what constitutes a 'high' value. In 1970 it was 10p!, the top four values (10p, 20p, 50p and £1) being larger size and recess printed.

10p high value

In 1977 the Machin design was adapted to a larger format for the, then, top three values (£1, £2 and £5), with later values being added to cover specific parcel post rates.

From 1988 to 1999 Machin high values were replaced by 'Castles', returning as four standard-size stamps, valued at £1·50, £2, £3 and £5, but recess-printed. Meanwhile the £1 had (in 1995) dropped to a 'low-value' (a standard-size stamp

in gravure) but with the added enhancement of being printed in 'Iriodin' ink, giving a shiny effect to the stamp's background. Then, in 2003, the remaining high values joined the £1 as standard-size, gravure stamps printed in Iriodin ink.

Large format £5

In February 2009, along with the 1st and 2nd class stamps and the 50p, all values from £1 upwards were re-issued as self-adhesives with U-shaped security slits and an iridescent 'ROYAL MAIL' overprint – but this change will be covered later on.

£1 in Iriodin ink

Less obvious than the ups and downs of the high values have been changes in the designs of the value numerals. These changes are well described in this catalogue, but had to be introduced as the space allowed for the value in the original decimal series was insufficient to accommodate some of the larger values which were needed subsequently, such as the 20½p. New, more compact numbers were introduced and some stamps appeared in both types shown in the catalogue listing.

Pricing in proportion small and large

In 2006 the Post Office introduced 'Pricing in Proportion', a system whereby the size and shape of a postal item would determine the cost of sending it, as well as its weight. 1st and 2nd class stamps were issued in two sizes, standard size for 'normal' letters and a larger size for 'large' letters, in each case the value being made clearer and placed at the top left of the stamp. It was felt, however, that this upset the balance of the smaller stamps and the denominator returned to its traditional position at lower left.

Printing methods

Over the 42-plus years the Machin design has been in use, no less than seven different printers have been involved in their production, using three basic printing methods, gravure, lithography and recess-printing (or intaglio). The changes have been partly the result of Royal Mail contracts, but also the result of business take-overs, with Harrison and Sons and the House of Questa both having been taken over by De La Rue, for example. The work of these different printers can be identified by specialists and offer yet another interesting aspect to the Machin Story.

As printing became cheaper towards the end of the 20th century and, indeed, through the advent of the home computer, accessible to all, the post office became more and more concerned about the danger of stamps being privately produced and, indeed, one or two quite passable attempts at forging postage stamps were made, defrauding the Post Office of many thousands of pounds. However, it was obvious that, though printing the counterfeit stamps was not a problem, perforating them was more difficult – and to make the job of the forger even more difficult, the Post Office introduced "elliptical" perforations as the sides of all Machins from 1993 onwards. These are separately listed in this catalogue, the numbers having a "Y" prefix, as opposed to the "X" prefixed numbers of stamps with "normal" perforations all round.

Uncancelled stamps

Although the elliptical perforations went a long way to curing the problem of stamp forgery, another way in which it was being defrauded remained a serious concern to the Post Office, the reuse of uncancelled stamps.

With the advance of automation and, it has to be said, lack of care on the part of some Post Office staff, envelopes and packages were arriving at the destinations without the stamps having been postmarked – and very often it was the higher value stamps on parcels and registered packages where the cancellation had been overlooked.

Security Machin

This led to "businesses" being set up to buy large quantities of "used" stamps, taking out the uncancelled ones, soaking them off and re-selling them at a heavy discount off face value. Faced with the loss of millions of pounds of revenue each year, the Post Office acted by introducing the new "security" Machins in February 2009. These were printed on a new self-adhesive paper with gum which could not be "soaked off" in the traditional way, with four U-shaped slits cut into the stamp, ensuring that the stamp would be destroyed if an attempt was made to peel it off the envelope. Finally the stamps had an iridescent "ROYAL MAIL" overprint, making it even more difficult for counterfeit stamps to be produced. As well as the most commonly used stamps, the 1st and 2nd class ("normal" and "large") stamps, the higher values most

often used on parcels and Special Delivery packages; 50p and all values from £1 up, have been produced in this form. They are separately listed in this catalogue with a "U" prefix, beginning with U2911.

Commemoratives and booklets

The Machin design has also been used for commemoratives. In 1990, to celebrate the 150th anniversary of the Penny Black, small-sized definitives incorporating the Machin head with that of Queen Victoria were issued in five values (with more than one paper and printing method being used for some of them). This design was revised ten years later, as a 1st class stamp in a commemorative stamp book.

Double head

Also in 2000 an adapted Machin design with a larger head against a white background replaced the standard gold 1st class Machin for the Millennium year. This stamp appeared in booklets as well as sheets.

Millenium Machin

The previous year a "prestige" stamp booklet entitled "Profile on Print" had included panes of four large-size Machins (in the format of the 1977 high values but 1st class stamps printed in lithography, with a colourless embossed Queen's head, letterpress (typography) and recess; this last stamp, engraved by the Swedish master-engraver Czeslaw Slania, being widely thought to be one of the most attractive stamps ever issued.

'Profile in Print' 1st class recess

Although not "commemoratives" in themselves Machin panes have usually been included in "Prestige" stamp booklets which either have a commemorative element or are linked to a special stamp issue. Such stamps frequently differ from those in sheets, providing something "special" for the purchaser of these booklets. The most obvious example came from the "First Wedgwood" booklet, issued in 1972, where one ½p stamp had a single phosphor at the left-hand side, while all other ½p stamps had two bands. This ½p stamp (SG ×842) is now catalogued at £55, against 10p for a "normal" ½p!

Subsequent booklets have included stamps with different phosphor arrangements, different perforations and, most commonly, different printing methods. Many of these are listed in this catalogue and are identifiable, not only through the notes in the catalogue listings, but also through their generally higher catalogue prices.

Regional and country stamps

Finally, it would be remiss not to mention that the Machin design was also used for "Regional" or "Country" stamps up to 2001, with the Queen's head and value being supplemented by the emblems of Northern Ireland, Scotland and Wales (and, from 1971 to 1973 only, the Isle of Man). These stamps went through their own changes of printer, print method, perforation and design adjustment, creating the potential for a collection no less interesting than that of the "national" Machin definitives.

Wales Regional

Indeed, since the Machin regionals have now been replaced by the "emblem" designs, and the collection now has a definite beginning and end, collecting Machin regionals may have a stronger appeal than their "national" cousins, where the story is far from over yet, and more and more new stamps are being added to the listings in this catalogue as the years go by!

How can Stanley Gibbons help you to build your collection?

Our History

Stanley Gibbons started trading in 1856 and we have been at the forefront of stamp collecting for more than 150 years, making us the world's oldest philatelic company. We can help you build your collection in a wide variety of ways – all with the backing of our unrivalled expertise.

When building a collection it helps to know what you have. You can use *Collect British Stamps* as a checklist to highlight all the items you currently own. You can then easily see where the gaps are that you need to fill.

Visit 399 Strand, London, UK

Our world famous stamp shop is a collector's paradise which aims to keep a full range of stock to sell at current catalogue price - so if there are any changes via a different catalogue, then prices will be adjusted accordingly. As well as stamps, the shop stocks albums, accessories and specialist philatelic books. Plan a visit now!

GB Specialist Department

When purchasing high value items you should definitely contact our specialist department for advice and guarantees on the items purchased. You need to make sure you consult the experts to ensure they help you make the right purchase. With Stanley Gibbons this comes with over 150 years of experience. For example, when buying early Victorian stamps our specialists will guide you through the prices – so a penny red SG 43 has many plate numbers which vary in value. We can explain what to look for and where, and help you plan your future collection.

Auctions and Valuations

You might find other ways of buying material to go into your collection, such as through auction – buying at auction can be great fun. You can buy collections and merge them with your own - not forgetting to check your *Collect British Stamps* checklist for gaps. Once again, you do need to make sure the condition of the collection you are buying is comparable to your own.

Stanley Gibbons Auctions have been running since the 1900's. They offer a range of auctions to suit all levels of collectors and dealers. You can of course also sell your collection or individual rare items through our public auctions and regular postal auctions. You can check out charges with the auction department directly (see contact details below).

Stanley Gibbons Publications

Our catalogues are trusted worldwide as the industry standard (see page xlv for more details).

To keep up to date with new issues you can follow the additions to this listing in our magazine *Gibbons Stamp Monthly*. This is a must-read for all collectors and dealers. It contains news, views and insights into all things philatelic, from beginner to specialist.

Completing the set

When is it cheaper to complete your collection by buying a whole set rather than item by item? You can use the prices in *Collect British Stamps*, which lists single item values and a complete set value, to check if it is better to buy the odd items missing, or a complete set. Some of the definitive sets can be built up over time. The current definitive set is augmented by the Post Office regularly.

Condition

Condition can make a big difference on the price you can pay for an item (see 'The Stanley Gibbons Guide to Stamp Pricing' on p xxviii). The prices in this catalogue are for items undamaged. When building your collection you do need to keep condition in mind and always buy the best condition you can find and afford. Collectors are reminded that for issues from 1936 to date, prices in the unused column are for unmounted mint. This means that the condition of the gum is the same as issued from the Post Office. If the gum is disturbed or has had an adhesion it can be classed as mounted. When buying issues prior to 1936 you should always look for the least amount of disturbance and adhesion. You do have to keep in mind the age of the issue when looking at the condition.

When buying philatelic items listed you need to make sure they are in the same condition as issued by the Post Office. This applies to Presentation packs, were the stamps are issued on a stock card with an information card and held together in a plastic wallet and also to Year Books, which should be in a slip case with a stock card of stamps. The prices quoted are for a complete item in good condition so make sure you check this – and of course that they are complete. You will find some items may appear in different format (e.g. language, different bindings, etc) which will be listed under the normal listing within this catalogue.

Ask the Experts

While you are building your collection, if you need help or guidance, you are welcome to come along to Stanley Gibbons in the Strand and ask for assistance. If you would like to have your collection appraised, you can arrange for a verbal evaluation Monday to Friday 9.00am – 4.30pm. We also provide insurance valuations should you require. Of course this up-to-date catalogue listing can assist with the valuation and may be presented to an insurance agent or company.

See the Stanley Gibbons Contact details: on page xxii.

Features Listing

An at-a-glace guide to what's in the Stanley Gibbons catalogues

Area	Feature	Collect British Stamps	Stamps of the World	Thematic Catalogues	Commonwealth and British Empire stamps and country catalogues	Comprehensive Catalogue, Parts 1-22 (including Commonwealth and British Empire stamps and country catalogues)	Great Britain Concise	Specialised catalogues
General	SG number	√	√	√		√	√	√
General	Specialised Catalogue number							√
General	Year of issue of first stamp in design	√	√	√		√	√	√
General	Exact date of issue of each design					√	√	√
General	Face value information	√	√	√		√	√	√
General	Historical and geographical information	√	√	√		√	√	√
General	General currency information, including dates used	√	√	√		√	√	√
General	Country name	√	√	√		√		
General	Booklet panes					√	√	√
General	Coil stamps					√		√
General	First Day Covers	√					√	√
General	Brief footnotes on key areas of note	√	√	√		√	√	√
General	Detailed footnotes on key areas of note					√	√	√
General	Extra background information					√	√	√
General	Miniature sheet information (including size in mm)	√	√	√		√	√	√
General	Sheetlets					√		
General	Stamp booklets					√	√	√
General	Perkins Bacon "Cancelled"					√		
General	PHQ Cards	√					√	√
General	Post Office Label Sheets						√	
General	Post Office Yearbooks	√					√	√
General	Presentation and Souvenir Packs	√					√	√
General	*Se-tenant* pairs	√				√	√	√
General	Watermark details - errors, varieties, positions					√	√	√
General	Watermark illustrations	√				√	√	√
General	Watermark types	√				√	√	√
General	Forgeries noted					√		√
General	Surcharges and overprint information	√	√	√		√	√	√
Design and Description	Colour description, simplified		√	√				
Design and Description	Colour description, extended	√				√	√	√
Design and Description	Set design summary information	√	√	√		√	√	√
Design and Description	Designer name					√	√	√
Design and Description	Short design description	√	√	√		√	√	√

Area	Feature	Collect British Stamps	Stamps of the World	Thematic Catalogues	Commonwealth and British Empire Stamps and country catalogues	Comprehensive Catalogue, Parts 1-22 (including Commonwealth catalogues)	Great Britain Concise	Specialised catalogues
Design and Description	Shade varieties					√	√	√
Design and Description	Type number	√	√			√	√	√
Illustrations	Multiple stamps from set illustrated	√				√	√	√
Illustrations	A Stamp from each set illustrated in full colour (where possible, otherwise mono)	√	√	√		√	√	√
Price	Catalogue used price	√	√	√		√	√	√
Price	Catalogue unused price	√	√	√		√	√	√
Price	Price - booklet panes					√	√	√
Price	Price - shade varieties					√	√	√
Price	On cover and on piece price					√	√	√
Price	Detailed GB pricing breakdown	√				√	√	√
Print and Paper	Basic printing process information	√	√	√		√	√	√
Print and Paper	Detailed printing process information, e.g. Mill sheets					√	√	√
Print and Paper	Paper information					√	√	√
Print and Paper	Detailed perforation information	√				√	√	√
Print and Paper	Details of research findings relating to printing processes and history							√
Print and Paper	Paper colour	√	√			√	√	√
Print and Paper	Paper description to aid identification					√	√	√
Print and Paper	Paper type					√	√	√
Print and Paper	Ordinary or chalk-surfaced paper					√	√	√
Print and Paper	Embossing omitted note							√
Print and Paper	Essays, Die Proofs, Plate Descriptions and Proofs, Colour Trials information							√
Print and Paper	Glazed paper					√	√	√
Print and Paper	Gum details					√		√
Print and Paper	Luminescence/Phosphor bands - general coverage	√				√	√	√
Print and Paper	Luminescence/Phosphor bands - specialised coverage							√
Print and Paper	Overprints and surcharges - including colour information	√	√	√		√	√	√
Print and Paper	Perforation/Imperforate information	√	√			√	√	√
Print and Paper	Perforation errors and varieties					√	√	√
Print and Paper	Print quantities					√		√
Print and Paper	Printing errors					√	√	√
Print and Paper	Printing flaws							√
Print and Paper	Printing varieties					√	√	√
Print and Paper	Punctured stamps - where official					√		
Print and Paper	Sheet positions					√	√	√
Print and Paper	Specialised plate number information							√
Print and Paper	Specimen overprints (only for Commonwealth & GB)					√	√	√
Print and Paper	Underprints						√	√
Print and Paper	Visible Plate numbers	√				√	√	√
Print and Paper	Yellow and Green paper listings					√		√
Index	Design index	√				√	√	

Stanley Gibbons Publications

1 *Commonwealth & British Empire Stamps 1840–1970*

Commonwealth Country Catalogues
Australia and Dependencies (5th edition, 2009)
Bangladesh, Pakistan & Sri Lanka
   (1st edition, 2004)
Belize, Guyana, Trinidad & Tobago
   (1st edition, 2009)
Brunei, Malaysia & Singapore
   (2nd edition, 2004)
Canada (3rd edition, 2008)
Central Africa (2nd edition, 2008)
Cyprus, Gibraltar & Malta (2nd edition, 2008)
East Africa with Egypt and Sudan
   (1st edition, 2006)
Eastern Pacific (1st edition, 2007)
Falkland Islands (3rd edition, 2008)
Hong Kong (2nd edition, 2007)
India (including Convention and Feudatory States)
   (3rd edition, 2009)
Indian Ocean (1st edition, 2006)
Ireland (4th edition, 2008)
Leeward Islands (1st edition, 2007)
New Zealand (3rd edition, 2009)
Northern Caribbean, Bahamas & Bermuda
   (2nd edition, 2009)
St. Helena & Dependencies (3rd edition, 2007)
Southern Africa (2nd edition, 2007)
West Africa (1st edition, 2009)
Western Pacific (2nd edition, 2009)
Windward Islands and Barbados
   (1st edition, 2007)

Foreign Countries
2 *Austria & Hungary* (7th edition, 2009)
3 *Balkans* (5th edition, 2009)
4 *Benelux* (5th edition, 2003)
5 *Czechoslovakia & Poland* (6th edition, 2002)
6 *France* (6th edition, 2006)
7 *Germany* (8th edition, 2007)
8 *Italy & Switzerland* (7th edition, 2010)
9 *Portugal & Spain* (5th edition, 2004)
10 *Russia* (6th edition, 2008)
11 *Scandinavia* (6th edition, 2008)
12 *Africa since Independence A-E* (2nd edition, 1983)
13 *Africa since Independence F-M* (1st edition, 1981)
14 *Africa since Independence N-Z* (1st edition, 1981)
15 *Central America* (3rd edition, 2007)
16 *Central Asia* (4th edition, 2006)

17 *China* (7th edition, 2006)
18 *Japan & Korea* (5th edition, 2008)
19 *Middle East* (7th edition, 2009)
20 *South America* (4th edition, 2008)
21 *South-East Asia* (4th edition, 2004)
22 *United States* (6th edition, 2005)

Great Britain Specialised Catalogues
Volume 1 *Queen Victoria* (15th edition, 2008)
Volume 2 *King Edward VII to King George VI*
            (13th edition, 2009)
Volume 3 *Queen Elizabeth II Pre-decimal issues*
            (11th edition, 2006)
Volume 4 *Queen Elizabeth II Decimal Definitive Issues – Part 1* (10th edition, 2008)
Volume 5 *Queen Elizabeth II Decimal Special Issues* (3rd edition, 1998 with 1998-99 and 2000/1 Supplements)

Thematic Catalogues
Stanley Gibbons Catalogues for use with **Stamps of the World.**
Collect Aircraft on Stamps (2nd edition, 2009)
Collect Birds on Stamps (5th edition, 2003)
Collect Chess on Stamps (2nd edition, 1999)
Collect Fish on Stamps (1st edition, 1999)
Collect Fungi on Stamps (2nd edition, 1997)
Collect Motor Vehicles on Stamps
   (1st edition 2004)

Other Publications
Philatelic Terms Illustrated (4th edition, 2003)
Collect British Stamps (61st edition, 2010)
Great Britain Concise Stamp Catalogue (24th edition, 2009)
How to Identify Stamps (4th edition, 2007)
Collect Channel Islands and Isle of Man Stamps
   (25th edition, 2009)
Great Britain Numbers Issued (3rd edition, 2008)
Enjoy Stamp Collecting (7th edition, 2006)

For other titles, and further details on the above, please see *www.stanleygibbons.com*

Guide to Entries

(A) Accession to the Throne

(B) Illustration – Generally all stamps illustrated. To comply with Post Office regulations illustrations are reduced to 75%, with overprints shown actual size.

(C) Illustration or Type Number – These numbers are used to help identify stamps, in the type column.

(D) Date of Issue – When a set of definitive stamps have been issued over several years the Year Date given is for the earliest issue, commemorative sets are set in chronological order.

(E) Phosphor Description – Phosphorised paper is activated by ultraviolet light.

(F) Perforations – The 'perforation' is the number of holes in a length of 2cm, as measured by the Stanley Gibbons *Instanta* gauge. From 1992 certain stamps occur with a large elliptical (oval) hole inserted in each line of vertical perforations. From 2009 certain stamps have U-shaped die-cut slits.

(G) Stanley Gibbons Catalogue Number – This is a unique number for each stamp to help the collector identify stamps, in the listing. The Stanley Gibbons numbering system is universally recognized as definitive, where insufficient numbers have been left to provide for additional stamps listings, some stamps will have a suffix letter after the catalogue number.

(H) Catalogue Value – Mint/Unused. Prices quoted for pre-1945 stamps are for lightly hinged examples. Prices quoted of unused King Edward VIII to Queen Elizabeth issues are for unmounted mint.

(I) Catalogue Value – Used. Prices generally refer to fine postally used examples.

Prices

Before February 1971 British currency was:

£1 = 20s One pound = twenty shillings *and*
1s = 12d One Shilling = 12 pence

Under decimalisation this became:

£1 = 100p One pound = one hundred (new) pence

Shown in Catalogue as	Explanation
10	10 pence
1.75	£1.75
15.00	£15
£150	£150
£2300	£2300

(J) Face Value – This refers to the value of the stamp and is sold at the Post Office when issued. Some modern stamps do not have their values in figures but instead shown as a letter.

(K) Type Number – Indicates a design type on which stamp is based. These are bold figures found below each illustration. The type numbers are also given in bold in the second column of figures alongside the stamp description to indicate the design of each stamp.

(L) Colour – Colour of stamps (if fewer than four colours, otherwise noted as 'multicoloured').

(M) Sets of Stamps – Two or more stamps with a common theme or subject.

(N) First Day Covers – Prices for first day covers are for complete sets used on plain covers or on special covers.

(O) Presentation Packs – Special packs consisting of the issue and slip-in cards with printed information inside a protective covering.

(P) PHQ Cards – Each card shows a large reproduction of a current British stamp.

(Q) Sets of Gutters – The term is used for a pair of stamps separated by part of the blank gutter margin or with Traffic Lights on the gutter margin.

(R) Footnote – Further information on background or key facts on issues.

(S) Other Types of Stamps – Postage Dues, Officials and Regional Issues

(T) Number Prefix – Stamps other than definitives and commemoratives have a prefix letter before the catalogue number.

QUEEN ELIZABETH II

A Accession to the Throne ———— ●6 February, 1952

B Illustration ————

C Illustration or Type Number ————

1862 *The Very Hungry Caterpillar* (Eric Carle)

E ● **1526** Butterfly Hat by Dai Rees

J Face Value

Nos. 2589/90, 2591/2, 2593/4 and 2595/6 were printed together, *se-tenant*, as horizontal pairs in sheets of 60(2 panes 6 × 5).

Animal Tales

D Date of Issue ———— ● **2006** (10 Jan.) One side phosphor band (2nd) or two ● phosphor bands (others). Perf 14½ ●

E Phosphor Description
F Perforations

			Unused	Used		
2589	**1856**	(2nd) multicoloured	30	35	☐	☐
		a. Horiz pair.				
		Nos. 2589/90	70	70	☐	☐
2590	**1857**	(2nd) multicoloured	30	35	☐	☐
2591	**1858**	(1st) multicoloured	45	50	☐	☐
		a. Horiz pair.				
		Nos. 2591/2	1·50	1·50	☐	☐
2592	**1859**	(1st) multicoloured	45	50	☐	☐
2593	**1860**	42p multicoloured	65	70	☐	☐
		a. Horiz pair.				
		Nos. 2593/4	3·75	3·75	☐	☐
2594	**1861**	42p multicoloured	65	70	☐	☐
2595	**1862**	68p multicoloured	1·00	1·10	☐	☐
		a. Horiz pair.				
		Nos. 2595/6	4·75	4·75	☐	☐
2596	**1863**	68p multicoloured	1·00	1·10	☐	☐
Set of 8			8·50	8·50	☐	
First Day Cover ●				8·00		☐
Presentation Pack			12·00		☐	
PHQ Cards (*set of* 8) ●			4·50	12·00	☐	☐
Set of 4 Gutter Blocks of 4			13·00		☐	
Set of 4 Traffic Light Gutter Blocks of 8			28·00		☐	

G Stanley Gibbons Catalogue Number

J Face Value

K Type Number

M Sets

O Special Packs

Q Gutter Combinations

H Catalogue Value – Unused

I Catalogue Value – Used

L Colour

N FDC for Complete Sets

P PHQ Cards

No. 2595 contains two die-cut holes.

R Footnotes ———— A design as No. 2592 but self-adhesive was also issued in sheets of 20 with each stamp accompanied by a *se-tenant* label.

S Postage Due ———— ● D 1

POSTAGE DUE STAMPS ●————————— **S** Other Types of Stamps

1968–69 Design size 21½ × 17½ mm. No wmk

T Number Prefix ●	D75	D **1**	4d blue	7·00	6·75	☐ ☐
	D76		8d red	50	1·00	☐ ☐

QUEEN VICTORIA

1837 (20 June)–1901 (22 Jan.)

| 5 | 8 | 6 |

9 Watermark extending over three stamps

IDENTIFICATION. In this checklist Victorian stamps are classified firstly according to which printing method was used –line-engraving, embossing or surface-printing.

Corner letters. Numerous stamps also have letters in all four, or just the lower corners. These were an anti-forgery device and the letters differ from stamp to stamp. If present in all four corners the upper pair are the reverse of the lower. Note the importance of these corner letters in the way the checklist is arranged.

Watermarks. Further classification depends on water-marks: these are illustrated in normal position, with stamps priced accordingly.

1 Line-engraved Issues

| 1 | 1a | 1b |

3 White lines added above and below head

2 Small Crown watermark

4 Large Crown watermark

Letters in lower corners

1840 Wmk Small Crown Type 2 Imperforate

| 2 | **1** | 1d black | £10000 | £275 | ☐ ☐ |
| 5 | **1a** | 2d blue | £27000 | £675 | ☐ ☐ |

1841

| 8 | **1b** | 1d red-brown | £500 | 25·00 | ☐ ☐ |
| 14 | **3** | 2d blue | £4250 | 75·00 | ☐ ☐ |

1854–57 (i) Wmk Small Crown Type 2 Perf 16

| 17 | **1b** | 1d red-brown | £275 | 25·00 | ☐ ☐ |
| 19 | **3** | 2d blue | £3500 | 90·00 | ☐ ☐ |

(ii) Wmk Small Crown Type 2 Perf 14

| 24 | **1b** | 1d red-brown | £500 | 60·00 | ☐ ☐ |
| 23 | **3** | 2d blue | £7500 | £200 | ☐ ☐ |

(iii) Wmk Large Crown Type 4 Perf 16

| 26 | **1b** | 1d red | £900 | £110 | ☐ ☐ |
| 27 | **3** | 2d blue | £10000 | £375 | ☐ ☐ |

(iv) Wmk Large Crown Type 4 Perf 14

| 40 | **1b** | 1d red | 45·00 | 10·00 | ☐ ☐ |
| 34 | **3** | 2d blue | £2000 | 60·00 | ☐ ☐ |

7

Letters in all four corners

Plate numbers. Stamps included a 'plate number' in their design and this affects valuation. The cheapest plates are priced here; see complete list of plate numbers overleaf.

1858–70 (i) Wmk Type 9 Perf 14

48	**7**	½d red	90·00	18·00	☐ ☐
(ii) Wmk Large Crown Type 4 Perf 14					
43	**5**	1d red	18·00	2·50	☐ ☐
51	**8**	1½d red	£400	60·00	☐ ☐
45	**6**	2d blue	£300	12·00	☐ ☐

Plate numbers on stamps 1858-70 having letters in all four corners

Positions of Plate Numbers

| Shows Plate 9 (½d) | Shows Plate 170 (1d, 2d) | Shows Plate 3 (1½d) |

HALFPENNY VALUE (SG 48)

48	*Plate 1*	£275	75·00	☐ ☐
48	*Plate 3*	£200	40·00	☐ ☐
48	*Plate 4*	£130	30·00	☐ ☐
48	*Plate 5*	90·00	18·00	☐ ☐
48	*Plate 6*	£100	18·00	☐ ☐
48	*Plate 8*	£500	£100	☐ ☐
48	*Plate 9*	£5500	£700	☐ ☐
48	*Plate 10*	£110	18·00	☐ ☐
48	*Plate 11*	£100	18·00	☐ ☐
48	*Plate 12*	£100	18·00	☐ ☐
48	*Plate 13*	£100	18·00	☐ ☐
48	*Plate 14*	£100	18·00	☐ ☐
48	*Plate 15*	£150	40·00	☐ ☐
48	*Plate 19*	£250	55·00	☐ ☐
48	*Plate 20*	£300	75·00	☐ ☐

PENNY VALUE (SG 43)

43	*Plate 71*	40·00	3·50	☐ ☐
43	*Plate 72*	45·00	4·50	☐ ☐
43	*Plate 73*	45·00	3·50	☐ ☐
43	*Plate 74*	45·00	2·50	☐ ☐
43	*Plate 76*	40·00	2·50	☐ ☐

43	*Plate 77*	—		☐	☐
43	*Plate 78*	£100	2·50	☐	☐
43	*Plate 79*	35·00	2·50	☐	☐
43	*Plate 80*	50·00	2·50	☐	☐
43	*Plate 81*	50·00	2·75	☐	☐
43	*Plate 82*	£100	4·50	☐	☐
43	*Plate 83*	£125	8·00	☐	☐
43	*Plate 84*	65·00	2·75	☐	☐
43	*Plate 85*	45·00	3·75	☐	☐
43	*Plate 86*	55·00	4·50	☐	☐
43	*Plate 87*	35·00	2·50	☐	☐
43	*Plate 88*	£150	8·50	☐	☐
43	*Plate 89*	45·00	2·50	☐	☐
43	*Plate 90*	45·00	2·50	☐	☐
43	*Plate 91*	60·00	6·50	☐	☐
43	*Plate 92*	40·00	2·50	☐	☐
43	*Plate 93*	55·00	2·50	☐	☐
43	*Plate 94*	50·00	5·50	☐	☐
43	*Plate 95*	45·00	2·50	☐	☐
43	*Plate 96*	50·00	2·50	☐	☐
43	*Plate 97*	45·00	4·00	☐	☐
43	*Plate 98*	55·00	6·50	☐	☐
43	*Plate 99*	60·00	5·50	☐	☐
43	*Plate 100*	65·00	2·75	☐	☐
43	*Plate 101*	65·00	10·00	☐	☐
43	*Plate 102*	50·00	2·50	☐	☐
43	*Plate 103*	55·00	4·00	☐	☐
43	*Plate 104*	80·00	5·50	☐	☐
43	*Plate 105*	£100	8·00	☐	☐
43	*Plate 106*	60·00	2·50	☐	☐
43	*Plate 107*	65·00	8·00	☐	☐
43	*Plate 108*	85·00	2·75	☐	☐
43	*Plate 109*	90·00	4·00	☐	☐
43	*Plate 110*	65·00	10·00	☐	☐
43	*Plate 111*	55·00	2·75	☐	☐
43	*Plate 112*	75·00	2·75	☐	☐
43	*Plate 113*	55·00	14·00	☐	☐
43	*Plate 114*	£280	14·00	☐	☐
43	*Plate 115*	£100	2·75	☐	☐
43	*Plate 116*	80·00	10·00	☐	☐
43	*Plate 117*	50·00	2·50	☐	☐
43	*Plate 118*	55·00	2·50	☐	☐
43	*Plate 119*	50·00	2·50	☐	☐
43	*Plate 120*	18·00	2·50	☐	☐
43	*Plate 121*	45·00	10·00	☐	☐
43	*Plate 122*	18·00	2·50	☐	☐
43	*Plate 123*	45·00	2·50	☐	☐
43	*Plate 124*	32·00	2·50	☐	☐
43	*Plate 125*	45·00	2·50	☐	☐
43	*Plate 127*	60·00	2·75	☐	☐
43	*Plate 129*	45·00	9·00	☐	☐
43	*Plate 130*	60·00	2·75	☐	☐
43	*Plate 131*	70·00	18·00	☐	☐
43	*Plate 132*	£150	25·00	☐	☐
43	*Plate 133*	£125	10·00	☐	☐
43	*Plate 134*	18·00	2·50	☐	☐
43	*Plate 135*	£100	28·00	☐	☐
43	*Plate 136*	£100	22·00	☐	☐
43	*Plate 137*	32·00	2·75	☐	☐
43	*Plate 138*	22·00	2·50	☐	☐
43	*Plate 139*	65·00	18·00	☐	☐
43	*Plate 140*	22·00	2·50	☐	☐
43	*Plate 141*	£125	10·00	☐	☐
43	*Plate 142*	75·00	28·00	☐	☐
43	*Plate 143*	65·00	16·00	☐	☐
43	*Plate 144*	£100	22·00	☐	☐

43	*Plate 145*	35·00	2·75	☐	☐
43	*Plate 146*	45·00	6·50	☐	☐
43	*Plate 147*	55·00	3·50	☐	☐
43	*Plate 148*	45·00	3·50	☐	☐
43	*Plate 149*	45·00	6·50	☐	☐
43	*Plate 150*	18·00	2·50	☐	☐
43	*Plate 151*	65·00	10·00	☐	☐
43	*Plate 152*	65·00	6·00	☐	☐
43	*Plate 153*	£110	10·00	☐	☐
43	*Plate 154*	55·00	2·50	☐	☐
43	*Plate 155*	55·00	2·75	☐	☐
43	*Plate 156*	50·00	2·50	☐	☐
43	*Plate 157*	55·00	2·50	☐	☐
43	*Plate 158*	35·00	2·50	☐	☐
43	*Plate 159*	35·00	2·50	☐	☐
43	*Plate 160*	35·00	2·50	☐	☐
43	*Plate 161*	65·00	8·00	☐	☐
43	*Plate 162*	55·00	8·00	☐	☐
43	*Plate 163*	55·00	3·50	☐	☐
43	*Plate 164*	55·00	3·50	☐	☐
43	*Plate 165*	50·00	2·50	☐	☐
43	*Plate 166*	50·00	6·50	☐	☐
43	*Plate 167*	50·00	2·50	☐	☐
43	*Plate 168*	55·00	9·00	☐	☐
43	*Plate 169*	65·00	8·00	☐	☐
43	*Plate 170*	40·00	2·50	☐	☐
43	*Plate 171*	18·00	2·50	☐	☐
43	*Plate 172*	35·00	2·50	☐	☐
43	*Plate 173*	75·00	10·00	☐	☐
43	*Plate 174*	35·00	2·50	☐	☐
43	*Plate 175*	65·00	4·00	☐	☐
43	*Plate 176*	65·00	2·75	☐	☐
43	*Plate 177*	45·00	2·50	☐	☐
43	*Plate 178*	65·00	4·00	☐	☐
43	*Plate 179*	55·00	2·75	☐	☐
43	*Plate 180*	65·00	5·50	☐	☐
43	*Plate 181*	50·00	2·50	☐	☐
43	*Plate 182*	£100	5·50	☐	☐
43	*Plate 183*	60·00	3·50	☐	☐
43	*Plate 184*	35·00	2·75	☐	☐
43	*Plate 185*	55·00	3·50	☐	☐
43	*Plate 186*	70·00	2·75	☐	☐
43	*Plate 187*	55·00	2·50	☐	☐
43	*Plate 188*	75·00	11·00	☐	☐
43	*Plate 189*	75·00	7·50	☐	☐
43	*Plate 190*	55·00	6·50	☐	☐
43	*Plate 191*	35·00	8·00	☐	☐
43	*Plate 192*	55·00	2·50	☐	☐
43	*Plate 193*	35·00	2·50	☐	☐
43	*Plate 194*	55·00	9·00	☐	☐
43	*Plate 195*	55·00	9·00	☐	☐
43	*Plate 196*	55·00	5·50	☐	☐
43	*Plate 197*	60·00	10·00	☐	☐
43	*Plate 198*	45·00	6·50	☐	☐
43	*Plate 199*	60·00	6·50	☐	☐
43	*Plate 200*	65·00	2·50	☐	☐
43	*Plate 201*	35·00	5·50	☐	☐
43	*Plate 202*	65·00	9·00	☐	☐
43	*Plate 203*	35·00	18·00	☐	☐
43	*Plate 204*	60·00	2·75	☐	☐
43	*Plate 205*	60·00	3·50	☐	☐
43	*Plate 206*	60·00	10·00	☐	☐
43	*Plate 207*	65·00	10·00	☐	☐
43	*Plate 208*	60·00	18·00	☐	☐
43	*Plate 209*	55·00	10·00	☐	☐
43	*Plate 210*	70·00	13·00	☐	☐

43	*Plate 211*	75·00	22·00	☐ ☐
43	*Plate 212*	65·00	12·00	☐ ☐
43	*Plate 213*	65·00	12·00	☐ ☐
43	*Plate 214*	70·00	20·00	☐ ☐
43	*Plate 215*	70·00	20·00	☐ ☐
43	*Plate 216*	75·00	20·00	☐ ☐
43	*Plate 217*	75·00	8·00	☐ ☐
43	*Plate 218*	70·00	9·00	☐ ☐
43	*Plate 219*	£100	75·00	☐ ☐
43	*Plate 220*	45·00	8·00	☐ ☐
43	*Plate 221*	75·00	18·00	☐ ☐
43	*Plate 222*	85·00	45·00	☐ ☐
43	*Plate 223*	£100	65·00	☐ ☐
43	*Plate 224*	£125	55·00	☐ ☐
43	*Plate 225*	£2800	£700	☐ ☐

Plates 69, 70, 75, 77, 126 and 128 were prepared but rejected. No stamps therefore exist, except for a very few from Plate 77 which somehow reached the public. Plate 177 stamps, by accident or design, are sometimes passed off as the rare Plate 77.

THREE-HALFPENNY VALUE (S.G. 52)

52	*Plate (1)*	£600	80·00	☐ ☐
52	*Plate 3*	£400	60·00	☐ ☐

Plate 1 did not have the plate number in the design. Plate 2 was not completed and no stamps exist.

TWOPENNY VALUE (S.G. 45)

45	*Plate 7*	£1400	50·00	☐ ☐
45	*Plate 8*	£1300	35·00	☐ ☐
45	*Plate 9*	£300	12·00	☐ ☐
45	*Plate 12*	£2200	£120	☐ ☐

Plates 10 and 11 were prepared but rejected.

2 Embossed Issues

Prices are for stamps cut square and with average to fine embossing. Stamps with exceptionally clear embossing are worth more.

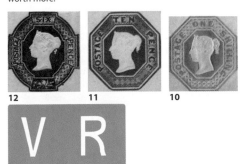

12   11   10

13

1847–54 Wmk 13 (6d), no wmk (others) Imperforate

59	**12**	6d lilac	£12000	£900	☐ ☐
57	**11**	10d brown	£8000	£1200	☐ ☐
54	**10**	1s green	£14000	£850	☐ ☐

3 Surface-printed Issues

IDENTIFICATION. Check first whether the design includes corner letters or not, as mentioned for 'Line-engraved Issues'. The checklist is divided up according to whether any letters are small or large, also whether they are white (uncoloured) or printed in the colour of the stamp. Further identification then depends on watermark.

PERFORATION. Except for Nos. 126/9 all the following issues of Queen Victoria are perf 14.

14

15   16   17

18   19   20 Emblems

No corner letters

1855–57 (i) Wmk Small Garter Type 15

62	**14**	4d red	£6500	£375	☐ ☐
(ii) Wmk Medium Garter Type 16					
65	**14**	4d red	£6000	£375	☐ ☐
(iii) Wmk Large Garter Type 17					
66a	**14**	4d red	£1350	£110	☐ ☐
(iv) Wmk Emblems Type 20					
70	**18**	6d lilac	£1100	95·00	☐ ☐
72	**19**	1s green	£1800	£260	☐ ☐

Plate numbers. Stamps Nos. 90/163 should be checked for the 'plate numbers' indicated, as this affects valuation (the cheapest plates are priced here). The mark 'Pl.' shows that several numbers exist, priced in separate list overleaf.

Plate numbers are the small numerals appearing in duplicate in some part of the frame design or adjacent to the lower corner letters (in the 5s value a single numeral above the lower inscription).

21   22   23

24   25

Small white corner letters

1862–64 Wmk Emblems Type 20, except 4d (Large Garter Type 17)

76	**21**	3d red	£2000	£250	☐ ☐
80	**22**	4d red	£1500	90·00	☐ ☐
84	**23**	6d lilac	£1700	90·00	☐ ☐

87	**24** 9d bistre	£3250	£350	☐	☐
90	**25** 1s green Pl.	£2500	£200	☐	☐

26   **27**   **28** Hyphen in SIX-PENCE

29   **30**   **31**

Large white corner letters

1865–67 Wmk Emblems Type 20 except 4d (Large Garter Type 17)

92	**26** 3d red (Plate 4)	£1500	£180	☐	☐
94	**27** 4d vermilion Pl.	£450	55·00	☐	☐
97	**28** 6d lilac Pl.	£900	80·00	☐	☐
98	**29** 9d straw Pl.	£4000	£500	☐	☐
99	**30** 10d brown (Plate 1)	*	£40000	☐	☐
101	**31** 1s green (Plate 4)	£2000	£200	☐	☐

32   **33** Spray of Rose   **34**

1867–80 Wmk Spray of Rose Type 33

103	**26** 3d red Pl.	£450	55·00	☐	☐
105	**28** 6d lilac (with hyphen) (Plate 6)	£1500	80·00	☐	☐
109	6d mauve (without hyphen) Pl.	£550	80·00	☐	☐
110	**29** 9d straw (Plate 4)	£2000	£275	☐	☐
112	**30** 10d brown Pl.	£2800	£300	☐	☐
117	**31** 1s green Pl.	£650	35·00	☐	☐
118	**32** 2s blue Pl.	£3000	£175	☐	☐
121	2s brown (Plate 1)	£20000	£3250	☐	☐

1872–73 Wmk Spray of Rose Type 33

122b	**34** 6d brown Pl.	£575	50·00	☐	☐
125	6d grey (Plate 12)	£1600	£225	☐	☐

PLATE NUMBERS ON STAMPS OF 1862–83

Small White Corner Letters (1862–64)

90	*Plate 2* 1s green	£2200	£200	☐	☐
90	*Plate 3*	£25000		☐	☐

Plate 2 is actually numbered as '1' and **Plate 3** as '2' on the stamps.

Large White Corner Letters (1865–83)

103	*Plate 4* 3d red	£1400	£250	☐	☐
103	*Plate 5*	£450	55·00	☐	☐
103	*Plate 6*	£475	55·00	☐	☐
103	*Plate 7*	£550	60·00	☐	☐
103	*Plate 8*	£525	55·00	☐	☐
103	*Plate 9*	£525	60·00	☐	☐

103	*Plate 10*	£750	£120	☐	☐
94	*Plate 7* 4d verm	£550	£100	☐	☐
94	*Plate 8*	£500	60·00	☐	☐
94	*Plate 9*	£500	60·00	☐	☐
94	*Plate 10*	£700	£130	☐	☐
94	*Plate 11*	£500	60·00	☐	☐
94	*Plate 12*	£475	55·00	☐	☐
94	*Plate 13*	£550	55·00	☐	☐
94	*Plate 14*	£600	85·00	☐	☐
97	*Plate 5* 6d lilac	£900	80·00	☐	☐
97	*Plate 6*	£3000	£150	☐	☐
109	*Plate 8* 6d mauve	£550	£120	☐	☐
109	*Plate 9*	£550	80·00	☐	☐
109	*Plate 10*	*	£28000	☐	☐
123	*Plate 11* 6d buff	£800	£100	☐	☐
123	*Plate 12*	£3000	£280	☐	☐
98	*Plate 4* 9d straw	£4000	£500	☐	☐
98	*Plate 5*	£18000		☐	☐
114	*Plate 1* 10d brown	£2800	£300	☐	☐
114	*Plate 2*	£40000	£12000	☐	☐
117	*Plate 4* 1s green	£1200	60·00	☐	☐
117	*Plate 5*	£650	35·00	☐	☐
117	*Plate 6*	£1000	35·00	☐	☐
117	*Plate 7*	£1200	70·00	☐	☐
119	*Plate 1* 2s blue	£3000	£175	☐	☐
119	*Plate 3*	*	£11000	☐	☐
127	*Plate 1* 5s red	£8250	£600	☐	☐
127	*Plate 2*	£12000	£1200	☐	☐

Large Coloured Corner Letters (1873–83)

139	*Plate 1* 2½d mauve	£525	80·00	☐	☐
139	*Plate 2*	£525	80·00	☐	☐
139	*Plate 3*	£800	£120	☐	☐
141	*Plate 3* 2½d mauve	£1100	£110	☐	☐
141	*Plate 4*	£425	50·00	☐	☐
141	*Plate 5*	£425	50·00	☐	☐
141	*Plate 6*	£425	50·00	☐	☐
141	*Plate 7*	£425	50·00	☐	☐
141	*Plate 8*	£425	50·00	☐	☐
141	*Plate 9*	£425	50·00	☐	☐
141	*Plate 10*	£475	65·00	☐	☐
141	*Plate 11*	£425	50·00	☐	☐
141	*Plate 12*	£425	50·00	☐	☐
141	*Plate 13*	£425	50·00	☐	☐
141	*Plate 14*	£425	50·00	☐	☐
141	*Plate 15*	£425	50·00	☐	☐
141	*Plate 16*	£425	50·00	☐	☐
141	*Plate 17*	£1400	£275	☐	☐
142	*Plate 17* 2½d blue	£475	55·00	☐	☐
142	*Plate 18*	£475	40·00	☐	☐
142	*Plate 19*	£475	40·00	☐	☐
142	*Plate 20*	£475	40·00	☐	☐
157	*Plate 21* 2½d blue	£400	35·00	☐	☐
157	*Plate 22*	£350	35·00	☐	☐
157	*Plate 23*	£350	28·00	☐	☐
144	*Plate 11* 3d red	£350	45·00	☐	☐
144	*Plate 12*	£400	45·00	☐	☐
144	*Plate 14*	£425	45·00	☐	☐
144	*Plate 15*	£350	45·00	☐	☐
144	*Plate 16*	£350	45·00	☐	☐
144	*Plate 17*	£400	45·00	☐	☐
144	*Plate 18*	£400	45·00	☐	☐
144	*Plate 19*	£350	45·00	☐	☐
144	*Plate 20*	£650	£100	☐	☐
158	*Plate 20* 3d red	£775	£140	☐	☐
158	*Plate 21*	£400	80·00	☐	☐

152	*Plate 15*	4d verm	£2400	£425
152	*Plate 16*		*	£28000
153	*Plate 15*	4d green	£1100	£275
153	*Plate 16*		£1000	£250
153	*Plate 17*		*	£17500
160	*Plate 17*	4d brown	£350	60·00
160	*Plate 18*		£350	60·00
147	*Plate 13*	6d grey	£400	60·00
147	*Plate 14*		£400	60·00
147	*Plate 15*		£400	60·00
147	*Plate 16*		£400	60·00
147	*Plate 17*		£750	£140
161	*Plate 17*	6d grey	£400	65·00
161	*Plate 18*		£350	65·00
150	*Plate 8*	1s green	£650	£120
150	*Plate 9*		£650	£120
150	*Plate 10*		£600	£140
150	*Plate 11*		£600	£120
150	*Plate 12*		£500	£100
150	*Plate 13*		£500	£100
150	*Plate 14*		*	£30000
163	*Plate 13*	1s brown	£675	£140
163	*Plate 14*		£550	£140

35   **36**   **37**

38

39 Maltese Cross   **40** Large Anchor

1867–83 (i) Wmk Maltese Cross Type 39 Perf 15½ × 15

126	**35**	5s red Pl.	£8250	£600
128	**36**	10s grey (Plate 1)	£50000	£2800
129	**37**	£1 brown (Plate 1)	£80000	£4000

(ii) Wmk Large Anchor Type 40 Perf 14

134	**35**	5s red (Plate 4)	£25000	£3250
131	**36**	10s grey (Plate 1)	£110000	£4800
132	**37**	£1 brown (Plate 1)	£125000	£9000
137	**38**	£5 orange (Plate 1)	£12000	£4500

41   **42**   **43**

44   **45**   **46**

47 Small anchor   **48** Orb   **49** Imperial Crown

Large coloured corner letters

1873–80 (i) Wmk Small Anchor Type 47

139	**41**	2½d mauve Pl.	£525	80·00

(ii) Wmk Orb Type 48

141	**41**	2½d mauve Pl.	£425	50·00
142		2½d blue Pl.	£475	40·00

(iii) Wmk Spray of Rose Type 33

143	**42**	3d red Pl.	£350	45·00
145	**43**	6d pale buff (Plate 13)	*	£20000
147		6d grey Pl.	£400	60·00
150	**44**	1s green Pl.	£500	£100
151		1s brown (Plate 13)	£4000	£600

(iv) Wmk Large Garter Type 17

152	**45**	4d vermilion Pl.	£2400	£425
153		4d green Pl.	£1000	£275
154		4d brown (Plate 17)	£2400	£475
156	**46**	8d orange (Plate 1)	£1500	£300

(50)   **(51)**

Surcharges in red

1880–83 Wmk Imperial Crown Type 49

157	**41**	2½d blue Pl.	£350	28·00
158	**42**	3d red Pl.	£400	80·00
159		3d on 3d lilac (surch Type 50)	£500	£130
160	**45**	4d brown Pl.	£350	60·00
161	**43**	6d grey Pl.	£350	65·00
162		6d on 6d lilac (surch Type 51)	£550	£130
163	**44**	1s brown Pl.	£550	£140

52   **53**   **54**

55   **56**

1880–81 Wmk Imperial Crown Type 49

164	**52**	½d green	45·00	12·00
166	**53**	1d brown	22·00	12·00
167	**54**	1½d brown	£200	45·00

| 168 | **55** | 2d red | £275 | 90·00 | ☐ ☐ |
| 169 | **56** | 5d indigo | £675 | £110 | ☐ ☐ |

57   Die I   Die II

1881 Wmk Imperial Crown Type 49
(a) 14 dots in each corner, Die I

| 171 | **57** | 1d lilac | £200 | 30·00 | ☐ ☐ |

(b) 16 dots in each corner, Die II

| 174 | **57** | 1d mauve | 2·50 | 1·50 | ☐ ☐ |

58   59

60

Coloured letters in the corners

1883–84 Wmk Anchor Type 40

178	**58**	2s 6d lilac	£500	£140	☐ ☐
181	**59**	5s red	£850	£200	☐ ☐
183	**60**	10s blue	£2000	£475	☐ ☐

61

1884 Wmk 3 Imperial Crowns Type 49

| 185 | **61** | £1 brown | £28000 | £2400 | ☐ ☐ |

1888 Wmk 3 Orbs Type 48

| 186 | **61** | £1 brown | £60000 | £3800 | ☐ ☐ |

1891 Wmk 3 Imperial Crowns Type 49

| 212 | **61** | £1 green | £3500 | £700 | ☐ ☐ |

62   63   64

65   66

1883–84 Wmk Imperial Crown Type 49 (sideways on horiz designs)

187	**52**	½d blue	25·00	8·00	☐ ☐
188	**62**	1½d lilac	£100	38·00	☐ ☐
189	**63**	2d lilac	£175	70·00	☐ ☐
190	**64**	2½d lilac	75·00	15·00	☐ ☐
191	**65**	3d lilac	£220	90·00	☐ ☐
192	**66**	4d dull green	£450	£185	☐ ☐
193	**62**	5d dull green	£450	£185	☐ ☐
194	**63**	6d dull green	£475	£200	☐ ☐
195	**64**	9d dull green	£950	£400	☐ ☐
196	**65**	1s dull green	£1100	£250	☐ ☐

The above prices are for stamps in the true dull green colour. Stamps which have been soaked, causing the colour to run are virtually worthless.

71   72   73

74   75   76

77   78   79

80   81   82

'Jubilee' Issue

1887–1900 The bicoloured stamps have the value tablets, or the frames including the value tablets, in the second colour. Wmk Imperial Crown Type 49

197	**71**	½d vermilion	1·50	1·00	☐ ☐
213		½d green*	1·75	2·00	☐ ☐
198	**72**	1½d purple and green	15·00	7·00	☐ ☐
200	**73**	2d green and red	28·00	12·00	☐ ☐
201	**74**	2½d purple on blue	22·00	3·00	☐ ☐
203	**75**	3d purple on yellow	22·00	3·25	☐ ☐
205	**76**	4d green and brown	30·00	13·00	☐ ☐
206	**77**	4½d green and red	10·00	40·00	☐ ☐
207a	**78**	5d purple and blue	35·00	11·00	☐ ☐
208	**79**	6d purple on red	30·00	10·00	☐ ☐
209	**80**	9d purple and blue	60·00	40·00	☐ ☐
210	**81**	10d purple and red	45·00	38·00	☐ ☐
211	**82**	1s green	£200	60·00	☐ ☐
214		1s green and red	50·00	£125	☐ ☐
Set of 14			£525	£325	☐ ☐

*The ½d No. 213 in blue is a colour changeling.

KING EDWARD VII

1901 (22 Jan.)–1910 (6 May)

83

84

85

86

87

88

89

90

91

92

93

94

95

96

97

297	**83**	6d purple	30·00	20·00	☐	☐
249	**90**	7d grey	12·00	20·00	☐	☐
307	**91**	9d purple and blue	60·00	60·00	☐	☐
311	**92**	10d purple and red	80·00	60·00	☐	☐
314	**93**	1s green and red	55·00	35·00	☐	☐
260	**94**	2s6d purple	£225	£140	☐	☐
263	**95**	5s red	£350	£200	☐	☐
265	**96**	10s blue	£850	£450	☐	☐
266	**97**	£1 green	£2000	£750	☐	☐
Set of 15 (to 1s)			£400	£275	☐	☐
(b) Perf 15 × 14						
279	**83**	½d green	40·00	45·00	☐	☐
281		1d red	35·00	15·00	☐	☐
283	**86**	2½d blue	22·00	15·00	☐	☐
285	**87**	3d purple on yellow	45·00	15·00	☐	☐
286	**88**	4d orange	30·00	15·00	☐	☐
Set of 5			£130	90·00	☐	☐

1902–13 Wmks Imperial Crown Type 49 (½d to 1s), Anchor
Type 40 (2s 6d to 10s), Three Crowns Type 49 (£1) (a) Perf 14

215	**83**	½d blue-green	2·75	1·50	☐	☐
217		½d yellow-green	2·75	1·50	☐	☐
219		1d red	2·75	1·50	☐	☐
224	**84**	1½d purple and green	70·00	18·00	☐	☐
291	**85**	2d green and red	28·00	20·00	☐	☐
231	**86**	2½d blue	20·00	10·00	☐	☐
232	**87**	3d purple on yellow	40·00	15·00	☐	☐
238	**88**	4d green and brown	40·00	18·00	☐	☐
240		4d orange	20·00	15·00	☐	☐
294	**89**	5d purple and blue	30·00	20·00	☐	☐

KING GEORGE V

1910 (6 May)–1936 (20 January)

PERFORATION. All the following issues are Perf 15 × 14 except vertical commemorative stamps which are 14 × 15, unless otherwise stated.

98 (Hair dark)   **99** (Lion unshaded)   **100**

1911–12 Wmk Imperial Crown Type 49

322	**98**	½d green	4·00	4·00	☐	☐
327	**99**	1d red	4·50	2·50	☐	☐

1912 Wmk Royal Cypher ('Simple') Type 100

335	**98**	½d green	40·00	40·00	☐	☐
336	**99**	1d red	30·00	30·00	☐	☐

  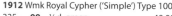

101 (Hair light)   **102** (Lion shaded)   **103**

1912 Wmk Imperial Crown Type 49

339	**101**	½d green	8·00	4·00	☐	☐
341	**102**	1d red	5·00	2·00	☐	☐

1912 Wmk Royal Cypher ('Simple') Type 100

344	**101**	½d green	7·00	3·00	☐	☐
345	**102**	1d red	8·00	4·50	☐	☐

1912 Wmk Royal Cypher ('Multiple') Type 103

346	**101**	½d green	12·00	8·00	☐	☐
350	**102**	1d red	18·00	10·00	☐	☐

104   **105**   **106**

107   **108**

1912–24 Wmk Royal Cypher Type 100

351	**105**	½d green	1·00	1·00	☐	☐
357	**104**	1d red	1·00	1·00	☐	☐
362	**105**	1½d brown	4·00	1·50	☐	☐
368	**106**	2d orange	4·00	3·00	☐	☐
371	**104**	2½d blue	12·00	4·00	☐	☐
375	**106**	3d violet	5·00	3·00	☐	☐
379		4d grey-green	15·00	2·00	☐	☐

381	**107**	5d brown	15·00	5·00	☐	☐
385		6d purple	15·00	7·00	☐	☐
		a. Perf 14	90·00	£110	☐	☐
387		7d olive-green	20·00	10·00	☐	☐
390		8d black on yellow	32·00	11·00	☐	☐
392	**108**	9d black	15·00	6·00	☐	☐
393a		9d olive-green	£110	30·00	☐	☐
394		10d blue	22·00	20·00	☐	☐
395		1s brown	20·00	4·00	☐	☐
Set of 15			£250	95·00	☐	☐

1913 Wmk Royal Cypher ('Multiple') Type 103

397	**105**	½d green	£150	£180	☐	☐
398	**104**	1d red	£225	£225	☐	☐

See also Nos. 418/29.

109   **110**

T 109. Background around portrait consists of horizontal lines

1913–18 Wmk Single Cypher Type 110 Perf 11 × 12

413a	**109**	2s 6d brown	£100	65·00	☐	☐
416		5s red	£250	£110	☐	☐
417		10s blue	£375	£160	☐	☐
403		£1 green	£2800	£1250	☐	☐
Set of 4			£3250	£1400	☐	☐

See also Nos. 450/2.

111

1924–26 Wmk Block Cypher Type 111

418	**105**	½d green	1·00	1·00	☐	☐
419	**104**	1d red	1·00	1·00	☐	☐
420	**105**	1½d brown	1·00	1·00	☐	☐
421	**106**	2d orange	2·50	2·50	☐	☐
422	**104**	2½d blue	5·00	3·00	☐	☐
423	**106**	3d violet	10·00	2·50	☐	☐
424		4d grey-green	12·00	2·50	☐	☐
425	**107**	5d brown	20·00	3·00	☐	☐
426a		6d purple	3·00	1·50	☐	☐
427	**108**	9d olive-green	12·00	3·50	☐	☐
428		10d blue	40·00	40·00	☐	☐
429		1s brown	22·00	3·00	☐	☐
Set of 12			£110	60·00	☐	☐

112   **112a**

British Empire Exhibition

1924–25 Wmk 111 Perf 14 (a) 23.4.24. Dated '1924'

430	**112**	1d red	10·00	11·00	☐	☐
431	**112a**	1½d brown	15·00	15·00	☐	☐
First Day Cover				£450		☐

(b) 9.5.25. Dated '1925'

432	**112**	1d red	15·00	30·00	☐	☐
433	**112a**	1½d brown	40·00	70·00	☐	☐
First Day Cover				£1700	☐	

113   **114**   **115**

116 St George and the Dragon

117

Ninth Universal Postal Union Congress

1929 (10 May) (a) Wmk 111

434	**113**	½d green	2·25	2·25	☐	☐
435	**114**	1d red	2·25	2·25	☐	☐
436		1½d brown	2·25	1·75	☐	☐
437	**115**	2½d blue	10·00	10·00	☐	☐
(b) Wmk 117 Perf 12						
438	**116**	£1 black	£750	£550	☐	☐
434/7		*Set of* 4	15·00	14·50	☐	☐
434/7		First Day Cover (4 vals.)		£600		☐
434/8		First Day Cover (5 vals.)		£9500		☐

118   **119**   **120**

121   **122**

1934–36 Wmk 111

439	**118**	½d green	50	50	☐	☐
440	**119**	1d red	50	50	☐	☐
441	**118**	1½d brown	50	50	☐	☐
442	**120**	2d orange	75	75	☐	☐
443	**119**	2½d blue	1·50	1·25	☐	☐
444	**120**	3d violet	1·50	1·25	☐	☐

445		4d grey-green	2·00	1·25	☐	☐
446	**121**	5d brown	6·50	2·75	☐	☐
447	**122**	9d olive-green	12·00	2·25	☐	☐
448		10d blue	15·00	10·00	☐	☐
449		1s brown	15·00	1·25	☐	☐
Set of 11			50·00	20·00	☐	☐

T **109** (re-engraved). Background around portrait consists of horizontal and diagonal lines

1934 Wmk 110 Perf 11 × 12

450	**109**	2s 6d brown	80·00	40·00	☐	☐
451		5s red	£175	85·00	☐	☐
452		10s blue	£350	80·00	☐	☐
Set of 3			£575	£190	☐	☐

123   **123a**

123b   **123c**

Silver Jubilee

1935 (7 May) Wmk 111

453	**123**	½d green	1·00	1·00	☐	☐
454	**123a**	1d red	1·50	2·00	☐	☐
455	**123b**	1½d brown	1·00	1·00	☐	☐
456	**123c**	2½d blue	5·00	6·00	☐	☐
Set of 4			8·00	9·25	☐	☐
First Day Cover				£600		☐

KING EDWARD VIII

1936 (20 Jan.–10 Dec.)

KING GEORGE VI

1936 (11 Dec.)–1952 (6 Feb.)

124

125

126 King George VI and Queen Elizabeth

127

1936 Wmk 125

457	**124**	½d	green	30	30	☐	☐
458		1d	red	60	50	☐	☐
459		1½d	brown	30	30	☐	☐
460		2½d	blue	30	85	☐	☐
Set of 4				1·25	1·75	☐	☐

First Day Covers

1 Sept. 1936	Nos. 457, 459/60	£150	☐
14 Sept. 1936	No. 458	£170	☐

Collectors are reminded that for issues from 1936 to date, prices in the unused column are for unmounted mint.

Coronation

1937 (13 May) Wmk 127

461	**126**	1½d	brown	30	30	☐	☐
First Day Cover				35·00			☐

128

129

130

King George VI and National Emblems

1937–47 Wmk 127

462	**128**	½d	green	30	25	☐	☐
463		1d	scarlet	30	25	☐	☐
464		1½d	brown	30	25	☐	☐
465		2d	orange	1·20	50	☐	☐
466		2½d	blue	40	25	☐	☐
467		3d	violet	5·00	1·00	☐	☐
468	**129**	4d	green	60	75	☐	☐
469		5d	brown	3·50	85	☐	☐
470		6d	purple	1·50	60	☐	☐
471	**130**	7d	green	5·00	60	☐	☐
472		8d	red	7·50	80	☐	☐
473		9d	deep green	6·50	80	☐	☐
474		10d	blue	7·00	80	☐	☐
474a		11d	plum	3·00	2·75	☐	☐
475		1s	brown	9·00	75	☐	☐
Set of 15				45·00	10·00	☐	☐

First Day Covers

10 May 1937	Nos. 462/3, 466	45·00	☐
30 July 1937	No. 464	45·00	☐
31 Jan. 1938	Nos. 465, 467	95·00	☐
21 Nov. 1938	Nos. 468/9	60·00	☐
30 Jan. 1939	No. 470	55·00	☐
27 Feb. 1939	Nos. 471/2	80·00	☐
1 May 1939	Nos. 473/4, 475	£450	☐
29 Dec. 1947	No. 474a	50·00	☐

For later printings of the lower values in apparently lighter shades and different colours, see Nos. 485/90 and 503/8.

130a King George VI

131

132

132a

133

1939–48 Wmk 133 Perf 14

476	**130a**	2s 6d	brown	70·00	6·00	☐	☐
476a		2s 6d	green	14·00	1·50	☐	☐
477	**131**	5s	red	20·00	2·00	☐	☐
478	**132**	10s	dark blue	£250	20·00	☐	☐
478a		10s	bright blue	35·00	5·00	☐	☐
478b	**132a**	£1	brown	20·00	26·00	☐	☐
Set of 6				£375	55·00	☐	☐

First Day Covers

21 Aug. 1939	No. 477	£800	☐
4 Sept. 1939	No. 476	£1750	☐
30 Oct. 1939	No. 478	£3000	☐
9 Mar. 1942	No. 476a	£1700	☐
30 Nov. 1942	No. 478a	£35000	☐
1 Oct. 1948	No. 478b	£300	☐

134 Queen Victoria and King George VI

**Centenary of
First Adhesive Postage Stamps**

1940 (6 May) Wmk 127 Perf 14½ × 14

479	**134**	½d	green	30	75	☐	☐
480		1d	red	1·00	75	☐	☐
481		1½d	brown	50	1·50	☐	☐
482		2d	orange	1·00	75	☐	☐
483		2½d	blue	2·25	50	☐	☐
484		3d	violet	3·00	3·50	☐	☐
Set of 6				8·75	5·25	☐	☐
First Day Cover					55·00		☐

Head as Nos. 462–7, but with lighter background

1941–42 Wmk 127

485	**128**	½d	pale green	30	30	☐	☐
486		1d	pale red	30	30	☐	☐
487		1½d	pale brown	60	80	☐	☐
488		2d	pale orange	50	50	☐	☐
489		2½d	light blue	30	30	☐	☐
490		3d	pale violet	2·50	1·00	☐	☐
Set of 6				3·50	2·75	☐	☐

First Day Covers

21 July 1941	No. 489	45·00	☐
11 Aug. 1941	No. 486	22·00	☐
1 Sept. 1941	No. 485	22·00	☐
6 Oct. 1941	No. 488	60·00	☐
3 Nov. 1941	No. 490	£110	☐
28 Sept. 1942	No. 487	55·00	☐

135 Symbols of Peace
and Reconstruction

136 Symbols of Peace
and Reconstruction

Victory

1946(11 June) Wmk 127

491	**135**	2½d	blue	20	20	☐	☐
492	**136**	3d	violet	20	50	☐	☐
First Day Cover					65·00		☐

137 King George VI
and Queen Elizabeth

138 King George VI
and Queen Elizabeth

Royal Silver Wedding

1948(26 Apr.) Wmk 127

493	**137**	2½d	blue	35	20	☐	☐
494	**138**	£1	blue	40·00	40·00	☐	☐
First Day Cover					£425		☐

1948(10 May)
Stamps of 1d and 2½d showing seaweed-gathering were on sale at eight Head Post Offices elsewhere in Great Britain, but were primarily for use in the Channel Islands and are listed there (see after Regional Issues).

139 Globe and Laurel
Wreath

140 Speed

141 Olympic Symbol

142 Winged Victory

149St George and the Dragon

150Royal Coat of Arms

1951(3 May) Wmk 133 Perf 11 × 12

509	**147**	2s 6d green	7·50	1·00	☐	☐
510	**148**	5s red	35·00	1·00	☐	☐
511	**149**	10s blue	15·00	7·50	☐	☐
512	**150**	£1 brown	45·00	18·00	☐	☐
Set of 4			£100	25·00	☐	☐
First Day Cover				£925		☐

Olympic Games

1948 (29 July) Wmk 127

495	**139**	2½d blue	35	10	☐	☐
496	**140**	3d violet	35	50	☐	☐
497	**141**	6d purple	2·50	75	☐	☐
498	**142**	1s brown	3·75	2·00	☐	☐
Set of 4			6·00	3·00	☐	☐
First Day Cover				45·00		☐

151 Commerce and Prosperity

152 Festival Symbol

Festival of Britain

1951 (3 May) Wmk 127

513	**151**	2½d red	20	15	☐	☐
514	**152**	4d blue	30	35	☐	☐
Set of 2			40	40	☐	☐
First Day Cover				38·00		☐

143 Two Hemispheres

144 U.P.U. Monument, Berne

145 Goddess Concordia, Globe and Points of Compass

146 Posthorn and Globe

75th Anniversary of Universal Postal Union

1949 (10 Oct.) Wmk 127

499	**143**	2½d blue	25	10	☐	☐
500	**144**	3d violet	25	50	☐	☐
501	**145**	6d purple	50	75	☐	☐
502	**146**	1s brown	1·00	1·25	☐	☐
Set of 4			1·50	2·50	☐	☐
First Day Cover				80·00		☐

4d as No. 468 and others as Nos. 485/9, but colours changed

1950–51 Wmk 127

503	**128**	½d pale orange	30	30	☐	☐
504		1d light blue	30	30	☐	☐
505		1½d pale green	65	60	☐	☐
506		2d pale brown	75	40	☐	☐
507		2½d pale red	60	40	☐	☐
508	**129**	4d light blue	2·00	1·75	☐	☐
Set of 6			4·00	3·25	☐	☐

First Day Covers

2 Oct. 1950	No. 508	£120	☐
3 May 1951	Nos. 503/7	55·00	☐

147 HMS Victory

148 White Cliffs of Dover

QUEEN ELIZABETH II

6 February, 1952

153 Tudor Crown

 154

 155

156

157

158

159

160

1952–54 Wmk 153

515	**154**	½d orange	10	15	☐	☐
516		1d blue	20	20	☐	☐
517		1½d green	10	20	☐	☐
518		2d brown	20	20	☐	☐
519	**155**	2½d red	15	15	☐	☐
520		3d lilac	1·50	90	☐	☐
521	**156**	4d blue	3·25	1·25	☐	☐
		4½d (See Nos. 577, 594, 609 and 616b)				
522	**157**	5d brown	75	3·50	☐	☐
523		6d purple	4·00	1·00	☐	☐
524		7d green	9·50	5·50	☐	☐
525	**158**	8d magenta	75	85	☐	☐
526		9d bronze-green	23·00	4·75	☐	☐
527		10d blue	18·00	4·75	☐	☐
528		11d plum	35·00	15·00	☐	☐
529	**159**	1s bistre	80	50	☐	☐
530	**160**	1s 3d green	4·50	3·25	☐	☐
531	**159**	1s 6d indigo	14·00	3·75	☐	☐
Set of 17			£100	40·00	☐	☐

First Day Covers

5 Dec. 1952	Nos. 517, 519	25·00	☐
6 July 1953	Nos. 522, 525, 529	50·00	☐
31 Aug. 1953	Nos. 515/16, 518	50·00	☐
2 Nov. 1953	Nos. 521, 530/1	£170	☐
18 Jan. 1954	Nos. 520, 523/4	£110	☐
8 Feb. 1954	Nos. 526/8	£225	☐

See also Nos. 540/56, 561/6, 570/94 and 599/618a and for stamps as Types **154/60** with face values in decimal currency see Nos. 2031/3, 2258/9, **MS**2326, **MS**2367 and 2378/9.

161

162

163

164

Coronation

1953 (3 June) Wmk 153

532	**161**	2½d red	20	25	☐	☐
533	**162**	4d blue	1·10	1·90	☐	☐
534	**163**	1s 3d green	5·00	3·00	☐	☐
535	**164**	1s 6d blue	10·00	4·75	☐	☐
Set of 4			16·00	9·00	☐	☐
First Day Cover				75·00		☐

For £1 values as Type **163** see Nos. **MS**2147 and 2380.

165 St Edward's Crown

166 Carrickfergus Castle

167 Caernarvon Castle

168 Edinburgh Castle

169 Windsor Castle

1955 (1–23 Sept.) Wmk 165 Perf 11 × 12

536	**166**	2s 6d brown	13·00	2·00	☐	☐
537	**167**	5s red	35·00	4·00	☐	☐
538	**168**	10s blue	85·00	14·00	☐	☐
539	**169**	£1 black	£130	35·00	☐	☐
Set of 4			£225	50·00	☐	☐
First Day Cover (Nos. 538/9) (1 Sept.)				£850		☐
First Day Cover (Nos. 536/7) (23 Sept.)				£650		☐

See also Nos. 595a/8a and 759/62.

1955–58 Wmk 165

540	**154**	½d orange	15	15	☐	☐
541		1d blue	30	15	☐	☐
542		1½d green	25	30	☐	☐
543		2d red-brown	25	35	☐	☐
543b		2d light red-brown	20	20	☐	☐
544	**155**	2½d red	20	25	☐	☐
545		3d lilac	25	25	☐	☐
546	**156**	4d blue	1·25	45	☐	☐
547	**157**	5d brown	6·00	6·00	☐	☐
548		6d purple	4·50	1·25	☐	☐

549		7d green	50·00	10·00	☐	☐
550	**158**	8d magenta	7·00	1·25	☐	☐
551		9d bronze-green	20·00	2·75	☐	☐
552		10d blue	20·00	2·75	☐	☐
553		11d plum	50	1·10	☐	☐
554	**159**	1s bistre	22·00	65	☐	☐
555	**160**	1s 3d green	30·00	1·60	☐	☐
556	**159**	1s 6d indigo	23·00	1·60	☐	☐
Set of 18			£160	27·00	☐	☐

170 Scout Badge and 'Rolling Hitch'   **171** 'Scouts coming to Britain'

172 Globe within a Compass   **173**

World Scout Jubilee Jamboree

1957 (1 Aug.) Wmk 165

557	**170**	2½d red	50	50	☐	☐
558	**171**	4d blue	75	1·50	☐	☐
559	**172**	1s 3d green	4·50	4·50	☐	☐
Set of 3			5·00	5·75	☐	☐
First Day Cover				25·00		☐

46th Inter Parliamentary Union Conference

1957 (12 Sept.) Wmk 165

560	**173**	4d blue	1·00	1·00	☐	☐
First Day Cover				£140		☐

Graphite-lined and Phosphor Issues

These are used in connection with automatic sorting machinery, originally experimentally at Southampton but now also operating elsewhere. In such areas these stamps were the normal issue, but from mid 1967 all low-value stamps bear phosphor markings.

The graphite lines were printed in black on the back, beneath the gum; two lines per stamp except for the 2d (see below).

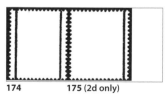

174   **175** (2d only)

(Stamps viewed from back)

In November 1959, phosphor bands, printed on the front, replaced the graphite. They are wider than the graphite, not easy to see, but show as broad vertical bands at certain angles to the light.

Values representing the rate for printed papers (and second class mail from 1968) have one band and others have two, three or four bands according to size and format. From 1972 onwards some commemorative stamps were printed with 'all-over' phosphor.

In the small stamps the bands are on each side with the single band at left (except where otherwise stated). In the large-size commemorative stamps the single band may be at left, centre or right varying in different issues. The bands are vertical on both horizontal and vertical designs except where otherwise stated.

See also notes on page 33.

Graphite-lined issue

1957 (19 Nov.) Two graphite lines on the back, except 2d value, which has one line. Wmk 165

561	**154**	½d orange	25	25	☐	☐
562		1d blue	40	40	☐	☐
563		1½d green	1·20	1·40	☐	☐
564		2d light red-brown	1·60	2·25	☐	☐
565	**155**	2½d red	8·50	7·00	☐	☐
566		3d lilac	80	50	☐	☐
Set of 6			12·00	10·50	☐	☐
First Day Cover				85·00		☐

See also Nos. 587/94.

176 Welsh Dragon   **177** Flag and Games Emblem

178 Welsh Dragon

Sixth British Empire and Commonwealth Games, Cardiff

1958 (18 July) Wmk 165

567	**176**	3d lilac	20	20	☐	☐
568	**177**	6d mauve	40	45	☐	☐
569	**178**	1s 3d green	2·25	2·40	☐	☐
Set of 3			2·50	2·75	☐	☐
First Day Cover				85·00		☐

179 Multiple Crowns

WATERMARK. All the following issues to No. 755 are Watermark 179 (sideways on the vertical commemorative stamps) unless otherwise stated.

1958–65 Wmk 179

570	**154**	½d orange	10	10	☐	☐
571		1d blue	10	10	☐	☐
572		1½d green	10	15	☐	☐
573		2d light red-brown	10	10	☐	☐
574	**155**	2½d red	10	20	☐	☐
575		3d lilac	10	20	☐	☐
576a	**156**	4d blue	15	15	☐	☐
577		4½d brown	10	25	☐	☐
578	**157**	5d brown	30	40	☐	☐
579		6d purple	30	25	☐	☐
580		7d green	50	45	☐	☐
581	**158**	8d magenta	60	40	☐	☐

582		9d bronze-green	60	40	☐ ☐
583		10d blue	1·00	50	☐ ☐
584	**159**	1s bistre	45	30	☐ ☐
585	**160**	1s 3d green	45	30	☐ ☐
586	**159**	1s 6d indigo	4·00	40	☐ ☐
Set of 17			8·00	4·25	☐ ☐
First Day Cover (No. 577) (9 Feb. 1959)				£250	☐

Graphite-lined issue

1958–59 Two graphite lines on the back, except 2d value, which has one line. Wmk 179

587	**154**	½d orange	9·00	9·00	☐ ☐
588		1d blue	2·00	1·50	☐ ☐
589		1½d green	90·00	80·00	☐ ☐
590		2d light red-brown	9·00	3·50	☐ ☐
591	**155**	2½d red	10·00	10·00	☐ ☐
592		3d lilac	50	65	☐ ☐
593	**156**	4d blue	5·50	5·00	☐ ☐
594		4½d brown	6·50	5·00	☐ ☐
Set of 8			85·00	70·00	☐ ☐

The prices quoted for Nos. 587 and 589 are for examples with inverted watermark. Stamps with upright watermark are priced at:½d £9 *mint*, £9 *used* and 1½d £90 *mint*, £80 *used*.

1959–63 Wmk 179 Perf 11 × 12

595a	**166**	2s 6d brown	35	40	☐ ☐
596a	**167**	5s red	1·20	50	☐ ☐
597a	**168**	10s blue	4·50	4·50	☐ ☐
598a	**169**	£1 black	13·00	8·00	☐ ☐
Set of 4			15·00	11·00	☐ ☐

Phosphor-Graphite issue

1959 (18 Nov.) Two phosphor bands on front and two graphite lines on back, except 2d value, which has one band on front and one line on back

		(a) Wmk 165			
599	**154**	½d orange	4·00	3·75	☐ ☐
600		1d blue	11·00	11·00	☐ ☐
601		1½d green	4·00	4·00	☐ ☐

		(b) Wmk 179			
605	**154**	2d light red-brown (1 band)	5·00	4·25	☐ ☐
606	**155**	2½d red	22·00	18·00	☐ ☐
607		3d lilac	10·00	8·00	☐ ☐
608	**156**	4d blue	20·00	16·00	☐ ☐
609		4½d brown	30·00	20·00	☐ ☐
Set of 8			85·00	70·00	☐ ☐

Phosphor issue

1960–67 Two phosphor bands on front, except where otherwise stated. Wmk 179

610	**154**	½d orange	10	15	☐ ☐
611		1d blue	10	10	☐ ☐
612		1½d green	15	15	☐ ☐
613		2d light red-brown (1 band)	16·00	18·00	☐ ☐
613a		2d light red-brown (2 bands)	10	15	☐ ☐
614	**155**	2½d red (2 bands)	20	30	☐ ☐
614a		2½d red (1 band)	60	75	☐ ☐
615		3d lilac (2 bands)	60	55	☐ ☐
615c		3d lilac (1 side band)	60	55	☐ ☐
615e		3d lilac (1 centre band)	40	45	☐ ☐
616a	**156**	4d blue	25	25	☐ ☐

616b		4½d brown	25	30	☐ ☐
616c	**157**	5d brown	25	35	☐ ☐
617		6d purple	30	30	☐ ☐
617a		7d green	55	50	☐ ☐
617b	**158**	8d magenta	40	45	☐ ☐
617c		9d bronze-green	60	55	☐ ☐
617d		10d blue	70	60	☐ ☐
617e	**159**	1s bistre	40	35	☐ ☐
618	**160**	1s 3d green	1·90	2·50	☐ ☐
618a	**159**	1s 6d indigo	2·00	2·00	☐ ☐
Set of 17 (one of each value)			7·50	8·00	☐ ☐

No. 615c exists with the phosphor band at the left or right of the stamp.

180 Postboy of 1660   **181** Posthorn of 1660

Tercentenary of Establishment of 'General Letter Office'

1960 (7 July)

619	**180**	3d lilac	50	50	☐ ☐
620	**181**	1s 3d green	3·75	4·25	☐ ☐
Set of 2			3·75	4·25	☐ ☐
First Day Cover				65·00	☐

182 Conference Emblem

First Anniversary of European Postal and Telecommunications Conference

1960 (19 Sept.)

621	**182**	6d green and purple	2·00	50	☐ ☐
622		1s 6d brown and blue	9·50	5·00	☐ ☐
Set of 2			11·00	5·50	☐ ☐
First Day Cover				65·00	☐

183 Thrift Plant

184 'Growth of Savings'   **185** Thrift Plant

Centenary of Post Office Savings Bank

1961 (28 Aug.)

623A	**183**	2½d black and red	25	25	☐	☐
624A	**184**	3d orange-brown and violet	20	20	☐	☐
625A	**185**	1s 6d red and blue	2·50	2·25	☐	☐
Set of 3			2·75	2·50	☐	☐
First Day Cover				75·00	☐	

186 C.E.P.T. Emblem

187 Doves and Emblem

188 Doves and Emblem

European Postal and Telecommunications (C.E.P.T.) Conference, Torquay

1961 (18 Sept.)

626	**186**	2d orange, pink and brown	15	10	☐	☐
627	**187**	4d buff, mauve and ultramarine	15	15	☐	☐
628	**188**	10d turquoise, green and blue	15	50	☐	☐
Set of 3			40	60	☐	☐
First Day Cover				6·00	☐	

189 Hammer Beam Roof, Westminster Hall

190 Palace of Westminster

Seventh Commonwealth Parliamentary Conference

1961 (25 Sept.)

629	**189**	6d purple and gold	25	25	☐	☐
630	**190**	1s 3d green and blue	2·50	2·75	☐	☐
Set of 2			2·75	3·00	☐	☐
First Day Cover				30·00	☐	

191 'Units of Productivity'

192 'National Productivity'

193 'Unified Productivity'

National Productivity Year

1962 (14 Nov.) Wmk 179 (inverted on 2½d and 3d)

631	**191**	2½d green and red	20	20	☐	☐
		p. Phosphor	60	50	☐	☐
632	**192**	3d blue and violet	50	25	☐	☐
		p. Phosphor	1·50	80	☐	☐
633	**193**	1s 3d red, blue and green	1·50	1·75	☐	☐
		p. Phosphor	35·00	22·00	☐	☐
Set of 3 (Ordinary)			2·00	1·90	☐	☐
Set of 3 (Phosphor)			30·00	22·00	☐	☐
First Day Cover (Ordinary)				55·00	☐	
First Day Cover (Phosphor)				£150	☐	

194 Campaign Emblem and Family

195 Children of Three Races

Freedom from Hunger

1963 (21 Mar.) Wmk 179 (inverted)

634	**194**	2½d crimson and pink	25	10	☐	☐
		p. Phosphor	3·00	1·25	☐	☐
635	**195**	1s 3d brown and yellow	1·90	1·90	☐	☐
		p. Phosphor	30·00	23·00	☐	☐
Set of 2 (Ordinary)			2·00	2·00	☐	☐
Set of 2 (Phosphor)			30·00	24·00	☐	☐
First Day Cover (Ordinary)				35·00	☐	
First Day Cover (Phosphor)				52·00	☐	

196 'Paris Conference'

Paris Postal Conference Centenary

1963 (7 May) Wmk 179 (inverted)

636	**196**	6d green and mauve	50	50	☐	☐
		p. Phosphor	6·00	7·00	☐	☐
First Day Cover (Ordinary)				16·00	☐	
First Day Cover (Phosphor)				37·00	☐	

197 Posy of Flowers

198 Woodland Life

National Nature Week

1963 (16 May)

637	**197**	3d multicoloured	15	15	☐	☐
		p. Phosphor	60	60	☐	☐
638	**198**	4½d multicoloured	35	35	☐	☐
		p. Phosphor	3·00	3·00	☐	☐
Set of 2 (Ordinary)			50	50	☐	☐
Set of 2 (Phosphor)			3·50	3·50	☐	☐
First Day Cover (Ordinary)				22·00	☐	
First Day Cover (Phosphor)				40·00	☐	

199 Rescue at Sea

200 19th-century Lifeboat

201 Lifeboatmen

Ninth International Lifeboat Conference, Edinburgh

1963 (31 May)

639	**199**	2½d	blue, black and red	25	25	☐ ☐
		p.	Phosphor	50	60	☐ ☐
640	**200**	4d	multicoloured	50	50	☐ ☐
		p.	Phosphor	50	60	☐ ☐
641	**201**	1s 6d	sepia, yellow and blue	3·00	3·25	☐ ☐
		p.	Phosphor	48·00	28·00	☐ ☐
Set of 3 (Ordinary)				3·25	3·50	☐ ☐
Set of 3 (Phosphor)				48·00	28·00	☐ ☐
First Day Cover (Ordinary)					35·00	☐
First Day Cover (Phosphor)					55·00	☐

202 Red Cross

203

204

Red Cross Centenary Congress

1963 (15 Aug.)

642	**202**	3d	red and lilac	25	25	☐ ☐
		p.	Phosphor	1·10	1·00	☐ ☐
643	**203**	1s 3d	red, blue and grey	3·00	3·00	☐ ☐
		p.	Phosphor	35·00	27·00	☐ ☐
644	**204**	1s 6d	red, blue and bistre	3·00	3·00	☐ ☐
		p.	Phosphor	35·00	27·00	☐ ☐
Set of 3 (Ordinary)				5·00	5·75	☐ ☐
Set of 3 (Phosphor)				65·00	55·00	☐ ☐
First Day Cover (Ordinary)					40·00	☐
First Day Cover (Phosphor)					90·00	☐

205 'Commonwealth Cable'

Opening of COMPAC (Trans-Pacific Telephone Cable)

1963 (3 Dec.)

645	**205**	1s 6d	blue and black	2·75	2·50	☐ ☐
		p.	Phosphor	16·00	15·50	☐ ☐
First Day Cover (Ordinary)					28·00	☐
First Day Cover (Phosphor)					40·00	☐

206 Puck and Bottom
(A Midsummer Nights Dream)

207 Feste
(Twelfth Night)

208 Balcony Scene
(Romeo and Juliet)

209 'Eve of Agincourt'
(Henry V)

210 Hamlet contemplating
Yorick's skull (Hamlet)
and Queen Elizabeth II

Shakespeare Festival

1964 (23 Apr.) Perf 11 × 12 (2s 6d) or 15 × 14 (others)

646	**206**	3d	bistre, black and violet-blue	15	15	☐ ☐
		p.	Phosphor	25	30	☐ ☐
647	**207**	6d	multicoloured	30	30	☐ ☐
		p.	Phosphor	75	1·00	☐ ☐
648	**208**	1s 3d	multicoloured	75	1·00	☐ ☐
		p.	Phosphor	4·00	6·50	☐ ☐
649	**209**	1s 6d	multicoloured	1·00	85	☐ ☐
		p.	Phosphor	8·00	8·00	☐ ☐
650	**210**	2s 6d	deep slate-purple	2·75	2·75	☐ ☐
Set of 5 (Ordinary)				4·50	4·50	☐ ☐
Set of 4 (Phosphor)				12·00	14·00	☐ ☐
First Day Cover (Ordinary)					12·00	☐
First Day Cover (Phosphor)					17·00	☐
Presentation Pack (Ordinary)				22·00		☐

PRESENTATION PACKS were first introduced by the G.P.O. for the Shakespeare Festival issue. The packs include one set of stamps and details of the designs, the designer and the stamp printer. They were issued for almost all later definitive and special issues.

211 Flats near Richmond Park
('Urban Development')

212 Shipbuilding Yards, Belfast
('Industrial Activity')

213 Beddgelert Forest Park, Snowdonia ('Forestry')

214 Nuclear Reactor, Dounreay ('Technological Development')

20th International Geographical Congress, London

1964 (1 July)

651	211	2½d	multicoloured	10	10	☐	☐
			p. Phosphor	40	50	☐	☐
652	212	4d	multicoloured	30	30	☐	☐
			p. Phosphor	1·25	1·25	☐	☐
653	213	8d	multicoloured	75	85	☐	☐
			p. Phosphor	2·50	2·75	☐	☐
654	214	1s 6d	multicoloured	3·50	3·50	☐	☐
			p. Phosphor	28·00	22·00	☐	☐
Set of 4 (Ordinary)				4·50	4·50	☐	☐
Set of 4 (Phosphor)				30·00	24·00	☐	☐
First Day Cover (Ordinary)					22·00	☐	
First Day Cover (Phosphor)					40·00	☐	
Presentation Pack (Ordinary)			£160			☐	

215 Spring Gentian

216 Dog Rose

217 Honeysuckle

218 Fringed Water Lily

Tenth International Botanical Congress, Edinburgh

1964 (5 Aug.)

655	215	3d	violet, blue and green	25	25	☐	☐
			p. Phosphor	40	40	☐	☐
656	216	6d	multicoloured	50	50	☐	☐
			p. Phosphor	2·50	2·75	☐	☐
657	217	9d	multicoloured	1·75	2·25	☐	☐
			p. Phosphor	4·50	4·00	☐	☐
658	218	1s 3d	multicoloured	2·50	2·50	☐	☐
			p. Phosphor	25·00	20·00	☐	☐
Set of 4 (Ordinary)				4·50	4·50	☐	☐
Set of 4 (Phosphor)				30·00	24·00	☐	☐
First Day Cover (Ordinary)					30·00	☐	
First Day Cover (Phosphor)					40·00	☐	
Presentation Pack (Ordinary)			£160			☐	

219 Forth Road Bridge

220 Forth Road and Railway Bridges

Opening of Forth Road Bridge

1964 (4 Sept.)

659	219	3d	black, blue and violet	10	10	☐	☐
			p. Phosphor	1·00	1·50	☐	☐
660	220	6d	blackish lilac, blue and red	40	40	☐	☐
			p. Phosphor	4·50	4·75	☐	☐
Set of 2 (Ordinary)				50	50	☐	☐
Set of 2 (Phosphor)				5·00	5·75	☐	☐
First Day Cover (Ordinary)					7·00	☐	
First Day Cover (Phosphor)					18·00	☐	
Presentation Pack (Ordinary)			£400			☐	

221 Sir Winston Churchill

221a Sir Winston Churchill

Churchill Commemoration

1965 (8 July)

661	221	4d	black and drab	10	10	☐	☐
			p. Phosphor	25	25	☐	☐
662	221a	1s 3d	black and grey	30	40	☐	☐
			p. Phosphor	2·50	3·00	☐	☐
Set of 2 (Ordinary)				40	50	☐	☐
Set of 2 (Phosphor)				2·75	3·25	☐	☐
First Day Cover (Ordinary)					7·00	☐	
First Day Cover (Phosphor)					9·00	☐	
Presentation Pack (Ordinary)			70·00			☐	

222 Simon de Montfort's Seal

223 Parliament Buildings (after engraving by Hollar, 1647)

700th Anniversary of Simon de Montfort's Parliament

1965 (19 July)

663	222	6d	green	20	20	☐	☐
			p. Phosphor	60	1·00	☐	☐
664	223	2s 6d	black, grey and drab	80	1·50	☐	☐
Set of 2 (Ordinary)				1·00	1·25	☐	☐
First Day Cover (Ordinary)					15·00	☐	
First Day Cover (Phosphor)					26·00	☐	
Presentation Pack (Ordinary)			75·00			☐	

224 Bandsmen and Banner

225 Three Salvationists

Salvation Army Centenary

1965 (9 Aug.)

665	**224**	3d multicoloured	25	25	☐	☐
		p. Phosphor	25	40	☐	☐
666	**225**	1s 6d multicoloured	1·00	1·50	☐	☐
		p. Phosphor	2·50	2·75	☐	☐
Set of 2 (Ordinary)			1·00	1·50	☐	☐
Set of 2 (Phosphor)			2·50	3·00	☐	☐
First Day Cover (Ordinary)				23·00	☐	
First Day Cover (Phosphor)				33·00	☐	

226 Lister's Carbolic Spray **227** Lister and Chemical Symbols

Centenary of Joseph Lister's Discovery of Antiseptic Surgery

1965 (1 Sept.)

667	**226**	4d indigo, chestnut and grey	25	15	☐	☐
		p. Phosphor	25	25	☐	☐
668	**227**	1s black, purple and blue	1·00	1·10	☐	☐
		p. Phosphor	2·00	2·50	☐	☐
Set of 2 (Ordinary)			1·00	1·25	☐	☐
Set of 2 (Phosphor)			2·25	2·50	☐	☐
First Day Cover (Ordinary)				12·00	☐	
First Day Cover (Phosphor)				15·00	☐	

228 Trinidad Carnival Dancers **229** Canadian Folk Dancers

Commonwealth Arts Festival

1965 (1 Sept.)

669	**228**	6d black and orange	20	20	☐	☐
		p. Phosphor	30	50	☐	☐
670	**229**	1s 6d black and violet	80	1·10	☐	☐
		p. Phosphor	2·50	3·50	☐	☐
Set of 2 (Ordinary)			1·00	1·25	☐	☐
Set of 2 (Phosphor)			2·75	3·50	☐	☐
First Day Cover (Ordinary)				16·50	☐	
First Day Cover (Phosphor)				22·00	☐	

230 Flight of Supermarine Spitfires **231** Pilot in Hawker Hurricane Mk I

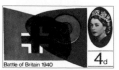 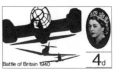

232 Wing-tips of Supermarine Spitfire and Messerschmitt Bf 109 **233** Supermarine Spitfires attacking Heinkel HE 111H Bomber

234 Supermarine Spitfire attacking Junkers Ju 87B 'Stuka' Dive Bomber **235** Hawker Hurricanes Mk I over Wreck of Dornier Do-17Z Bomber

The above were issued together se-tenant in blocks of six (3 × 2) within the sheet.

236 Anti-aircraft Artillery in Action **237** Air Battle over St Paul's Cathedral

25th Anniversary of Battle of Britain

1965 (13 Sept.)

671	**230**	4d olive and black	25	25	☐	☐
		a. Block of 6. Nos. 671/6	8·00	8·00	☐	☐
		p. Phosphor	50	50	☐	☐
		pa. Block of 6. Nos. 671p/6p	10·00	12·00	☐	☐
672	**231**	4d olive, blackish olive and black	25	25	☐	☐
		p. Phosphor	50	50	☐	☐
673	**232**	4d multicoloured	25	25	☐	☐
		p. Phosphor	50	50	☐	☐
674	**233**	4d olive and black	25	25	☐	☐
		p. Phosphor	50	50	☐	☐
675	**234**	4d olive and black	25	25	☐	☐
		p. Phosphor	50	50	☐	☐
676	**235**	4d multicoloured	25	25	☐	☐
		p. Phosphor	50	50	☐	☐
677	**236**	9d violet, orange and purple	1·75	1·75	☐	☐
		p. Phosphor	1·75	2·50	☐	☐
678	**237**	1s 3d multicoloured	1·75	1·75	☐	☐
		p. Phosphor	1·75	2·50	☐	☐
Set of 8 (Ordinary)			8·00	8·00	☐	
Set of 8 (Phosphor)			10·00	12·00	☐	
First Day Cover (Ordinary)				25·00	☐	
First Day Cover (Phosphor)				28·00	☐	
Presentation Pack (Ordinary)			70·00		☐	

238 Tower and Georgian Buildings **239** Tower and Nash Terrace, Regent's Park

Opening of Post Office Tower

1965 (8 Oct.)

679	**238**	3d yellow, blue and green	10	15	☐	☐
		p. Phosphor	15	15	☐	☐
680	**239**	1s 3d green and blue	30	45	☐	☐
		p. Phosphor	30	50	☐	☐
Set of 2 (Ordinary)			40	60	☐	☐
Set of 2 (Phosphor)			45	65	☐	☐
First Day Cover (Ordinary)				6·50	☐	
First Day Cover (Phosphor)				7·00	☐	
Presentation Pack (Ordinary)			6·50		☐	
Presentation Pack (Phosphor)			6·50		☐	

240 U.N. Emblem   **241** I.C.Y. Emblem

20th Anniversary of UNO and International Co-operation Year

1965 (25 Oct.)

681	**240**	3d black, orange and blue	25	20	☐	☐
		p. Phosphor	25	30	☐	☐
682	**241**	1s 6d black, purple and blue	1·00	80	☐	☐
		p. Phosphor	2·75	3·00	☐	☐
Set of 2 (Ordinary)			1·00	1·00	☐	☐
Set of 2 (Phosphor)			2·50	3·25	☐	☐
First Day Cover (Ordinary)				12·00	☐	
First Day Cover (Phosphor)				14·00	☐	

242 Telecommunications Network   **243** Radio Waves and Switchboard

I.T.U. Centenary

1965 (15 Nov.)

683	**242**	9d multicoloured	50	40	☐	☐
		p. Phosphor	1·00	75	☐	☐
684	**243**	1s 6d multicoloured	1·50	1·25	☐	☐
		p. Phosphor	4·25	5·25	☐	☐
Set of 2 (Ordinary)			1·50	1·60	☐	☐
Set of 2 (Phosphor)			4·25	6·00	☐	☐
First Day Cover (Ordinary)				17·00	☐	
First Day Cover (Phosphor)				20·00	☐	

244 Robert Burns (after Skirving chalk drawing)   **245** Robert Burns (after Nasmyth portrait)

Burns Commemoration

1966 (25 Jan.)

685	**244**	4d black, indigo and blue	15	15	☐	☐
		p. Phosphor	25	50	☐	☐
686	**245**	1s 3d black, blue and orange	40	70	☐	☐
		p. Phosphor	2·25	2·25	☐	☐

Set of 2 (Ordinary)		55	85	☐ ☐
Set of 2 (Phosphor)		2·50	2·25	☐ ☐
First Day Cover (Ordinary)			4·00	☐
First Day Cover (Phosphor)			6·00	☐
Presentation Pack (Ordinary)		60·00		☐

246 Westminster Abbey   **247** Fan Vaulting, Henry VII Chapel

900th Anniversary of Westminster Abbey

1966 (28 Feb.) Perf 15 × 14 (3d) or 11 × 12 (2s 6d)

687	**246**	3d black, brown and blue	15	20	☐	☐
		p. Phosphor	20	25	☐	☐
688	**247**	2s 6d black	55	80	☐	☐
Set of 2			70	1·00	☐	
First Day Cover (Ordinary)				6·00	☐	
First Day Cover (Phosphor)				14·00	☐	
Presentation Pack (Ordinary)			55·00		☐	

 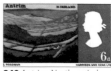

248 View near Hassocks, Sussex   **249** Antrim, Northern Ireland

250 Harlech Castle, Wales   **251** Cairngorm Mountains, Scotland

Landscapes

1966 (2 May)

689	**248**	4d black, yellow-green and blue	10	15	☐	☐
		p. Phosphor	10	15	☐	☐
690	**249**	6d black, green and blue	15	20	☐	☐
		p. Phosphor	15	20	☐	☐
691	**250**	1s 3d black, yellow and blue	25	35	☐	☐
		p. Phosphor	25	35	☐	☐
692	**251**	1s 6d black, orange and blue	40	35	☐	☐
		p. Phosphor	40	40	☐	☐
Set of 4 (Ordinary)			80	95	☐	☐
Set of 4 (Phosphor)			80	1·00	☐	☐
First Day Cover (Ordinary)				7·00	☐	
First Day Cover (Phosphor)				8·50	☐	

252 Players with Ball

253 Goalmouth Mêlée   **254** Goalkeeper saving Goal

World Cup Football Championship

1966 (1 June)

693	**252**	4d	multicoloured	10	25	☐	☐
		p.	Phosphor	10	25	☐	☐
694	**253**	6d	multicoloured	15	25	☐	☐
		p.	Phosphor	15	25	☐	☐
695	**254**	1s 3d	multicoloured	50	1·00	☐	☐
		p.	Phosphor	50	1·00	☐	☐
Set of 3 (Ordinary)				70	1·00	☐	☐
Set of 3 (Phosphor)				50	1·00	☐	☐
First Day Cover (Ordinary)					20·00		☐
First Day Cover (Phosphor)					22·00		☐
Presentation Pack (Ordinary)				15·00		☐	

255 Black-headed Gull   **256** Blue Tit

257 European Robin   **258** Blackbird

The above were issued *se-tenant* in blocks of four within the sheet.

British Birds

1966 (8 Aug.)

696	**255**	4d	multicoloured	20	20	☐	☐
		a.	Block of 4. Nos. 696/9	1·00	2·00	☐	☐
		p.	Phosphor	20	20	☐	☐
		pa.	Block of 4. Nos. 696p/9p	75	2·00	☐	☐
697	**256**	4d	multicoloured	20	20	☐	☐
		p.	Phosphor	20	20	☐	☐
698	**257**	4d	multicoloured	20	20	☐	☐
		p.	Phosphor	20	20	☐	☐
699	**258**	4d	multicoloured	20	20	☐	☐
		p.	Phosphor	20	20	☐	☐
Set of 4 (Ordinary)				1·00	2·00	☐	☐
Set of 4 (Phosphor)				75	2·00	☐	☐
First Day Cover (Ordinary)					8·00		☐
First Day Cover (Phosphor)					8·00		☐
Presentation Pack (Ordinary)				11·00		☐	

259 Cup Winners

England's World Cup Football Victory

1966 (18 Aug.)

700	**259**	4d	multicoloured	30	30	☐	☐
First Day Cover					13·00		☐

260 Jodrell Bank Radio Telescope   **261** British Motor-cars

262 SR N6 Hovercraft   **263** Windscale Reactor

British Technology

1966 (19 Sept.)

701	**260**	4d	black and lemon	15	10	☐	☐
		p.	Phosphor	10	10	☐	☐
702	**261**	6d	red, blue and orange	25	20	☐	☐
		p.	Phosphor	15	25	☐	☐
703	**262**	1s 3d	multicoloured	50	40	☐	☐
		p.	Phosphor	35	40	☐	☐
704	**263**	1s 6d	multicoloured	50	60	☐	☐
		p.	Phosphor	50	60	☐	☐
Set of 4 (Ordinary)				1·00	1·10	☐	☐
Set of 4 (Phosphor)				1·00	1·10	☐	☐
First Day Cover (Ordinary)					5·00		☐
First Day Cover (Phosphor)					5·00		☐
Presentation Pack (Ordinary)				12·00		☐	

264   **265**

266   **267**

268   **269**

The above show battle scenes, they were issued together *se-tenant* in horizontal strips of six within the sheet.

270 Norman Ship

271 Norman Horsemen attacking Harold's Troops

900th Anniversary of Battle of Hastings

1966 (14 Oct.) Designs show scenes from Bayeux Tapestry
Wmk 179 (sideways on 1s 3d)

705	**264**	4d multicoloured	10	10	☐	☐
		a. Strip of 6. Nos. 705/10	1·90	2·25	☐	☐
		p. Phosphor	10	10	☐	☐
		pa. Strip of 6. Nos. 705p/10p	1·90	2·25	☐	☐
706	**265**	4d multicoloured	10	10	☐	☐
		p. Phosphor	10	10	☐	☐
707	**266**	4d multicoloured	10	10	☐	☐
		p. Phosphor	10	10	☐	☐
708	**267**	4d multicoloured	10	10	☐	☐
		p. Phosphor	10	10	☐	☐
709	**268**	4d multicoloured	10	10	☐	☐
		p. Phosphor	10	10	☐	☐
710	**269**	4d multicoloured	10	10	☐	☐
		p. Phosphor	10	25	☐	☐
711	**270**	6d multicoloured	10	10	☐	☐
		p. Phosphor	10	10	☐	☐
712	**271**	1s 3d multicoloured	20	75	☐	☐
		p. Phosphor	20	75	☐	☐
Set of 8 (Ordinary)			2·00	2·25	☐	☐
Set of 8 (Phosphor)			2·00	2·25	☐	☐
First Day Cover (Ordinary)				8·00	☐	
First Day Cover (Phosphor)				9·00	☐	
Presentation Pack (Ordinary)			9·00		☐	

272 King of the Orient

273 Snowman

Christmas

1966 (1 Dec.) Wmk 179 (upright on 1s 6d)

713	**272**	3d multicoloured	10	25	☐	☐
		p. Phosphor	10	25	☐	☐
714	**273**	1s 6d multicoloured	30	50	☐	☐
		p. Phosphor	30	50	☐	☐
Set of 2 (Ordinary)			40	40	☐	☐
Set of 2 (Phosphor)			40	45	☐	☐
First Day Cover (Ordinary)				2·50	☐	
First Day Cover (Phosphor)				2·00	☐	
Presentation Pack (Ordinary)			12·00		☐	

274 Sea Freight

275 Air Freight

European Free Trade Association (EFTA)

1967 (20 Feb.)

715	**274**	9d multicoloured	25	20	☐	☐
		p. Phosphor	25	20	☐	☐
716	**275**	1s 6d multicoloured	50	45	☐	☐
		p. Phosphor	25	40	☐	☐
Set of 2 (Ordinary)			50	65	☐	☐
Set of 2 (Phosphor)			50	60	☐	☐
First Day Cover (Ordinary)				3·00	☐	
First Day Cover (Phosphor)				3·00	☐	
Presentation Pack (Ordinary)			3·50		☐	

276 Hawthorn and Bramble

277 Larger Bindweed and Viper's Bugloss

278 Ox-eye Daisy, Coltsfoot and Buttercup

279 Bluebell, Red Campion and Wood Anemone

T **276/9** were issued together *se-tenant* in blocks of four within the sheet.

280 Dog Violet

281 Primroses

British Wild Flowers

1967 (24 Apr.)

717	**276**	4d multicoloured	20	20	☐	☐
		a. Block of 4. Nos. 717/20	80	2·25	☐	☐
		p. Phosphor	10	15	☐	☐
		pa Block of 4. Nos. 717p/20p	50	2·00	☐	☐
718	**277**	4d multicoloured	20	20	☐	☐
		p. Phosphor	10	15	☐	☐
719	**278**	4d multicoloured	20	20	☐	☐
		p. Phosphor	10	15	☐	☐
720	**279**	4d multicoloured	20	20	☐	☐
		p. Phosphor	10	15	☐	☐
721	**280**	9d multicoloured	20	25	☐	☐
		p. Phosphor	15	25	☐	☐
722	**281**	1s 9d multicoloured	25	35	☐	☐
		p. Phosphor	20	30	☐	☐
Set of 6 (Ordinary)			1·00	2·25	☐	☐
Set of 6 (Phosphor)			75	2·00	☐	☐
First Day Cover (Ordinary)				5·00	☐	
First Day Cover (Phosphor)				5·00	☐	
Presentation Pack (Ordinary)			6·00		☐	
Presentation Pack (Phosphor)			6·00		☐	

282 (value at left)　　**282a** (value at right)

　I　　　　II

Two types of the 2d.

I.　Value spaced away from left side of stamp.

II.　Value close to left side from new multi-positive. This results in the portrait appearing in the centre, thus conforming with the other values.

1967–69 Two phosphor bands, except where otherwise stated. No wmk.

723	**282**	½d orange-brown	10	20	☐	☐
724		1d olive (2 bands)	10	10	☐	☐
725		1d olive (1 centre band)	30	35	☐	☐
726		2d lake-brown (Type I) (2 bands)	10	15	☐	☐
727		2d lake-brown (Type II) (2 bands)	15	20	☐	☐
728		2d lake-brown (Type II) (1 centre band)	70	90	☐	☐
729		3d violet (1 centre band)	15	10	☐	☐
730		3d violet (2 bands)	30	35	☐	☐
731		4d sepia (2 bands)	10	10	☐	☐
732		4d olive-brown (1 centre band)	10	10	☐	☐
733		4d vermilion (1 centre band)	10	10	☐	☐
734		4d vermilion (1 side band)	1·50	1·90	☐	☐
735		5d blue	10	10	☐	☐
736		6d purple	20	25	☐	☐
737	**282a**	7d emerald	40	35	☐	☐
738		8d vermilion	20	45	☐	☐
739		8d turquoise-blue	50	60	☐	☐
740		9d green	40	25	☐	☐
741	**282**	10d drab	50	50	☐	☐
742		1s violet	45	25	☐	☐
743		1s 6d blue and deep blue	50	50	☐	☐
		c. Phosphorised paper	80	80	☐	☐
744		1s 9d orange and black	50	45	☐	☐
Set of 16 (one of each value and colour)			4·00	4·00	☐	☐
Presentation Pack (one of each value)			12·00		☐	
Presentation Pack (German)			£140		☐	
First Day Covers						
5 June 1967		Nos. 731, 742, 744	3·00		☐	
8 Aug. 1967		Nos. 729, 740, 743	3·00		☐	
5 Feb. 1968		Nos. 723/4, 726, 736	3·00		☐	
1 July 1968		Nos. 735, 737/8, 741	3·00		☐	

No. 734 exists with phosphor band at the left or right.

283 'Master Lambton' (Sir Thomas Lawrence)

284 'Mares and Foals in a Landscape' (George Stubbs)

285 'Children Coming Out of School' (L. S. Lowry)

British Paintings

1967 (10 July) Two phosphor bands. No wmk

748	**283**	4d multicoloured	10	10	☐	☐
749	**284**	9d multicoloured	15	15	☐	☐
750	**285**	1s 6d multicoloured	25	35	☐	☐
Set of 3			30	50	☐	☐
First Day Cover				2·50		☐
Presentation Pack				5·50		☐

286 Gipsy Moth IV

Sir Francis Chichester's World Voyage

1967 (24 July) Three phosphor bands. No wmk

751	**286**	1s 9d multicoloured	20	20	☐	☐
First Day Cover				1·00		☐

287 Radar Screen　　　　**288** *Penicillium notatum*

289 Vickers VC-10 Jet Engines　**290** Television Equipment

British Discovery and Invention

1967 (19 Sept.) Two phosphor bands (except 4d. three bands). Wmk 179 (sideways on 1s 9d)

752	**287**	4d yellow, black and vermilion	10	10	☐	☐
753	**288**	1s multicoloured	10	20	☐	☐
754	**289**	1s 6d multicoloured	20	25	☐	☐
755	**290**	1s 9d multicoloured	20	30	☐	☐
Set of 4			50	75	☐	☐
First Day Cover				2·00		☐
Presentation Pack				4·00		☐

NO WATERMARK. All the following issues are on unwatermarked paper unless otherwise stated.

291 'The Adoration of the Shepherds' (School of Seville)

292 'Madonna and Child' (Murillo)

293 'The Adoration of the Shepherds' (Louis le Nain)

Christmas

1967 Two phosphor bands (except 3d, one phosphor band)

756	**291**	3d multicoloured (27 Nov.)	10	15	☐	☐
757	**292**	4d multicoloured (18 Oct.)	10	15	☐	☐
758	**293**	1s 6d multicoloured (27 Nov.)	15	15	☐	☐
Set of 3			30	30	☐	☐
First Day Covers (2)				1·50	☐	

Gift Pack 1967

1967 (27 Nov.) Comprises Nos. 715p/22p and 748/58

GP758c Gift Pack		3·00	☐

1967–68 No wmk. Perf 11 × 12

759	**166**	2s 6d brown	30	45	☐	☐
760	**167**	5s red	70	75	☐	☐
761	**168**	10s blue	7·75	4·00	☐	☐
762	**169**	£1 black	7·50	4·50	☐	☐
Set of 4			15·00	8·00	☐	☐

294 Tarr Steps, Exmoor

295 Aberfeldy Bridge

296 Menai Bridge

297 M4 Viaduct

British Bridges

1968 (29 Apr.) Two phosphor bands

763	**294**	4d multicoloured	10	10	☐	☐
764	**295**	9d multicoloured	10	15	☐	☐
765	**296**	1s 6d multicoloured	15	25	☐	☐
766	**297**	1s 9d multicoloured	20	30	☐	☐
Set of 4			50	70	☐	☐
First Day Cover				1·50	☐	
Presentation Pack		3·00			☐	

298 'TUC' and Trades Unionists

299 Mrs Emmeline Pankhurst (statue)

300 Sopwith Camel and English Electric Lightning Fighters

301 Captain Cook's *Endeavour* and Signature

British Anniversaries. Events described on stamps

1968 (29 May) Two phosphor bands

767	**298**	4d multicoloured	10	10	☐	☐
768	**299**	9d violet, grey and black	10	15	☐	☐
769	**300**	1s multicoloured	15	15	☐	☐
770	**301**	1s 9d ochre and brown	35	35	☐	☐
Set of 4			50	50	☐	☐
First Day Cover				4·00		☐
Presentation Pack			3·00		☐	

302 'Queen Elizabeth I' (Unknown Artist)

303 'Pinkie' (Lawrence)

304 'Ruins of St Mary Le Port' (John Piper)

305 'The Hay Wain' (John Constable)

British Paintings

1968 (12 Aug.) Two phosphor bands

771	**302**	4d multicoloured	10	10	☐	☐
772	**303**	1s multicoloured	10	20	☐	☐
773	**304**	1s 6d multicoloured	20	25	☐	☐
774	**305**	1s 9d multicoloured	25	40	☐	☐
Set of 4			50	85	☐	☐
First Day Cover				2·00		☐
Presentation Pack			3·50		☐	
Presentation Pack (German)			12·00		☐	

Gift Pack 1968

1968 (16 Sept.) Comprises Nos. 763/74

GP774c Gift Pack	6·00	☐
GP774d Gift Pack (German)	38·00	☐

Collectors Pack 1968

1968 (16 Sept.) Comprises Nos. 752/8 and 763/74

CP774e Collectors Pack	7·00	☐

306 Girl and Boy with Rocking Horse

307 Girl with Doll's House   **308** Boy with Train Set

Christmas

1968 (25 Nov.) Two phosphor bands (except 4d, one centre phosphor band)

775	**306**	4d multicoloured	10	15	☐	☐
776	**307**	9d multicoloured	15	25	☐	☐
777	**308**	1s 6d multicoloured	15	50	☐	☐
Set of 3			30	50	☐	☐
First Day Cover				1·00		☐
Presentation Pack			5·00		☐	
Presentation Pack (German)			14·00		☐	

309 Queen Elizabeth 2

310 Elizabethan Galleon   **311** East Indiaman

312 Cutty Sark

313 Great Britain

314 Mauretania I

The 9d and 1s values were arranged in horizontal strips of three and pairs respectively throughout the sheet.

British Ships

1969 (15 Jan.) One horiz phosphor band (5d), two phosphor bands (9d) or two vert phosphor bands at right (1s)

778	**309**	5d multicoloured	10	15	☐	☐
779	**310**	9d multicoloured	10	25	☐	☐
		a. Strip of 3. Nos. 779/81	1·25	1·50	☐	☐
780	**311**	9d multicoloured	10	25	☐	☐
781	**312**	9d multicoloured	10	25	☐	☐
782	**313**	1s multicoloured	40	35	☐	☐
		a. Pair. Nos. 782/3	1·25	1·50	☐	☐
783	**314**	1s multicoloured	40	35	☐	☐
Set of 6			2·50	3·00	☐	☐
First Day Cover				5·00		☐
Presentation Pack			4·50		☐	
Presentation Pack (German)			40·00		☐	

   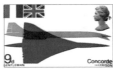

315 Concorde in Flight   **316** Plan and Elevation Views

317 Concorde's Nose and Tail

First Flight of Concorde

1969 (3 Mar.) Two phosphor bands

784	**315**	4d multicoloured	25	25	☐	☐
785	**316**	9d multicoloured	55	75	☐	☐
786	**317**	1s 6d deep blue, grey and light blue	75	1·00	☐	☐
Set of 3			1·00	1·50	☐	☐
First Day Cover				3·00		☐
Presentation Pack			12·00		☐	
Presentation Pack (German)			40·00		☐	

318 (See also Type **357**)

1969 (5 Mar.) P 12

787	**318**	2s 6d brown	35	30	☐	☐
788		5s lake	1·75	60	☐	☐
789		10s ultramarine	6·00	7·00	☐	☐
790		£1 black	3·25	1·50	☐	☐
Set of 4			10·00	8·50	☐	☐

First Day Cover	9·50		☐
Presentation Pack	16·00		☐
Presentation Pack (German)	80·00		☐

319 Page from the *Daily Mail*,
and Vickers FB-27 Vimy Aircraft

320 Europa and C.E.P.T.
Emblems

321 I.L.O. Emblem

322 Flags of N.A.T.O. Countries

323 Vickers FB-27 Vimy Aircraft
and Globe showing Flight

Anniversaries. Events described on stamps

1969 (2 Apr.) Two phosphor bands

791	**319**	5d	multicoloured	10	15	☐ ☐
792	**320**	9d	multicoloured	15	25	☐ ☐
793	**321**	1s	claret, red and blue	15	25	☐ ☐
794	**322**	1s 6d	multicoloured	15	30	☐ ☐
795	**323**	1s 9d	olive, yellow and turquoise-green	20	40	☐ ☐
Set of 5				50	1·00	☐ ☐
First Day Cover					3·00	☐
Presentation Pack				3·50		☐
Presentation Pack (German)				65·00		☐

324 Durham Cathedral

325 York Minster

326 St Giles' Cathedral,
Edinburgh

327 Canterbury Cathedral

The above were issued together *se-tenant* in blocks of four
within the sheet.

328 St Paul's Cathedral

329 Liverpool Metropolitan
Cathedral

British Architecture (Cathedrals)

1969 (28 May) Two phosphor bands

796	**324**	5d	multicoloured	10	10	☐ ☐
		a.	Block of 4. Nos. 796/9	1·10	1·25	☐ ☐
797	**325**	5d	multicoloured	10	10	☐ ☐
798	**326**	5d	multicoloured	10	10	☐ ☐
799	**327**	5d	multicoloured	10	10	☐ ☐
800	**328**	9d	multicoloured	25	30	☐ ☐
801	**329**	1s 6d	multicoloured	25	35	☐ ☐
Set of 6				1·10	1·50	☐ ☐
First Day Cover					3·00	☐
Presentation Pack				3·25		☐
Presentation Pack (German)				30·00		☐

330 The King's Gate,
Caernarvon Castle

331 The Eagle Tower,
Caernarvon Castle

332 Queen Eleanor's
Gate, Caernarvon Castle

333 Celtic Cross,
Margam Abbey

The 5d values were printed *se-tenant* in strips of three
throughout the sheet.

334 Prince Charles

Investiture of H.R.H. The Prince of Wales

1969 (1 July) Two phosphor bands

802	**330**	5d	multicoloured	10	15	☐ ☐
		a.	Strip of 3. Nos. 802/4	50	1·00	☐ ☐
803	**331**	5d	multicoloured	10	15	☐ ☐
804	**332**	5d	multicoloured	10	15	☐ ☐
805	**333**	9d	multicoloured	15	30	☐ ☐
806	**334**	1s	black and gold	15	30	☐ ☐
Set of 5				60	1·20	☐ ☐
First Day Cover					1·50	☐
Presentation Pack				3·00		☐
Presentation Pack (German)				30·00		☐

335 Mahatma Gandhi

Gandhi Centenary Year

1969 (13 Aug.) Two phosphor bands

807	**335**	1s 6d multicoloured	30	30	☐	☐
First Day Cover				1·00		☐

Collectors Pack 1969

1969 (15 Sept.) Comprises Nos. 775/86 and 791/807

CP807b	Collectors Pack	25·00	☐

336 National Giro

337 Telecommunications – International Subscriber Dialling

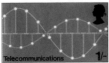

338 Telecommunications – Pulse Code Modulation

339 Postal Mechanisation – Automatic Sorting

British Post Office Technology

1969 (1 Oct.) Two phosphor bands. Perf 13½ × 14

808	**336**	5d multicoloured	10	10	☐	☐
809	**337**	9d green, blue and black	20	25	☐	☐
810	**338**	1s green, lavender and black	20	25	☐	☐
811	**339**	1s 6d multicoloured	25	50	☐	☐
Set of 4			70	1·00	☐	☐
First Day Cover				1·50		☐
Presentation Pack			3·00		☐	

340 Herald Angel

341 The Three Shepherds

342 The Three Kings

Christmas

1969 (26 Nov.) Two phosphor bands (5d, 1s 6d) or one centre band (4d)

812	**340**	4d multicoloured	10	10	☐	☐
813	**341**	5d multicoloured	15	15	☐	☐
814	**342**	1s 6d multicoloured	20	20	☐	☐
Set of 3			30	30	☐	☐
First Day Cover				1·00		☐
Presentation Pack			3·00		☐	

343 Fife Harling

344 Cotswold Limestone

345 Welsh Stucco

346 Ulster Thatch

British Rural Architecture

1970 (11 Feb.) Two phosphor bands

815	**343**	5d multicoloured	10	10	☐	☐
816	**344**	9d multicoloured	10	25	☐	☐
817	**345**	1s multicoloured	15	25	☐	☐
818	**346**	1s 6d multicoloured	20	40	☐	☐
Set of 4			50	75	☐	☐
First Day Cover				1·50		☐
Presentation Pack			4·00		☐	

347 Signing the Declaration of Arbroath

348 Florence Nightingale attending Patients

349 Signing of International Co-operative Alliance

350 Pilgrims and *Mayflower*

351 Sir William Herschel, Francis Baily, Sir John Herschel and Telescope

Anniversaries. Events described on stamps

1970 (1 Apr.) Two phosphor bands

819	**347**	5d multicoloured	10	10	☐	☐
820	**348**	9d multicoloured	15	15	☐	☐
821	**349**	1s multicoloured	20	25	☐	☐
822	**350**	1s 6d multicoloured	20	30	☐	☐
823	**351**	1s 9d multicoloured	25	30	☐	☐
Set of 5			75	1·00	☐	☐
First Day Cover				2·00		☐
Presentation Pack			3·00		☐	

352 'Mr Pickwick and Sam' *(Pickwick Papers)*

353 'Mr and Mrs Micawber' *(David Copperfield)*

354 'David Copperfield and Betsy Trotwood' *(David Copperfield)*

355 'Oliver asking for more' *(Oliver Twist)*

356 'Grasmere' (from engraving by J. Farrington, R.A.)

The 5d values were issued together *se-tenant* in blocks of four within the sheet.

Literary Anniversaries. Events described on stamps

1970 (3 June) Two phosphor bands

824	**352**	5d multicoloured	10	25	☐	☐
		a. Block of 4. Nos. 824/7	75	1·50	☐	☐
825	**353**	5d multicoloured	10	25	☐	☐
826	**354**	5d multicoloured	10	25	☐	☐
827	**355**	5d multicoloured	10	25	☐	☐
828	**356**	1s 6d multicoloured	25	50	☐	☐
Set of 5			1·00	1·50	☐	☐
First Day Cover				2·00		☐
Presentation Pack			3·00		☐	

356a

357 (Value redrawn)

Decimal Currency

1970 (17 June)–72 10p and some printings of the 50p were issued on phosphor paper. Perf 12

829	**356a**	10p cerise	50	75	☐	☐
830		20p olive-green	60	25	☐	☐
831		50p ultramarine	1·50	40	☐	☐
831b	**357**	£1 black (6 Dec. 1972)	3·50	80	☐	☐
Set of 4			6·00	2·00	☐	☐
First Day Cover (Nos. 829/31)				2·75		☐
First Day Cover (No. 831b)				3·00		☐
Presentation Pack (P.O Pack No. 18)						
	(Nos. 829/31)		10·00		☐	
Presentation Pack (P.O Pack No. 38)						
	(Nos. 830/1, 790 or 831b)		17·00		☐	

358 Runners
359 Swimmers

360 Cyclists

Ninth British Commonwealth Games, Edinburgh

1970 (15 July) Two phosphor bands. Perf 13½ × 14

832	**358**	5d pink, emerald, greenish yellow and yellow-green	25	25	☐	☐
833	**359**	1s 6d greenish blue, lilac, brown and Prussian blue	50	50	☐	☐
834	**360**	1s 9d yellow-orange, lilac, salmon and red-brown	50	50	☐	☐
Set of 3			75	75	☐	☐
First Day Cover				1·20		☐
Presentation Pack			3·00		☐	

Collectors Pack 1970

1970 (14 Sept.) Comprises Nos. 808/28 and 832/4

CP834a Collectors Pack		25·00	☐

361 1d Black (1840)
362 1s Green (1847)
363 4d Carmine (1855)

'Philympia 70' Stamp Exhibition

1970 (18 Sept.) Two phosphor bands. Perf 14 × 14½

835	**361**	5d multicoloured	25	10	☐	☐
836	**362**	9d multicoloured	25	30	☐	☐
837	**363**	1s 6d multicoloured	25	45	☐	☐
Set of 3			50	75	☐	☐
First Day Cover				1·50		☐
Presentation Pack			3·00		☐	

364 Shepherds and Apparition of the Angel

365 Mary, Joseph and Christ in Manger

366 The Wise Men bearing Gifts

Christmas

1970 (25 Nov.) Two phosphor bands (5d, 1s 6d) or one centre phosphor band (4d)

838	**364**	4d	multicoloured	15	10	☐	☐
839	**365**	5d	multicoloured	15	15	☐	☐
840	**366**	1s 6d	multicoloured	25	30	☐	☐
Set of 3				50	50	☐	☐
First Day Cover					1·00		☐
Presentation Pack					2·75	☐	

PRINTING PROCESSES

There is a basic distinction between stamps printed byphotogravure and those printed by lithography. Sorting the two is not as difficult as it sounds and with a little experience it should become easy to tell which method of production was employed for a particular stamp.

The tiny dots of the printing screen give uneven edges to the values on photogravure stamps (right). Litho values have clean, clear outlines (left).

All you need is a reasonably good glass giving a magnification of 34 or more (310 is even better!).

The image on a photogravure stamp is created from a pattern or 'screen', of minute dots which are not evident when looking at the stamp without a glass but show up quite clearly under magnification, especially in the Queen's face and around the margin of the stamp design where it meets the white background of the paper. Now look at the value; here also, what looks to the naked eye like a straight line is in fact made up of rows of tiny little dots.

'Screens' of dots are also used in the production of litho printed stamps but they are only required where the printer is attempting to produce shades and tints as is necessary in the Queen's head portion of the stamp. Where solid colour is used, as in the background of the majority of values, there is no need to resort to a screen of dots and the background is printed as a solid mass of colour. If you look at the margins or the values of stamps produced in this way you will not see any evidence of dots—just a clear clean break between the inked portion of the stamp and the uninked white of the paper.

367   **367a**

Two types of the 3p., 10p. and 26p. (Nos. X930/c, X886/b and X971/b).

I   II

I   II

I   II

Decimal Currency

1971–96. Type 367

(a) Printed in photogravure by Harrison and Sons (except for some ptgs of Nos. X879 and X913 which were produced by Enschedé) with phosphor bands. Perf 15×14

X841	½p	turquoise-blue (2 bands)	10	10	☐	☐
X842	½p	turquoise-blue (1 side band)	55·00	30·00	☐	☐
X843	½p	turquoise-blue (1 centre band)	40	25	☐	☐
X844	1p	crimson (2 bands)	10	15	☐	☐
X845	1p	crimson (1 centre band)	25	20	☐	☐
X846	1p	crimson ('all-over' phosphor)	15	25	☐	☐
X847	1p	crimson (1 side band)	1·00	1·25	☐	☐
X848	1½p	black (2 bands)	15	25	☐	☐
X849	2p	myrtle-green (face value as in T **367**) (2 bands)	15	20	☐	☐
X850	2p	myrtle-green (face value as in T **367**) ('all-over' phosphor)	25	30	☐	☐
X851	2½p	magenta (1 centre band)	20	15	☐	☐
X852	2½p	magenta (1 side band)	1·50	1·75	☐	☐
X853	2½p	magenta (2 bands)	25	50	☐	☐
X854	2½p	rose-red (2 bands)	40	60	☐	☐
X855	3p	ultramarine (2 bands)	20	25	☐	☐
X856	3p	ultramarine (1 centre band)	15	20	☐	☐
X857	3p	bright magenta (Type I) (2 bands)	35	35	☐	☐
X858	3½p	olive-grey (2 bands)	25	30	☐	☐
X859	3½p	olive-grey (1 centre band)	30	35	☐	☐

X860	3½p purple-brown				
	(1 centre band)	1·25	1·25	☐	☐
X861	4p ochre-brown (2 bands)	20	25	☐	☐
X862	4p greenish blue				
	(2 bands)	1·75	2·00	☐	☐
X863	4p greenish blue				
	(1 centre band)	1·50	1·90	☐	☐
X864	4p greenish blue				
	(1 side band)	2·00	2·00	☐	☐
X865	4½p grey-blue (2 bands)	25	30	☐	☐
X866	5p pale violet (2 bands)	20	20	☐	☐
X867	5p claret (1 centre band)	2·00	2·25	☐	☐
X868	5½p violet (2 bands)	25	30	☐	☐
X869	5½p violet (1 centre band)	25	30	☐	☐
X870	6p light emerald (2 bands)	25	20	☐	☐
X871	6½p greenish blue (2 bands)	30	35	☐	☐
X872	6½p greenish blue				
	(1 centre band)	25	20	☐	☐
X873Ea	6½p greenish blue				
	(1 side band)	60	60	☐	☐
X874	7p purple-brown				
	(2 bands)	30	35	☐	☐
X875	7p purple-brown				
	(1 centre band)	25	30	☐	☐
X876Ea	7p purple-brown				
	(1 side band)	45	50	☐	☐
X877	7½p chestnut (2 bands)	25	35	☐	☐
X878	8p rosine (2 bands)	30	30	☐	☐
X879	8p rosine (1 centre band)	30	30	☐	☐
X880	8p rosine (1 side band)	60	75	☐	☐
X881	8½p yellowish green				
	(2 bands)	30	30	☐	☐
X882	9p yellow-orange and black				
	(2 bands)	45	55	☐	☐
X883	9p deep violet (2 bands)	35	30	☐	☐
X884	9½p purple (2 bands)	35	45	☐	☐
X885	10p orange-brown and				
	chestnut (2 bands)	35	35	☐	☐
X886	10p orange-brown (Type I)				
	(2 bands)	35	30	☐	☐
	b. Type II	22·00	22·00	☐	☐
X887	10p orange-brown (Type I)				
	('all-over'phosphor)	35	45	☐	☐
X888	10p orange-brown (Type I)				
	(1 centre band)	35	25	☐	☐
X889	10p orange-brown (Type I)				
	(1 side band)	70	80	☐	☐
X890	10½p yellow (2 bands)	40	45	☐	☐
X891	10½p blue (2 bands)	45	50	☐	☐
X892	11p brown-red (2 bands)	40	30	☐	☐
X893	11½p drab (1 centre band)	40	35	☐	☐
X894	11½p drab (1 side band)	55	70	☐	☐
X895	12p yellowish green				
	(2 bands)	45	45	☐	☐
X896	12p bright emerald				
	(1 centre band)	45	45	☐	☐
X897	12p bright emerald				
	(1 sideband)	80	85	☐	☐
X898	12½p light emerald				
	(1 centre band)	45	40	☐	☐
X899	12½p light emerald				
	(1 side band)	70	75	☐	☐
X900	13p pale chestnut				
	(1 centre band)	40	40	☐	☐
X901	13p pale chestnut				
	(1 side band)	50	60	☐	☐

X902	14p grey-blue				
	(2 bands)	75	80	☐	☐
X903	14p deep blue				
	(1 centre band)	45	50	☐	☐
X904	14p deep blue				
	(1 side band)	4·00	4·00	☐	☐
X905	15p bright blue				
	(1 centre band)	65	65	☐	☐
X906Ea	15p bright blue				
	(1 side band)	3.00	3.00	☐	☐
X907	15½p pale violet (2 bands)	60	65	☐	☐
X908	16p olive-drab (2 bands)	1·25	1·40	☐	☐
X909	17p grey-blue (2 bands)	60	60	☐	☐
X910	17p deep blue				
	(1 centre band)	80	85	☐	☐
X911Ea	17p deep blue				
	(1 side band)	1·25	1.25	☐	☐
X912	18p deep olive-grey				
	(2 bands)	70	80	☐	☐
X913	18p bright green				
	(1 centre band)	60	60	☐	☐
X914	19p bright orange-red				
	(2 bands)	1·50	1·50	☐	☐
X915	20p dull purple (2 bands)	1·20	90	☐	☐
X916	20p brownish black				
	(2 bands)	1·50	1·60	☐	☐
X917	22p bright orange-red				
	(2 bands)	1·50	1·25	☐	☐
X917a	25p rose-red (2 bands)	7·00	7·00	☐	☐
X918	26p rosine (Type I)				
	(2 bands)	7·00	7·50	☐	☐
X919	31p purple (2 bands)	15·00	15·00	☐	☐
X920	34p ochre-brown (2 bands)	7·00	7·50	☐	☐
X921	50p ochre-brown (2 bands)	2·00	75	☐	☐
X922	50p ochre (2 bands)	4·50	4·50	☐	☐

(b) Printed in photogravure by Harrison and Sons on phosphorised paper. Perf 15 × 14

X924	½p turquoise-blue	10	15	☐	☐
X925	1p crimson	10	15	☐	☐
X926	2p myrtle-green (face value				
	as in T **367**)	15	20	☐	☐
X927	2p deep green (smaller				
	value as in T **367a**)	20	20	☐	☐
X928	2p myrtle-green (smaller				
	value as in T 367a)	3·25	3·25	☐	☐
X929	2½p rose-red	15	20	☐	☐
X930	3p bright magenta (Type I)	20	25	☐	☐
	c. Type II	90	70	☐	☐
X931	3½p purple-brown	50	60	☐	☐
X932	4p greenish blue	25	40	☐	☐
X933	4p new blue	20	25	☐	☐
X934	5p pale violet	30	35	☐	☐
X935	5p dull red-brown	25	30	☐	☐
X936	6p yellow-olive	30	30	☐	☐
X937	7p brownish red	1·10	1·25	☐	☐
X938	8½p yellowish green	40	50	☐	☐
X939	10p orange-brown (Type I)	35	35	☐	☐
X940	10p dull orange (Type II)	40	35	☐	☐
X941	11p brown-red	70	80	☐	☐
X942	11½p ochre-brown	55	55	☐	☐
X943	12p yellowish green	45	45	☐	☐
X944	13p olive-grey	45	50	☐	☐
X945	13½p purple-brown	60	60	☐	☐
X946	14p grey-blue	50	50	☐	☐
X947	15p ultramarine	60	60	☐	☐
X948	15½p pale violet	60	50	☐	☐

X949	16p olive-drab	rr	55	
X950	16½p pale chestnut	80	80	
X951	17p light emerald	60	60	
X952	17p grey-blue	60	60	
X953	17½p pale chestnut	70	75	
X954	18p deep violet	70	70	
X955	18p deep olive-grey	75	60	
X956	19p bright orange-red	80	60	
X957	19½p olive-grey	2·00	2·00	
X958	20p dull purple	1·00	75	
X959	20p turquoise-green	75	70	
X960	20p brownish black	1·00	1·00	
X961	20½p ultramarine	1·25	1·25	
X962	22p blue	90	75	
X963	22p yellow-green	90	80	
X964	22p bright orange-red	90	80	
X965	23p brown-red	1·25	1·10	
X966	23p bright green	1·10	1·10	
X967	24p violet	1·40	1·50	
X968	24p Indian red	2·00	1·60	
X969	24p chestnut	80	80	
X970	25p purple	1·00	1·00	
X971	26p rosine (Type I)	1·10	80	
	b. Type II	3·50	4·00	
X972	26p drab	1·50	1·25	
X973	27p chestnut	1·25	1·25	
X974	27p violet	1·50	1·25	
X975	28p deep violet	1·25	1·25	
X976	28p ochre	1·40	1·25	
X977	28p deep bluish grey	1·40	1·25	
X978	29p ochre-brown	1·75	1·75	
X979	29p deep mauve	1·75	1·75	
X980	30p deep olive-grey	1·25	1·25	
X981	31p purple	1·25	1·25	
X982	31p ultramarine	1·60	1·50	
X983	32p greenish blue	1·90	1·75	
X984	33p light emerald	1·75	1·60	
X985	34p ochre-brown	1·75	1·75	
X986	34p deep bluish grey	2·00	1·90	
X987	34p deep mauve	1·75	1·75	
X988	35p sepia	1·60	1·60	
X989	35p yellow	1·75	1·60	
X990	37p rosine	2·00	1·75	
X991	39p bright mauve	1·75	1·75	

(c) Printed in photogravure by Harrison and Sons on ordinary paper. Perf 15×14

X992	50p ochre-brown	1·75	70	
X993	75p grey-black (smaller values as T **367a**)	3·25	1·50	

(d) Printed in photogravure by Harrison and Sons on ordinary paper or phosphorised paper. Perf 15 × 14

X994	50p ochre	2·00	70	

(e) Printed in lithography by John Waddington. Perf 14

X996	4p greenish blue (2 bands)	25	35	
X997	4p greenish blue (phosphorised paper)	45	40	
X998	20p dull purple (2 bands)	1·25	1·20	
X999	20p dull purple (phosphorised paper)	1·75	1·20	

(f) Printed in lithography by Questa. Perf 14 (Nos. X1000, X1003/4 and X1023) or 15×14 (others)

X1000	2p emerald-green (face value as in T **367**) (phosphorised paper)	20	25	
	a. Perf 15 × 14	35	35	

X1001	2p bright green and deep green (smaller value as in T **367a**) (phosphorised paper)	75	70	
X1002	4p greenish blue (phosphorised paper)	70	75	
X1003	5p light violet (phosphorised paper)	40	40	
X1004	5p claret (phosphorised paper)	50	50	
	a. Perf 15 × 14	65	60	
X1005	13p pale chestnut (1 centre band)	70	75	
X1006	13p pale chestnut (1 side band)	75	75	
X1007	14p deep blue (1 centre band)	2·00	2·00	
X1008	17p deep blue (1 centre band)	80	80	
X1009	18p deep olive-grey (phosphorised paper)	90	95	
X1010	18p deep olive-grey (2 bands)	7·50	7·50	
X1011	18p bright green (1 centre band)	75	75	
X1012	18p bright green (1 side band)	1·25	1·40	
X1013	19p bright orange-red (phosphorised paper)	2·20	2·00	
X1014	20p dull purple (phosphorised paper)	1·40	1·40	
X1015	22p yellow-green (2 bands)	9·00	9·00	
X1016	22p bright orange-red (phosphorised paper)	1·00	90	
X1017	24p chestnut (phosphorised paper)	90	1·10	
X1018	24p chestnut (2 bands)	1·40	1·40	
X1019	33p light emerald (phosphorised paper)	2·50	2·50	
X1020	33p light emerald (2 bands)	1·50	1·50	
X1021	34p bistre-brown (2 bands)	7·50	7·50	
X1022	39p bright mauve (2 bands)	1·50	1·60	
X1023	75p black (face value as T **367**) (ordinary paper)	3·00	1·50	
	a. Perf 15×14	4·00	2·25	
X1024	75p brownish grey and black (smaller value as T **367a**) (ordinary paper)	9·00	8·50	

(g) Printed in lithography by Walsall. Perf 14

X1050	2p deep green (phosphorised paper)	1·10	1·10	
X1051	14p deep blue (1 side band)	4·50	4·50	
X1052	19p bright orange-red (2 bands)	3·00	3·00	
X1053	24p chestnut (phosphorised paper)	1·10	1·25	
X1054	29p deep mauve (2 bands)	3·00	3·00	
X1055	29p deep mauve (phosphorised paper)	4·50	4·50	
X1056	31p ultramarine (phosphorised paper)	1·40	1·40	
X1057	33p light emerald (phosphorised paper)	1·25	1·25	
X1058	39p bright mauve (phosphorised paper)	1·60	1·60	

Presentation Pack (P.O. Pack No. 26) (contains ½p
  (X841), 1p (X844), 1½p (X848), 2p (X849), 2½p
  (X851), 3p (X855), 3½p (X858), 4p (X861), 5p
  (X866), 6p (X870), 7½p(X877), 9p (X882))   5·00   ☐

Presentation Pack ('Scandinavia 71')
  (contents as above)   30·00   ☐

Presentation Pack (P.O. Pack No. 37) (contains ½p
  (X841), 1p (X844), 1½p (X848), 2p (X849), 2½p
  (X851), 3p (X855 or X856), 3½p (X858 or X859),
  4p (X861), 4½p (X865), 5p (X866), 5½p (X868 or
  X869), 6p (X870), 7½p (X877),8p (X878), 9p
  (X882), 10p (X885))   30·00   ☐

Later issues of this pack included the 6½p (X871) or the 6½p
(X872) and 7p (X874).

Presentation Pack (P.O. Pack No. 90) (contains ½p
  (X841), 1p (X844), 1½p (X848), 2p (X849), 2½p
  (X851), 3p (X856), 5p (X866), 6½p (X872), 7p
  (X874 or X875), 7½p (X877), 8p (X878), 8½p
  (X881), 9p (X883), 9½p (X884), 10p (X886),
  10½p (X890), 11p (X892), 20p (X915), 50p
  (X921))   5·00   ☐

Presentation Pack (P.O. Pack No. 129a) (contains
  2½p (X929), 3p (X930), 4p (X996), 10½p (X891),
  11½p (X893), 11½p (X942), 12p (X943), 13p
  (X944), 13½p (X945), 14p (X946), 15p (X947),
  15½p (X948), 17p (X951), 17½p (X953),18p
  (X954), 22p (X962), 25p (X970), 75p
  (X1023)   20·00   ☐

Presentation Pack (P.O. Pack No. 1) (contains ½p
  (X924), 1p (X925), 2p (X1000), 3p (X930), 3½p
  (X931), 4p (X997), 5p (X1004), 10p (X888), 12½p
  (X898), 16p (X949), 16½p (X950), 17p (X952),
  20p (X999), 20½p (X961), 23p (X965), 26p
  (X971), 28p (X975), 31p (X981), 50p (X992),
  75p (X1023))   40·00   ☐

Presentation Pack (P.O. Pack No. 5) (contains ½p
  (X924), 1p (X925), 2p (X1000a), 3p (X930), 4p
  (X997), 5p (X1004a), 10p (X939), 13p (X900),
  16p (X949), 17p (X952), 18p (X955), 20p (X999),
  22p (X963), 24p (X967), 26p (X971), 28p (X975),
  31p (X981), 34p (X985), 50p (X992), 75p
  (X1023a))   36·00   ☐

Presentation Pack (P.O. Pack No. 9) (contains 1p
  (X925), 2p (X1000a), 3p (X930), 4p (X997), 5p
  (X1004a), 7p (X937), 10p (X939), 12p (X896),
  13p (X900), 17p (X952), 18p (X955), 20p (X999),
  22p (X963), 24p (X967), 26p (X971), 28p (X975),
  31p (X981), 34p (X985), 50p (X992), 75p
  (X1023a))   40·00   ☐

Presentation Pack (P.O. Pack No. 15) (contains
  14p (X903), 19p (X956), 20p (X959), 23p (X966),
  27p (X973), 28p (X976), 32p (X983), 35p
  (X988))   12·00   ☐

Presentation Pack (P.O. Pack No. 19) (contains
  15p (X905), 20p (X906), 24p (X968), 29p (X979),
  30p (X980), 34p (X986), 37p (X990))   10·00   ☐

Presentation Pack (P.O. Pack No. 22) (contains
  10p (X940), 17p (X910), 22p (X964), 26p (X972),
  27p (X974),31p (X982), 33p (X984))   9·00   ☐

Presentation Pack (P.O. Pack No. 24) (contains
  1p (X925), 2p (X927), 3p (X930), 4p (X933), 5p
  (X935), 10p (X940), 17p (X910), 20p (X959), 22p
  (X964), 26p (X972), 27p (X974), 30p (X980), 31p
  (X982), 32p (X983), 33p (X984), 37p (X990),
  50p (X994),
  75p (X993))   30·00   ☐

Presentation Pack (P.O. Pack No. 25) (contains 6p
  (X936), 18p (X913), 24p (X969), 28p (X977), 34p
  (X987), 35p (X989), 39p (X991))   9·00   ☐

First Day Covers

Date	Contents	Price	
15 Feb. 1971	½p, 1p, 1½p, 2p, 2½p, 3p, 3½p, 4p, 5p, 6p, 7½p, 9p (Nos. X841, X844, X848/9, X851, X855, X858, X861, X866, X870, X877, X882) (Covers carry 'POSTING DELAYED BY THE POST OFFICE STRIKE 1971' cachet)	2·50	☐
11 Aug. 1971	10p (No. X885)	1·50	☐
24 Oct. 1973	4½p, 5½p, 8p (Nos. X865, X868, X878)	1·50	☐
4 Sept. 1974	6½p (No. X871)	1·50	☐
15 Jan. 1975	7p (No. X874)	1·00	☐
24 Sept. 1975	8½p (No. X881)	1·50	☐
25 Feb. 1976	9p, 9½p, 10p, 10½p, 11p, 20p (Nos. X883/4, X886, X890, X892, X915)	3·50	☐
2 Feb. 1977	50p (No. X921)	1·75	☐
26 April 1978	10½p (No. X891)	1·20	☐
15 Aug. 1979	11½p, 13p, 15p (Nos. X942, X944, X947)	1·75	☐
30 Jan. 1980	4p, 12p, 13½p, 17p, 17½p, 75p (Nos. X996, X943, X945, X951, X953, X1023)	3·25	☐
22 Oct. 1980	3p, 22p (Nos. X930, X962)	1·50	☐
14 Jan. 198	2½p, 11½p, 14p, 15½p, 18p, 25p (Nos. X929, X893, X946, X948, X954, X970)	2·00	☐
27 Jan. 1982	5p, 12½p, 16½p, 19½p, 26p, 29p (Nos. X1004, X898, X950, X957, X971, X978)	3·50	☐
30 Mar. 1983	3½p, 16p, 17p, 20½p, 23p, 28p, 31p (Nos. X931, X949, X952, X961, X965, X975, X981)	5·00	☐
28 Aug. 1984	13p, 18p, 22p, 24p, 34p (Nos. X900, X955, X963, X967, X985)	3·00	☐
29 Oct. 1985	7p, 12p (Nos. X937, X896)	3·00	☐
23 Aug. 1988	14p, 19p, 20p, 23p, 27p, 28p, 32p, 35p (Nos. X903, X956, X959, X966, X973, X976, X983, X988)	6·00	☐
26 Sept. 1989	15p, 20p, 24p, 29p, 30p, 34p, 37p (Nos. X905, X960, X968, X979/80, X986, X990)	5·00	☐
4 Sept. 1990	10p, 17p, 22p, 26p, 27p, 31p, 33p (Nos. X940, X910, X964, X972, X974, X982, X984)	5·50	☐
10 Sept. 1991	6p, 18p, 24p, 28p, 34p, 35p, 39p (Nos. X936, X913, X969, X977, X987, X989, X991)	6·00	☐

For similar stamps, but with elliptical perforations see Nos.
Y1667/1803 in 1993.

PHOSPHOR BANDS. See notes on page 15.
Phosphor bands are applied to the stamps, after the design
has been printed, by a separate cylinder. On issues with 'all-
over' phosphor the 'band' covers the entire stamp. Parts of the
stamp covered by phosphor bands, or the entire surface for
'all-over' phosphor versions, appear matt.
Nos. X847, X852, X864, X873, X876, X880, X889, X894, X897,
X899, X901, X906, X911, X1006 and X1012 exist with the
phosphor band at the left or right of the stamp.

PHOSPHORISED PAPER. First introduced as an experiment for a limited printing of the 1s 6d value (No. 743c) in 1969, this paper has the phosphor, to activate the automatic sorting machinery, added to the paper coating before the stamps were printed. Issues on this paper have a completely shiny surface. Although not adopted after this first trial further experiments on the 8½p in 1976 led to this paper being used for new printings of current values.

368 'A Mountain Road'
(T.P. Flanagan)

369 'Deer's Meadow'
(Tom Carr)

370 'Slieve na brock'
(Colin Middleton)

'Ulster '71' Paintings

1971 (16 June) Two phosphor bands

881	**368**	3p multicoloured	25	25	☐	☐
882	**369**	7½p multicoloured	50	50	☐	☐
883	**370**	9p multicoloured	50	50	☐	☐
Set of 3			1·00	1·00	☐	☐
First Day Cover				1·75		☐
Presentation Pack			6·00		☐	

371 John Keats (150th Death Anniv)

372 Thomas Gray (Death Bicentenary)

373 Sir Walter Scott
(Birth Bicentenary)

Literary Anniversaries. Events described above

1971 (28 July) Two phosphor bands

884	**371**	3p black, gold and blue	25	10	☐	☐
885	**372**	5p black, gold and olive	45	50	☐	☐
886	**373**	7½p black, gold and brown	45	45	☐	☐
Set of 3			1·00	1·10	☐	☐
First Day Cover				2·00		☐
Presentation Pack			6·00		☐	

374 Servicemen and Nurse of 1921

375 Roman Centurion

376 Rugby Football, 1871

British Anniversaries. Events described on stamps

1971 (25 Aug.) Two phosphor bands

887	**374**	3p multicoloured	25	25	☐	☐
888	**375**	7½p multicoloured	50	50	☐	☐
889	**376**	9p multicoloured	50	50	☐	☐
Set of 3			1·00	1·00		☐
First Day Cover				2·50		☐
Presentation Pack				6·00		☐

377 Physical Sciences Building, University College of Wales, Aberystwyth

378 Faraday Building, Southampton University

379 Engineering Department, Leicester University

380 Hexagon Restaurant, Essex University

British Architecture (Modern University Buildings)

1971 (22 Sept.) Two phosphor bands

890	**377**	3p multicoloured	10	10	☐	☐
891	**378**	5p multicoloured	25	20	☐	☐
892	**379**	7½p ochre, black and purple-brown	45	55	☐	☐
893	**380**	9p multicoloured	75	80	☐	☐
Set of 4			1·25	1·50	☐	☐
First Day Cover				2·00		☐
Presentation Pack			8·00		☐	

Collectors Pack 1971

1971 (29 Sept.) Comprises Nos. 835/40 and 881/93

CP893a Collectors Pack		60·00	☐

381 Dream of the Wise Men

382 Adoration of the Magi

390 Ralph Vaughan Williams and Score

383 Ride of the Magi

Christmas

1971 (13 Oct.) Two phosphor bands (3p, 7½p) or one centre phosphor band (2½p)

894	**381**	2½p multicoloured	10	10	☐	☐
895	**382**	3p multicoloured	10	10	☐	☐
896	**383**	7½p multicoloured	55	75	☐	☐
Set of 3			50	75	☐	☐
First Day Cover				2·00		☐
Presentation Pack			4·50		☐	

384 Sir James Clark Ross

385 Sir Martin Frobisher

386 Henry Hudson

387 Capt. Robert F. Scott

British Polar Explorers

1972 (16 Feb.) Two phosphor bands

897	**384**	3p multicoloured	10	10	☐	☐
898	**385**	5p multicoloured	15	15	☐	☐
899	**386**	7½p multicoloured	45	50	☐	☐
900	**387**	9p multicoloured	70	85	☐	☐
Set of 4			1·25	1·50	☐	☐
First Day Cover				2·50		☐
Presentation Pack			5·25		☐	

388 Statuette of Tutankhamun

389 19th-century Coastguard

Anniversaries. Events described on stamps

1972 (26 Apr.) Two phosphor bands

901	**388**	3p multicoloured	25	25	☐	☐
902	**389**	7½p multicoloured	50	50	☐	☐
903	**390**	9p multicoloured	50	50	☐	☐
Set of 3			1·00	1·00	☐	☐
First Day Cover				2·25		☐
Presentation Pack			4·25		☐	

391 St Andrew's, Greensted - juxta-Ongar, Essex

392 All Saints, Earls Barton, Northants

393 St Andrew's, Letheringsett, Norfolk

394 St Andrew's, Helpringham, Lincs

395 St Mary the Virgin, Huish Episcopi, Somerset

British Architecture (Village Churches)

1972 (21 June) Two phosphor bands

904	**391**	3p multicoloured	10	10	☐	☐
905	**392**	4p multicoloured	10	20	☐	☐
906	**393**	5p multicoloured	15	20	☐	☐
907	**394**	7½p multicoloured	50	75	☐	☐
908	**395**	9p multicoloured	50	80	☐	☐
Set of 5			1·25	1·90	☐	☐
First Day Cover				2·75		☐
Presentation Pack			10·00		☐	

'Belgica '72' Souvenir Pack

1972 (24 June) Comprises Nos. 894/6 and 904/8
CP908b Souvenir Pack   10·00   ☐

396 Microphones, 1924–69   **397** Horn Loudspeaker

398 TV Camera, 1972   **399** Oscillator and Spark
Transmitter, 1897

Broadcasting Anniversaries. Events described on stamps

1972 (13 Sept.) Two phosphor bands

909	**396**	3p multicoloured	10	10	☐	☐
910	**397**	5p multicoloured	10	20	☐	☐
911	**398**	7½p multicoloured	45	50	☐	☐
912	**399**	9p multicoloured	50	50	☐	☐
Set of 4			1·00	1·25	☐	☐
First Day Cover				2·75	☐	
Presentation Pack			4·25		☐	

400 Angel holding   **401** Angel playing
Trumpet   Lute

402 Angel playing Harp

Christmas

1972 (18 Oct.) Two phosphor bands (3p, 7½p) or one centre
phosphor band (2½p)

913	**400**	2½p multicoloured	10	10	☐	☐
914	**401**	3p multicoloured	10	10	☐	☐
915	**402**	7½p multicoloured	50	45	☐	☐
Set of 3			60	45	☐	☐
First Day Cover				1·50	☐	
Presentation Pack			4·00		☐	

403 Queen Elizabeth II   **404** Europe
and Prince Philip

Royal Silver Wedding

1972 (20 Nov.) 3p 'all-over' phosphor, 20p without phosphor

916	**403**	3p brownish black, deep blue and silver	25	25	☐	☐
917		20p brownish black, reddish purple and silver	1·00	1·00	☐	☐
Set of 2			1·00	1·00	☐	☐
First Day Cover				1·50		☐
Presentation Pack			4·00		☐	
Presentation Pack (Japanese)			9·50		☐	
Souvenir Book			4·00		☐	
Gutter Pair (3p)			80		☐	
Traffic Light Gutter Pair (3p)			20·00		☐	

Collectors Pack 1972

1972 (20 Nov.) Comprises Nos. 897/917
CP918a Collectors Pack   30·00   ☐
Nos. 920/1 were issued horizontally *se-tenant* throughout the
sheet.

Britain's Entry into European Communities

1973 (3 Jan.) Two phosphor bands

919	**404**	3p multicoloured	25	25	☐	☐
920		5p multicoloured (blue jigsaw)	25	50	☐	☐
		a. Pair. Nos. 920/1	1·00	1·00	☐	☐
921		5p multicoloured (green jigsaw)	25	50	☐	☐
Set of 3			1·00	1·00	☐	☐
First Day Cover				2·00		☐
Presentation Pack			3·00		☐	

405 Oak Tree

British Trees (1st Issue)

1973 (28 Feb.) Two phosphor bands

922	**405**	9p multicoloured	35	40	☐	☐
First Day Cover				1·75		☐
Presentation Pack			2·75		☐	

See also No. 949

406 David Livingstone

407 H. M. Stanley

The above were issued horizontally *se-tenant* throughout the sheet.

408 Sir Francis Drake

409 Sir Walter Raleigh

410 Charles Sturt

British Explorers

1973 (18 Apr.) 'All-over' phosphor

923	**406**	3p multicoloured	40	25	☐	☐
		a. Pair. Nos. 923/4	80	1·00	☐	☐
924	**407**	3p multicoloured	40	25	☐	☐
925	**408**	5p multicoloured	40	50	☐	☐
926	**409**	7½p multicoloured	40	50	☐	☐
927	**410**	9p multicoloured	40	75	☐	☐
Set of 5			1·50	2·50	☐	☐
First Day Cover				2·50		☐
Presentation Pack			4·50		☐	

411

412

413

County Cricket 1873–1973

1973 (16 May) Designs show sketches of W. G. Grace by Harry Furniss. Queen's head in gold. 'All-over' phosphor

928	**411**	3p black and brown	25	25	☐	☐
929	**412**	7½p black and green	75	75	☐	☐
930	**413**	9p black and blue	1·25	1·00	☐	☐
Set of 3			1·75	1·50	☐	☐
First Day Cover				3·00		☐
Presentation Pack			4·50		☐	
Souvenir Book			7·00			
PHQ Card (No. 928)			70·00	£275	☐	☐

The PHQ Card did not become available until mid-July. The used price quoted is for an example used in July or August 1973.

414 'Self-portrait'
(Sir Joshua Reynolds)

415 'Self-portrait'
(Sir Henry Raeburn)

416 'Nelly O'Brien'
(Sir Joshua Reynolds)

417 'Rev R. Walker
(The Skater)'
(Sir Henry Raeburn)

British Paintings. 250th Birth Anniv of Sir Joshua Reynolds and 150th Death Anniv of Sir Henry Raeburn

1973 (4 July) 'All-over' phosphor

931	**414**	3p multicoloured	10	10	☐	☐
932	**415**	5p multicoloured	30	30	☐	☐
933	**416**	7½p multicoloured	30	30	☐	☐
934	**417**	9p multicoloured	60	60	☐	☐
Set of 4			1·20	1·20	☐	☐
First Day Cover				2·00		☐
Presentation Pack			3·25		☐	

418 Court Masque Costumes

419 St Paul's Church, Covent Garden

420 Prince's Lodging, Newmarket

421 Court Masque Stage Scene

The 3p and 5p values were printed horizontally *se-tenant* within the sheet.

400th Anniversary of the Birth of Inigo Jones (architect and designer)

1973 (15 Aug.) 'All-over' phosphor

935	**418**	3p deep mauve, black and gold	10	25	☐	☐
		a. Pair. Nos. 935/6	30	50	☐	☐
936	**419**	3p deep brown, black and gold	10	25	☐	☐
937	**420**	5p blue, black and gold	35	50	☐	☐
		a. Pair. Nos. 937/8	1·00	1·00	☐	☐
938	**421**	5p grey-olive, black and gold	35	50	☐	☐
Set of 4			1·25	1·25	☐	☐
First Day Cover				2·00		☐
Presentation Pack			3·50		☐	
PHQ Card (No. 936)			£200	£200	☐	☐

422 Palace of Westminster seen from Whitehall

423 Palace of Westminster seen from Millbank

19th Commonwealth Parliamentary Conference

1973 (12 Sept.) 'All-over' phosphor

939	**422**	8p black, grey and pale buff	45	50	☐	☐
940	**423**	10p gold and black	45	40	☐	☐
Set of 2			75	75	☐	☐
First Day Cover				1·50		☐
Presentation Pack			3·00		☐	
Souvenir Book			7·00		☐	
PHQ Card (No. 939)			40·00	£150	☐	☐

424 Princess Anne and Captain Mark Phillips

Royal Wedding

1973 (14 Nov.) 'All-over' phosphor

941	**424**	3½p violet and silver	25	25	☐	☐
942		20p brown and silver	1·00	75	☐	☐
Set of 2			1·00	75	☐	☐
First Day Cover				1·50		☐
Presentation Pack			2·75		☐	
PHQ Card (No. 941)			9·00	50·00	☐	☐
Set of 2 Gutter Pairs			2·75		☐	
Set of 2 Traffic Light Gutter Pairs			£110		☐	

425

426

427

428

429

430 'Good King Wenceslas, the Page and Peasant'

The 3p values depict the carol 'Good King Wenceslas' and were printed horizontally *se-tenant* within the sheet.

Christmas

1973 (28 Nov.) One phosphor band (3p) or 'all-over' phosphor (3½p)

943	**425**	3p multicoloured	20	25	☐	☐
		a. Strip of 5. Nos. 943/7	2·25	2·50	☐	☐
944	**426**	3p multicoloured	20	25	☐	☐
945	**427**	3p multicoloured	20	25	☐	☐
946	**428**	3p multicoloured	20	25	☐	☐
947	**429**	3p multicoloured	20	25	☐	☐
948	**430**	3½p multicoloured	20	25	☐	☐
Set of 6			2·25	2·50	☐	☐
First Day Cover				2·50		☐
Presentation Pack			4·00		☐	

Collectors Pack 1973

1973 (28 Nov.) Comprises Nos. 919/48

CP948k Collectors Pack		27·00	☐

431 Horse Chestnut

British Trees (2nd issue)

1974 (27 Feb.) 'All-over' phosphor

949	**431**	10p multicoloured	40	35	☐	☐
First Day Cover				1·25	☐	
Presentation Pack			2·50		☐	
PHQ Card			£150	£150	☐	☐
Gutter Pair			2·00		☐	
Traffic Light Gutter Pair			65·00		☐	

432 First Motor Fire-engine, 1904

433 Prize-winning Fire-engine, 1863

434 First Steam Fire-engine, 1830

435 Fire-engine, 1766

Bicentenary of the Fire Prevention (Metropolis) Act

1974 (24 Apr.) 'All-over' phosphor

950	**432**	3½p multicoloured	25	10	☐	☐
951	**433**	5½p multicoloured	25	30	☐	☐
952	**434**	8p multicoloured	50	50	☐	☐
953	**435**	10p multicoloured	50	50	☐	☐
Set of 4			1·25	1·25	☐	☐
First Day Cover				3·00		☐
Presentation Pack			3·00		☐	
PHQ Card (No. 950)			£140	£150	☐	☐
Set of 4 Gutter Pairs			4·00		☐	
Set of 4 Traffic Light Gutter Pairs			60·00		☐	

436 P & O Packet *Peninsular*, 1888

437 Farman H.F. III Biplane, 1911

438 Airmail-blue Van and Postbox, 1930

439 Imperial Airways Short S.21 Flying Boat *Maia*, 1937

Centenary of Universal Postal Union

1974 (12 June) 'All-over' phosphor

954	**436**	3½p multicoloured	25	10	☐	☐
955	**437**	5½p multicoloured	25	30	☐	☐
956	**438**	8p multicoloured	25	35	☐	☐
957	**439**	10p multicoloured	50	40	☐	☐
Set of 4			1·00	1·00	☐	☐

First Day Cover		2·00	☐
Presentation Pack		3·00	☐
Set of 4 Gutter Pairs		3·00	☐
Set of 4 Traffic Light Gutter Pairs		45·00	☐

440 Robert the Bruce   **441** Owain Glyndŵr

442 Henry V   **443** The Black Prince

Medieval Warriors

1974 (10 July) 'All-over' phosphor

958	**440**	4½p multicoloured	25	10	☐	☐
959	**441**	5½p multicoloured	25	35	☐	☐
960	**442**	8p multicoloured	50	50	☐	☐
961	**443**	10p multicoloured	50	50	☐	☐
Set of 4			1·25	1·25	☐	☐
First Day Cover				3·00		☐
Presentation Pack			4·00		☐	
PHQ Cards (*set of* 4)			28·00	65·00	☐	☐
Set of 4 Gutter Pairs			4·00		☐	
Set of 4 Traffic Light Gutter Pairs			60·00		☐	

444 Churchill in Royal yacht Squadron Uniform   **445** Prime Minister, 1940

446 Secretary for War and Air, 1919   **447** War Correspondent, South Africa, 1899

Birth Centenary of Sir Winston Churchill

1974 (9 Oct.) Queen's head and inscription in silver. 'All-over' phosphor

962	**444**	4½p green and blue	20	15	☐	☐
963	**445**	5½p grey and black	35	35	☐	☐
964	**446**	8p rose and lake	60	50	☐	☐
965	**447**	10p stone and brown	60	50	☐	☐
Set of 4			1·60	1·50	☐	☐
First Day Cover				2·00		☐

Presentation Pack	3·50		☐
Souvenir Book	3·00		☐
PHQ Card (No. 963)	6·00	32·00	☐ ☐
Set of 4 Gutter Pairs	4·00		☐
Set of 4 Traffic Light Gutter Pairs	34·00		☐

448 Adoration of the Magi (York Minister, *c* 1355)

449 The Nativity (St Helen's Church, Norwich, *c* 1480)

450 Virgin and Child (Ottery St Mary Church, *c* 1350)

451 Virgin and Child (Worcester Cathedral, *c* 1224)

Christmas

1974 (27 Nov.) Designs show church roof bosses. One phosphor band (3½p) or 'all-over' phosphor (others)

966	**448**	3½p multicoloured	10	10	☐	☐
967	**449**	4½p multicoloured	10	10	☐	☐
968	**450**	8p multicoloured	25	50	☐	☐
969	**451**	10p multicoloured	50	50	☐	☐
Set of 4			1·00	1·00	☐	☐
First Day Cover				2·00		☐
Presentation Pack			3·00		☐	
Set of 4 Gutter Pairs			3·50		☐	
Set of 4 Traffic Light Gutter Pairs			36·00		☐	

Collectors Pack 1974

1974 (27 Nov.) Comprises Nos. 949/69

CP969a Collectors Pack		13·00	☐

452 Invalid in Wheelchair

Health and Handicap Funds

1975 (22 Jan.) 'All-over' phosphor

970	**452**	4½p + 1½p azure and blue	25	25	☐	☐
First Day Cover				1·00		☐
Gutter Pair			50		☐	
Traffic Light Gutter Pair			2·25		☐	

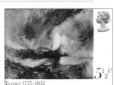

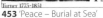

453 'Peace – Burial at Sea'

454 'Snowstorm – Steamer off a Harbour's Mouth'

455 'The Arsenal, Venice'

456 'St Laurent'

Birth Bicentenary of J. M. W. Turner (painter)

1975 (19 Feb.) 'All-over' phosphor

971	**453**	4½p multicoloured	25	25	☐	☐
972	**454**	5½p multicoloured	25	25	☐	☐
973	**455**	8p multicoloured	25	50	☐	☐
974	**456**	10p multicoloured	50	50	☐	☐
Set of 4			1·00	1·00		☐
First Day Cover				1·50		☐
Presentation Pack			3·00		☐	
PHQ Card (No. 972)			42·00	34·00	☐	☐
Set of 4 Gutter Pairs			2·25		☐	
Set of 4 Traffic Light Gutter Pairs			8·00		☐	

457 Charlotte Square, Edinburgh

458 The Rows, Chester

The above were printed horizontally *se-tenant* throughout the sheet.

459 Royal Observatory, Greenwich

460 St George's Chapel, Windsor

461 National Theatre, London

European Architectural Heritage Year

1975 (23 Apr.) 'All-over' phosphor

975	**457**	7p multicoloured	15	15	☐	☐
		a. Pair. Nos. 975/6	90	1·00	☐	☐
976	**458**	7p multicoloured	15	15	☐	☐
977	**459**	8p multicoloured	40	30	☐	☐
978	**460**	10p multicoloured	40	30	☐	☐
979	**461**	12p multicoloured	40	35	☐	☐
Set of 5			1·50	1·40		☐
First Day Cover				2·50		☐
Presentation Pack			3·00		☐	
PHQ Cards (Nos. 975/7)			11·00	40·00	☐	☐
Set of 5 Gutter Pairs			5·50		☐	
Set of 5 Traffic Light Gutter Pairs			22·00		☐	

462 Sailing Dinghies

463 Racing Keel Boats

470 Palace of Westminster

464 Cruising Yachts

465 Multihulls

62nd Inter-Parliamentary Union Conference

1975 (3 Sept.) 'All-over' phosphor

988	**470**	12p multicoloured		50	40	☐	☐
First Day Cover					80		☐
Presentation Pack				1·75		☐	
Gutter Pair				1·00		☐	
Traffic Light Gutter Pair				3·00		☐	

Sailing

1975 (11 June) 'All-over' phosphor

980	**462**	7p multicoloured		25	20	☐	☐
981	**463**	8p multicoloured		35	40	☐	☐
982	**464**	10p multicoloured		35	45	☐	☐
983	**465**	12p multicoloured		50	50	☐	☐
Set of 4				1·25	1·25	☐	☐
First Day Cover					2·00		☐
Presentation Pack				2·50		☐	☐
PHQ Card (No. 981)				5·75	30·00	☐	☐
Set of 4 Gutter Pairs				2·50		☐	
Set of 4 Traffic Light Gutter Pairs				25·00		☐	

471 Emma and
Mr Woodhouse (*Emma*)

472 Catherine Morland
(*Northanger Abbey*)

466 Stephenson's *Locomotion*,
1825

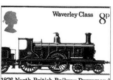

467 *Abbotsford*, 1876

473 Mr Darcy (*Pride
and Prejudice*)

474 Mary and Henry
Crawford (*Mansfield Park*)

468 *Caerphilly Castle*, 1923

469 High Speed Train, 1975

Birth Bicentenary of Jane Austen (novelist)

1975 (22 Oct.) 'All-over' phosphor

989	**471**	8½p multicoloured		25	20	☐	☐
990	**472**	10p multicoloured		45	45	☐	☐
991	**473**	11p multicoloured		45	45	☐	☐
992	**474**	13p multicoloured		50	50	☐	☐
Set of 4				1·50	1·25	☐	☐
First Day Cover					2·50		☐
Presentation Pack				3·00		☐	
PHQ Cards (*set of 4*)				24·00	42·00	☐	☐
Set of 4 Gutter Pairs				2·50		☐	
Set of 4 Traffic Light Gutter Pairs				7·00		☐	

150th Anniversary of Public Railways

1975 (13 Aug.) 'All-over' phosphor

984	**466**	7p multicoloured		25	25	☐	☐
985	**467**	8p multicoloured		50	50	☐	☐
986	**468**	10p multicoloured		50	50	☐	☐
987	**469**	12p multicoloured		40	50	☐	☐
Set of 4				1·50	1·50	☐	☐
First Day Cover					2·50		☐
Presentation Pack				3·00		☐	
Souvenir Book				4·00		☐	
PHQ Cards (*set of 4*)				70·00	72·00	☐	☐
Set of 4 Gutter Pairs				3·00		☐	
Set of 4 Traffic Light Gutter Pairs				12·00		☐	

475 Angels with Harp and Lute **476** Angel with Mandolin

477 Angel with Horn   **478** Angel with Trumpet

Christmas

1975 (26 Nov.) One phosphor band (6½p). phosphor-inked (8½p) (background) or 'all-over' phosphor (others)

993	**475**	6½p	multicoloured	25	25	☐ ☐
994	**476**	8½p	multicoloured	25	40	☐ ☐
995	**477**	11p	multicoloured	50	45	☐ ☐
996	**478**	13p	multicoloured	50	45	☐ ☐
Set of 4				1·25	1·25	☐ ☐
First Day Cover					1·50	☐
Presentation Pack				3·00		☐
Set of 4 Gutter Pairs				2·75		☐
Set of 4 Traffic Light Gutter Pairs				9·00		☐

Collectors Pack 1975

1975 (26 Nov.) Comprises Nos. 970/96

CP996a	Collectors Pack	9·00	☐

479 Housewife   **480** Policeman

481 District Nurse   **482** Industrialist

Telephone Centenary

1976 (10 Mar.) 'All-over' phosphor

997	**479**	8½p	multicoloured	25	20	☐ ☐
998	**480**	10p	multicoloured	40	40	☐ ☐
999	**481**	11p	multicoloured	50	50	☐ ☐
1000	**482**	13p	multicoloured	60	60	☐ ☐
Set of 4				1·50	1·50	☐ ☐
First Day Cover					1·50	☐
Presentation Pack				3·00		☐
Set of 4 Gutter Pairs				2·75		☐
Set of 4 Traffic Light Gutter Pairs				9·00		☐

483 Hewing Coal (Thomas Hepburn)   **484** Machinery (Robert Owen)

485 Chimney Cleaning (Lord Shaftesbury)   **486** Hands clutching Prison Bars (Elizabeth Fry)

Social Reformers

1976 (28 Apr.) 'All-over' phosphor

1001	**483**	8½p	multicoloured	25	20	☐ ☐
1002	**484**	10p	multicoloured	40	40	☐ ☐
1003	**485**	11p	black, slate-grey and drab	50	50	☐ ☐
1004	**486**	13p	slate-grey, black and green	60	60	☐ ☐
Set of 4				1·50	1·50	☐ ☐
First Day Cover					1·50	☐
Presentation Pack				2·75		☐
PHQ Card (No. 1001)				6·00	20·00	☐ ☐
Set of 4 Gutter Pairs				2·75		☐
Set of 4 Traffic Light Gutter Pairs				9·00		☐

487 Benjamin Franklin (bust by Jean-Jacques Caffieri)

Bicentenary of American Revolution

1976 (2 June) 'All-over' phosphor

1005	**487**	11p	multicoloured	50	50	☐ ☐
First Day Cover					1·50	☐
Presentation Pack				1·50		☐
PHQ Card				5·00	20·00	☐ ☐
Gutter Pair				75		☐
Traffic Light Gutter Pair				2·50		☐

488 'Elizabeth of Glamis'   **489** 'Grandpa Dickson'

490 *'Rosa Mundi'*   **491** *'Sweet Briar'*

Centenary of Royal National Rose Society

1976 (30 June) 'All-over' phosphor

1006	**488**	8½p multicoloured	15	10	☐	☐
1007	**489**	10p multicoloured	40	40	☐	☐
1008	**490**	11p multicoloured	50	50	☐	☐
1009	**491**	13p multicoloured	65	65	☐	☐
Set of 4			1·50	1·50	☐	☐
First Day Cover				1·50		☐
Presentation Pack			3·00		☐	
PHQ Cards (*set of* 4)			30·00	38·00	☐	☐
Set of 4 Gutter Pairs			3·00		☐	
Set of 4 Traffic Light Gutter Pairs			10·00		☐	

492 Archdruid

493 Morris Dancing

494 Scots Piper

495 Welsh Harpist

British Cultural Traditions

1976 (4 Aug.) 'All-over' phosphor

1010	**492**	8½p multicoloured	25	20	☐	☐
1011	**493**	10p multicoloured	40	40	☐	☐
1012	**494**	11p multicoloured	45	45	☐	☐
1013	**495**	13p multicoloured	60	60	☐	☐
Set of 4			1·50	1·50	☐	☐
First Day Cover				2·00		☐
Presentation Pack			2·50		☐	
PHQ Cards (*set of* 4)			18·00	30·00	☐	☐
Set of 4 Gutter Pairs			3·00		☐	
Set of 4 Traffic Light Gutter Pairs			12·00		☐	

496 The Canterbury
Tales

497 The Tretyse of
Love

498 Game and Playe
of Chesse

499 Early Printing
Press

500th Anniversary of British Printing

1976 (29 Sept.) 'All-over' phosphor

1014	**496**	8½p black, blue and gold	25	20	☐	☐
1015	**497**	10p black, olive-green and gold	40	40	☐	☐
1016	**498**	11p black, grey and gold	45	45	☐	☐
1017	**499**	13p brown, ochre and gold	60	60	☐	☐
Set of 4			1·50	1·50	☐	☐
First Day Cover				1·75		☐
Presentation Pack			2·75		☐	
PHQ Cards (*set of* 4)			10·00	28·00	☐	☐
Set of 4 Gutter Pairs			3·00		☐	
Set of 4 Traffic Light Gutter Pairs			7·00		☐	

500 Virgin and Child

501 Angel with Crown

502 Angel appearing to
Shepherds

503 The Three Kings

Christmas

1976 (24 Nov.) Designs show English medieval embroidery. One phosphor band (6½p) or 'all-over' phosphor (others)

1018	**500**	6½p multicoloured	25	25	☐	☐
1019	**501**	8½p multicoloured	35	25	☐	☐
1020	**502**	11p multicoloured	40	45	☐	☐
1021	**503**	13p multicoloured	45	50	☐	☐
Set of 4			1·25	1·25	☐	☐
First Day Cover				1·50		☐
Presentation Pack			2·75		☐	
PHQ Cards (*set of* 4)			4·50	26·00	☐	☐
Set of 4 Gutter Pairs			2·75		☐	
Set of 4 Traffic Light Gutter Pairs			7·00		☐	

Collectors Pack 1976

1976 (24 Nov.) Comprises Nos. 997/1021

CP1021a	Collectors Pack	13·50	☐

504 Lawn Tennis

505 Table Tennis

506 Squash

507 Badminton

Racket Sports

1977 (12 Jan.) Phosphorised paper

1022	**504**	8½p multicoloured	25	20	☐	☐
1023	**505**	10p multicoloured	40	40	☐	☐
1024	**506**	11p multicoloured	45	40	☐	☐
1025	**507**	13p multicoloured	45	50	☐	☐
Set of 4			1·25	1·25	☐	☐
First Day Cover				2·00		☐
Presentation Pack			3·00		☐	
PHQ Cards (set of 4)			8·00	24·00	☐	☐
Set of 4 Gutter Pairs			3·00		☐	
Set of 4 Traffic Light Gutter Pairs			7·50		☐	

508

1977 (2 Feb.)–**87** Type 508 Ordinary paper

1026		£1 green and olive	3·00	25	☐	☐
1026b	£1·30	drab and deep greenish blue	5·50	6·00	☐	☐
1026c	£1·33	pale mauve and grey-black	7·50	8·00	☐	☐
1026d	£1·41	drab and deep greenish blue	8·50	8·50	☐	☐
1026e	£1·50	pale mauve and grey-black	6·00	5·00	☐	☐
1026f	£1·60	drab and deep greenish blue	6·50	7·00	☐	☐
1027		£2 green and brown	9·00	50	☐	☐
1028		£5 pink and blue	22·00	3·00	☐	☐
Set of 8			60·00	32·00	☐	☐
Presentation pack (P.O. Pack No. 91 (small size)) (Nos. 1026, 1027/8)			30·00		☐	
Presentation Pack (P.O. Pack No 13 (large size)) (Nos. 1026, 1027/8)			£180		☐	
Presentation Pack (P.O. Pack No. 14) (No. 1026f)			22·00		☐	
Set of 8 Gutter Pairs			£140		☐	
Set of 8 Gutter Pairs			£170		☐	

First Day Covers

2 Feb. 1977	Nos. 1026, 1027/8	14·00	☐
3 Aug. 1983	No. 1026b	£6·50	☐
28th Aug. 1984	No. 1026c.	8·00	☐
17 Sept. 1985	No. 1026d	9·00	☐
2 Sept. 1986	No. 1026e	6·50	☐
15 Sept. 1987	No. 1026f	8·50	☐

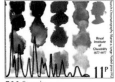

509 Steroids — Conformational Analysis

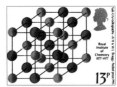

510 Vitamin C — Synthesis

511 Starch — Chromatography

512 Salt — Crystallography

Centenary of Royal Institute of Chemistry

1977 (2 Mar.) 'All-over' phosphor

1029	**509**	8½p multicoloured	25	20	☐	☐
1030	**510**	10p multicoloured	45	45	☐	☐
1031	**511**	11p multicoloured	45	45	☐	☐
1032	**512**	13p multicoloured	45	45	☐	☐
Set of 4			1·25	1·25	☐	☐
First Day Cover				1·50		☐
Presentation Pack			3·00		☐	
PHQ Cards (set of 4)			8·00	18·00	☐	☐
Set of 4 Gutter Pairs			3·00		☐	
Set of 4 Traffic Light Gutter Pairs			7·00		☐	

513

Silver Jubilee

1977 (11 May–15 June) 'All-over' phosphor

1033	**513**	8½p multicoloured	25	25	☐	☐
1034		9p multicoloured	25	25	☐	☐
1035		10p multicoloured	25	25	☐	☐
1036		11p multicoloured	50	50	☐	☐
10347		13p multicoloured	50	50	☐	☐
Set of 5			1·75	1·75	☐	☐
First Day Cover (2)				2·50		☐
Presentation Pack (ex 9p)			2·00		☐	
Souvenir Book (ex 9p)			3·00		☐	
PHQ Cards (set of 5)			14·00	20·00	☐	☐
Set of 5 Gutter Pairs			3·50		☐	
Set of 5 Traffic Light Gutter Pairs			6·00		☐	

517 'Gathering of Nations'

Commonwealth Heads of Government Meeting, London

1977 (8 June) 'All-over' phosphor

1038	**517**	13p black, deep green, rose and silver	50	50	☐	☐
First Day Cover				1·50		☐
Presentation Pack			1·50		☐	
PHQ Card			5·00	6·00	☐	☐
Gutter Pair			1·00		☐	
Traffic Light Gutter Pair			1·50		☐	

518 Hedgehog

519 Brown Hare

520 Red Squirrel

521 Otter

522 Badger

T **518/22** were printed together, *se-tenant*, throughout the sheet.

British Wildlife

1977 (5 Oct.) 'All-over' phosphor

1039	**518**	9p multicoloured	25	20	☐	☐
		a. Strip of 5. Nos.1039/43	1·50	1·75	☐	☐
1040	**519**	9p multicoloured	25	20	☐	☐
1041	**520**	9p multicoloured	25	20	☐	☐
1042	**521**	9p multicoloured	25	20	☐	☐
1043	**522**	9p multicoloured	25	20	☐	☐
Set of 5			1·50	1·75	☐	☐

First Day Cover		3·00	☐
Presentation Pack		2·50	☐
PHQ Cards (*set of 5*)		3·00	7·00	☐ ☐
Gutter Strip of 10		3·00	☐
Traffic Light Gutter Strip of 10		5·00	☐

523 'Three French Hens, Two Turtle Doves and a Partridge in a Pear Tree'

524 'Six Geese a laying, Five Gold Rings, Four Colly Birds'

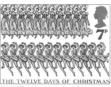

525 'Eight Maids a-milking, Seven Swans a-swimming'

526 'Ten Pipers piping, Nine Drummers drumming'

527 'Twelve Lords a-leaping, Eleven Ladies Dancing'

528 'A Partridge in a Pear Tree'

T **523/8** depict the carol 'The Twelve Days of Christmas'.
T **523/7** were printed horizontally *se-tenant* throughout the sheet.

Christmas

1977 (23 Nov.) One centre phosphor band (7p) or 'all-over' phosphor (9p)

1044	**523**	7p multicoloured	20	15	☐	☐
		a. Strip of 5. Nos. 1044/8	1·50	1·50	☐	☐
1045	**524**	7p multicoloured	20	15	☐	☐
1046	**525**	7p multicoloured	20	15	☐	☐
1047	**526**	7p multicoloured	20	15	☐	☐
1048	**527**	7p multicoloured	20	15	☐	☐
1049	**528**	9p multicoloured	35	30	☐	☐
Set of 6			1·25	1·50	☐	
First Day Cover				2·25		☐
Presentation Pack			2·25		☐	
PHQ Cards (*set of 6*)			3·00	6·00	☐	☐
Set of 6 Gutter Pairs			3·00		☐	
Set of 6 Traffic Light Gutter Pairs			5·50		☐	

Collectors Pack 1977

1977 (23 Nov.) Comprises Nos. 1022/5, 1029/49

CP1049b	Collectors Pack	9·00	☐

529 Oil — North Sea Production Platform

530 Coal — Modern Pithead

531 Natural Gas — Flame Rising from Sea

532 Electricity — Nuclear Power Station and Uranium Atom

Energy Resources

1978 (25 Jan.) 'All-over' phosphor

1050	**529**	9p multicoloured	25	25
1051	**530**	10½p multicoloured	25	25
1052	**531**	11p multicoloured	50	50
1053	**532**	13p multicoloured	50	50
Set of 4			1·25	1·25
First Day Cover				1·50
Presentation Pack			2·00	
PHQ Cards (*set of* 4)			3·00	6·00
Set of 4 Gutter Pairs			2·75	
Set of 4 Traffic Light Gutter Pairs			4·50	

533 Tower of London

534 Holyroodhouse

535 Caernarvon Castle

536 Hampton Court Palace

British Architecture (Historic Buildings)

1978 (1 Mar.) 'All-over' phosphor

1054	**533**	9p multicoloured	25	20
1055	**534**	10½p multicoloured	25	40
1056	**535**	11p multicoloured	60	40
1057	**536**	13p multicoloured	60	40
Set of 4			1·50	1·25
First Day Cover				1·50

Presentation Pack	2·00		
PHQ Cards (*set of* 4)	3·00	6·00	
Set of 4 Gutter Pairs	3·00		
Set of 4 Traffic Light Gutter Pairs	4·50		
MS1058 121 × 90 mm. Nos. 1054/7	1·50	1·75	
First Day Cover		2·00	

No. **MS**1058 was sold at 53½p, the premium being used for the London 1980 Stamp Exhibition.

537 State Coach

538 St Edward's Crown

539 The Sovereign's Orb

540 Imperial State Crown

25th Anniversary of Coronation

1978 (31 May) 'All-over' phosphor

1059	**537**	9p gold and blue	35	25
1060	**538**	10½p gold and red	45	45
1061	**539**	11p gold and green	45	45
1062	**540**	13p gold and violet	50	50
Set of 4			1·50	1·50
First Day Cover				1·50
Presentation Pack			2·00	
Souvenir Book			3·00	
PHQ Cards (*set of* 4)			3·00	6·00
Set of 4 Gutter Pairs			3·00	
Set of 4 Traffic Light Gutter Pairs			4·25	

541 Shire Horse

542 Shetland Pony

543 Welsh Pony

544 Thoroughbred

Horses

1978 (5 July) 'All-over' phosphor

1063	**541**	9p multicoloured	20	10	☐	☐
1064	**542**	10½p multicoloured	35	40	☐	☐
1065	**543**	11p multicoloured	35	45	☐	☐
1066	**544**	13p multicoloured	45	50	☐	☐
Set of 4			1·25	1·25	☐	☐
First Day Cover				1·50	☐	
Presentation Pack			1·75		☐	
PHQ Cards (*set of* 4)			2·25	5·75	☐	☐
Set of 4 Gutter Pairs			3·00		☐	
Set of 4 Traffic Light Gutter Pairs			4·50		☐	

545 Penny-farthing and 1884 Safety Bicycle **546** 1920 Touring Bicycles

547 Modern Small-wheel Bicycles **548** 1978 Road-racers

Centenaries of Cyclists Touring Club and British Cycling Federation

1978 (2 Aug.) 'All-over' phosphor

1067	**545**	9p multicoloured	25	20	☐	☐
1068	**546**	10½p multicoloured	35	40	☐	☐
1069	**547**	11p multicoloured	40	40	☐	☐
1070	**548**	13p multicoloured	50	50	☐	☐
Set of 4			1·25	1·25	☐	☐
First Day Cover				1·50	☐	
Presentation Pack			1·75		☐	
PHQ Cards (*set of* 4)			2·25	5·00	☐	☐
Set of 4 Gutter Pairs			2·75		☐	
Set of 4 Traffic Light Gutter Pairs			4·50		☐	

549 Singing Carols round the Christmas Tree **550** The Waits

551 18th-Century Carol Singers **552** 'The Boar's Head Carol'

Christmas

1978 (22 Nov.) One centre phosphor band (7p) or 'all-over' phosphor (others)

1071	**549**	7p multicoloured	25	25	☐	☐
1072	**550**	9p multicoloured	25	25	☐	☐
1073	**551**	11p multicoloured	50	50	☐	☐
1074	**552**	13p multicoloured	50	50	☐	☐
Set of 4			1·25	1·25	☐	☐
First Day Cover				1·50	☐	
Presentation Pack			1·75		☐	
PHQ Cards (*set of* 4)			2·25	5·00	☐	☐
Set of 4 Gutter Pairs			2·50		☐	
Set of 4 Traffic Light Gutter Pairs			4·25		☐	

Collectors Pack 1978

1978 (22 Nov.) Comprises Nos. 1050/7, 1059/74

CP1074a Collectors Pack		10·00	☐

553 Old English Sheepdog **554** Welsh Springer Spaniel

555 West Highland Terrier **556** Irish Setter

Dogs

1979 (7 Feb.) 'All-over' phosphor

1075	**553**	9p multicoloured	25	20	☐	☐
1076	**554**	10½p multicoloured	40	40	☐	☐
1077	**555**	11p multicoloured	40	40	☐	☐
1078	**556**	13p multicoloured	40	50	☐	☐
Set of 4			1·25	1·25	☐	☐
First Day Cover				1·50	☐	
Presentation Pack			1·75		☐	
PHQ Cards (*set of* 4)			2·50	5·00	☐	☐
Set of 4 Gutter Pairs			2·50		☐	
Set of 4 Traffic Light Gutter Pairs			4·25		☐	

557 Primrose **558** Daffodil

559 Bluebell   **560** Snowdrop

Spring Wild Flowers

1979 (21 Mar.) 'All-over' phosphor

1079	**557**	9p multicoloured	25	20	☐	☐
1080	**558**	10½p multicoloured	25	45	☐	☐
1081	**559**	11p multicoloured	50	45	☐	☐
1082	**560**	13p multicoloured	50	40	☐	☐
Set of 4			1·25	1·25	☐	☐
First Day Cover				1·50		☐
Presentation Pack			1·75		☐	
PHQ Cards (*set of* 4)			2·50	4·50	☐	☐
Set of 4 Gutter Pairs			2·50		☐	
Set of 4 Traffic Light Gutter Pairs			4·25		☐	

561   **562**

563   **564**

T **561/4** show hands placing the flags of the member nations into ballot boxes.

First Direct Elections to European Assembly

1979 (9 May) Phosphorised paper

1083	**561**	9p multicoloured	25	20	☐	☐
1084	**562**	10½p multicoloured	35	35	☐	☐
1085	**563**	11p multicoloured	40	40	☐	☐
1086	**564**	13p multicoloured	45	40	☐	☐
Set of 4			1·25	1·25	☐	☐
First Day Cover				1·50		☐
Presentation Pack			1·75		☐	
PHQ Cards (*set of* 4)			2·25	4·50	☐	☐
Set of 4 Gutter Pairs			2·50		☐	
Set of 4 Traffic Light Gutter Pairs			4·25		☐	

565 'Saddling "Mahmoud" for the Derby, 1936' (Sir Alfred Munnings)

566 'The Liverpool Great National Steeple Chase, 1839' (aquatint by F. C.Turner)

567 'The First Spring Meeting, Newmarket, 1793' (J.N. Sartorius)

568 'Racing at Dorsett Ferry, Windsor, 1684' (Francis Barlow)

Horseracing Paintings and Bicentenary of The Derby (9p)

1979 (6 June) 'All-over' phosphor

1087	**565**	9p multicoloured	25	25	☐	☐
1088	**566**	10½p multicoloured	25	25	☐	☐
1089	**567**	11p multicoloured	50	50	☐	☐
1090	**568**	13p multicoloured	50	50	☐	☐
Set of 4			1·25	1·25	☐	☐
First Day Cover				1·50		☐
Presentation Pack			1·75		☐	
PHQ Cards (*set of* 4)			2·25	4·50	☐	☐
Set of 4 Gutter Pairs			2·50		☐	
Set of 4 Traffic Light Gutter Pairs			4·25		☐	

569 *The Tale of Peter Rabbit* (Beatrix Potter)

570 *The Wind in the Willows* (Kenneth Grahame)

571 *Winnie-the-Pooh* (A.A. Milne)

572 *Alice's Adventures in Wonderland* (Lewis Carroll)

T **569/72** depict original illustrations from the four books.

International Year of the Child

1979 (11 July) 'All-over' phosphor

1091	**569**	9p multicoloured	30	25	☐	☐
1092	**570**	10½p multicoloured	35	35	☐	☐
1093	**571**	11p multicoloured	40	40	☐	☐
1094	**572**	13p multicoloured	60	60	☐	☐
Set of 4			1·50	1·50	☐	☐
First Day Cover				1·50		☐
Presentation Pack			1·75		☐	
PHQ Cards (*set of* 4)			2·50	4·50	☐	☐
Set of 4 Gutter Pairs			3·50		☐	
Set of 4 Traffic Light Gutter Pairs			4·25		☐	

573 Sir Rowland Hill, 1795-1879

574 General Post, c 1839

575 London Post, c 1839

576 Uniform Postage, 1840

Death Centenary of Sir Rowland Hill (postal reformer)

1979 (22 Aug.–24 Oct.) 'All-over' phosphor

1095	**573**	10p multicoloured	25	20	☐	☐
1096	**574**	11½p multicoloured	25	35	☐	☐
1097	**575**	13p multicoloured	50	45	☐	☐
1098	**576**	15p multicoloured	75	50	☐	☐
Set of 4			1·50	1·50	☐	☐
First Day Cover				1·50		☐
Presentation Pack			1·50		☐	
PHQ Cards (set of 4)			2·25	4·25	☐	☐
Set of 4 Gutter Pairs			3·00		☐	
Set of 4 Traffic Light Gutter Pairs			4·25		☐	
MS1099 89 × 121 mm. Nos. 1095/8			1·25	1·50	☐	☐
First Day Cover (24 Oct.)				1·50		☐

No. **MS**1099 was sold at 59½p, the premium being used for the London 1980 Stamp Exhibition.

577 Policeman on the Beat

578 Policeman directing Traffic

579 Mounted Policewoman

580 River Patrol Boat

150th Anniversary of Metropolitan Police

1979 (26 Sept.) Phosphorised paper

1100	**577**	10p multicoloured	30	20	☐	☐
1101	**578**	11½p multicoloured	35	35	☐	☐
1102	**579**	13p multicoloured	40	55	☐	☐
1103	**580**	15p multicoloured	60	55	☐	☐

Set of 4	1·50	1·50	☐	☐
First Day Cover		1·50		☐
Presentation Pack	1·75		☐	
PHQ Cards (set of 4)	2·25	4·25	☐	☐
Set of 4 Gutter Pairs	3·00		☐	
Set of 4 Traffic Light Gutter Pairs	4·25		☐	

581 The Three Kings

582 Angel appearing to the Shepherds

583 The Nativity

584 Mary and Joseph travelling to Bethlehem

585 The Annunciation

Christmas

1979 (21 Nov.) One centre phosphor band (8p) or phosphorised paper (others)

1104	**581**	8p multicoloured	25	20	☐	☐
1105	**582**	10p multicoloured	25	25	☐	☐
1106	**583**	11½p multicoloured	25	35	☐	☐
1107	**584**	13p multicoloured	50	50	☐	☐
1108	**585**	15p multicoloured	50	50	☐	☐
Set of 5			1·50	1·50	☐	☐
First Day Cover				1·50		☐
Presentation Pack			2·00		☐	
PHQ Cards (set of 5)			2·50	4·25	☐	☐
Set of 5 Gutter Pairs			3·50		☐	
Set of 5 Traffic Light Gutter Pairs			4·50		☐	

Collectors Pack 1979

1979 (21 Nov.) Comprises Nos. 1075/98, 1100/8

CP1108a	Collectors Pack	12·00	☐

586 Common Kingfisher

587 Dipper

588 Moorhen   **589** Yellow Wagtails

Centenary of Wild Bird Protection Act

1980 (16 Jan.) Phosphorised paper

1109	**586**	10p multicoloured	20	10	☐	☐
1110	**587**	11½p multicoloured	40	35	☐	☐
1111	**588**	13p multicoloured	50	55	☐	☐
1112	**589**	15p multicoloured	50	55	☐	☐
Set of 4			1·50	1·50	☐	☐
First Day Cover				1·50		☐
Presentation Pack			1·50		☐	
PHQ Cards (*set of* 4)			2·25	4·50	☐	
Set of 4 Gutter Pairs			3·50		☐	

590 Rocket approaching Moorish Arch, Liverpool

591 First and Second Class Carriages passing through Olive Mount Cutting

592 Third Class Carriage and Sheep Truck crossing Chat Moss

593 Horsebox and Carriage Truck near Bridgewater Canal

594 Goods Truck and Mail - coach at Manchester

T **590/4** were printed together, *se-tenant*, in horizontal strips of 5 throughout the sheet.

150th Anniversary of Liverpool and Manchester Railway

1980 (12 Mar.) Phosphorised paper

1113	**590**	12p multicoloured	20	15	☐	☐
		a. Strip of 5.				
		Nos. 1113/17	1·75	1·75	☐	☐
1114	**591**	12p multicoloured	20	15	☐	☐
1115	**592**	12p multicoloured	20	15	☐	☐
1116	**593**	12p multicoloured	20	15	☐	☐
1117	**594**	12p multicoloured	20	15	☐	☐

Set of 5		1·75	1·75	☐ ☐
First Day Cover			1·75	☐
Presentation Pack		2·00		☐
PHQ Cards (*set of* 5)		3·25	4·50	☐ ☐
Gutter block of 10		3·75		☐

595 Montage of London Buildings

'London 1980' International Stamp Exhibition

1980 (9 Apr.–7 May) Phosphorised paper. Perf 14½ × 14

1118	**595**	50p agate	1·50	1·50	☐	☐
First Day Cover				1·50		☐
Presentation Pack			1·75		☐	
PHQ Card			2·25	3·00	☐	☐
Gutter Pair			3·25		☐	
MS1119 90 × 123 mm. No. 1118			1·50	1·75	☐	☐
First Day Cover (7 May)				2·00		☐

No. **MS**1119 was sold at 75p, the premium being used for the exhibition.

596 Buckingham Palace

597 The Albert Memorial

598 Royal Opera House

599 Hampton Court

600 Kensington Palace

London Landmarks

1980 (7 May) Phosphorised paper

1120	**596**	10½p multicoloured	25	10	☐	☐
1121	**597**	12p multicoloured	25	15	☐	☐
1122	**598**	13½p multicoloured	40	50	☐	☐
1123	**599**	15p multicoloured	50	75	☐	☐
1124	**600**	17½p multicoloured	75	75	☐	☐
Set of 5			2·00	2·00	☐	☐
First Day Cover				2·00		☐
Presentation Pack			2·00		☐	
PHQ Cards (*set of* 5)			2·25	3·00	☐	☐
Set of 5 Gutter Pairs			4·25		☐	

601 Charlotte Brontë (*Jane Eyre*)   **602** George Eliot (*The Mill on the Floss*)

603 Emily Brontë (*Wuthering Heights*)   **604** Mrs Gaskell (*North and South*)

T **601/4** show authoresses and scenes from their novels.
T **601/2** also include the 'Europa' C.E.P.T. emblem.

Famous Authoresses

1980 (9 July) Phosphorised paper

1125	**601**	12p multicoloured	35	20	☐	☐
1126	**602**	13½p multicoloured	40	45	☐	☐
1127	**603**	15p multicoloured	40	45	☐	☐
1128	**604**	17½p multicoloured	50	50	☐	☐
Set of 4			1·50	1·50	☐	☐
First Day Cover				1·50		☐
Presentation Pack			1·75		☐	
PHQ Cards (*set of* 4)			2·50	3·00	☐	☐
Set of 4 Gutter Pairs			3·75		☐	

605 Queen Elizabeth the Queen Mother

80th Birthday of Queen Elizabeth the Queen Mother

1980 (4 Aug.) Phosphorised paper

1129	**605**	12p multicoloured	75	75	☐	☐
First Day Cover				1·50		☐
PHQ Card			2·25	1·75	☐	☐
Gutter Pair			1·50		☐	

606 Sir Henry Wood   **607** Sir Thomas Beecham

608 Sir Malcolm Sargent   **609** Sir John Barbirolli

British Conductors

1980 (10 Sept.) Phosphorised paper

1130	**606**	12p multicoloured	30	10	☐	☐
1131	**607**	13½p multicoloured	45	40	☐	☐
1132	**608**	15p multicoloured	50	55	☐	☐
1133	**609**	17½p multicoloured	50	55	☐	☐
Set of 4			1·50	1·50	☐	☐
First Day Cover				1·75		☐
Presentation Pack			1·75		☐	
PHQ Cards (*set of* 4)			2·25	3·75	☐	☐
Set of 4 Gutter Pairs			3·75		☐	

610 Running   **611** Rugby

612 Boxing   **613** Cricket

Sports Centenaries

1980 (10 Oct.) Phosphorised paper. Perf 14 × 14½

1134	**610**	12p multicoloured	25	20	☐	☐
1135	**611**	13½p multicoloured	50	50	☐	☐
1136	**612**	15p multicoloured	50	45	☐	☐
1137	**613**	17½p multicoloured	50	50	☐	☐

Set of 4	1·50	1·50	☐ ☐
First Day Cover		1·75	☐
Presentation Pack	1·75		☐
PHQ Cards (set of 4)	2·25	3·75	☐ ☐
Set of 4 Gutter Pairs	3·75		☐

Centenaries:—12p Amateur Athletics Association; 13½p Welsh Rugby Union; 15p Amateur Boxing Association; 17½p First England v Australia Test Match.

614 Christmas Tree

615 Candles

616 Apples and Mistletoe

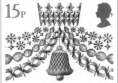
617 Crown, Chains and Bell

618 Holly

Christmas

1980 (19 Nov.) One centre phosphor band (10p) or phosphorised paper (others)

1138	**614**	10p multicoloured	20	10	☐ ☐
1139	**615**	12p multicoloured	20	20	☐ ☐
1140	**616**	13½p multicoloured	40	40	☐ ☐
1141	**617**	15p multicoloured	55	50	☐ ☐
1142	**618**	17½p multicoloured	55	50	☐ ☐
Set of 5			1·75	1·50	☐ ☐
First Day Cover				1·75	☐
Presentation Pack			2·00		☐
PHQ Cards (set of 5)			2·25	4·00	☐ ☐
Set of 5 Gutter Pairs			4·50		☐

Collectors Pack 1980

1980 (19 Nov.) Comprises Nos. 1109/18, 1120/42

CP1142a Collectors Pack	15·00	☐

619 St Valentine's Day

620 Morris Dancers

621 Lammastide

622 Medieval Mummers

T **619/20** also include the 'Europa' C.E.P.T. emblem.

Folklore

1981 (6 Feb.) Phosphorised paper

1143	**619**	14p multicoloured	25	25	☐ ☐
1144	**620**	18p multicoloured	50	50	☐ ☐
1145	**621**	22p multicoloured	75	80	☐ ☐
1146	**622**	25p multicoloured	1·00	1·10	☐ ☐
Set of 4			2·25	2·50	☐ ☐
First Day Cover				2·00	☐
Presentation Pack			2·25		☐
PHQ Cards (set of 4)			2·25	3·25	☐ ☐
Set of 4 Gutter Pairs			5·25		☐

623 Blind Man with Guide Dog

624 Hands spelling 'Deaf' in Sign Language

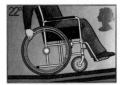
625 Disabled Man in Wheelchair

626 Disabled Artist painting with Foot

International Year of the Disabled

1981 (25 Mar.) Phosphorised paper

1147	**623**	14p multicoloured	50	25	☐ ☐
1148	**624**	18p multicoloured	50	50	☐ ☐
1149	**625**	22p multicoloured	75	85	☐ ☐
1150	**626**	25p multicoloured	1·00	1·00	☐ ☐
Set of 4			2·25	2·50	☐ ☐
First Day Cover				2·50	☐
Presentation Pack			2·25		☐
PHQ Cards (set of 4)			2·25	3·25	☐ ☐
Set of 4 Gutter Pairs			4·25		☐

627 *Aglais urticae*

628 *Maculinea arion*

629 *Inachis io*

630 *Carterocephalus palaemon*

636 Prince Charles and Lady Diana Spencer

Butterflies

1981 (13 May) Phosphorised paper

1151	**627**	14p multicoloured	25	20	☐	☐
1152	**628**	18p multicoloured	75	70	☐	☐
1153	**629**	22p multicoloured	70	85	☐	☐
1154	**630**	25p multicoloured	75	85	☐	☐
Set of 4			2·25	2·50	☐	☐
First Day Cover				2·50	☐	
Presentation Pack			2·25		☐	
PHQ Cards (*set of* 4)			2·25	6·00	☐	☐
Set of 4 Gutter Pairs			4·75		☐	

Royal Wedding

1981 (22 July) Phosphorised paper

1160	**636**	14p multicoloured	75	25	☐	☐
1161		25p multicoloured	1·50	1·50	☐	☐
Set of 2			2·25	1·50	☐	☐
First Day Cover				2·75		☐
Presentation Pack			3·00		☐	
Souvenir Book			3·00		☐	
PHQ Cards (*set of* 2)			2·50	5·00	☐	☐
Set of 2 Gutter Pairs			4·00		☐	

631 Glenfinnan, Scotland

632 Derwentwater, England

637 'Expeditions'

638 'Skills'

633 Stackpole Head, Wales

634 Giant's Causeway, N. Ireland

639 'Service'

640 'Recreation'

635 St Kilda, Scotland

50th Anniversary of National Trust for Scotland (British landscapes)

1981 (24 June) Phosphorised paper

1155	**631**	14p multicoloured	15	25	☐	☐
1156	**632**	18p multicoloured	45	50	☐	☐
1157	**633**	20p multicoloured	70	75	☐	☐
1158	**634**	22p multicoloured	75	1·00	☐	☐
1159	**635**	25p multicoloured	90	1·00	☐	☐
Set of 5			2·50	3·00	☐	☐
First Day Cover				3·25		☐
Presentation Pack			3·00		☐	
PHQ Cards (*set of* 5)			2·50	5·00	☐	☐
Set of 5 Gutter Pairs			6·00		☐	

25th Anniversary of Duke of Edinburgh's Award Scheme

1981 (12 Aug.) Phosphorised paper. Perf 14

1162	**637**	14p multicoloured	25	20	☐	☐
1163	**638**	18p multicoloured	45	50	☐	☐
1164	**639**	22p multicoloured	80	80	☐	☐
1165	**640**	25p multicoloured	90	1·00	☐	☐
Set of 4			2·25	2·50	☐	☐
First Day Cover				2·50		☐
Presentation Pack			2·50		☐	
PHQ Cards (*set of* 4)			2·50	4·50	☐	☐
Set of 4 Gutter Pairs			5·00		☐	

641 Cockle-dredging from *Lindsey II*

642 Hauling Trawl Net

643 Lobster Potting   **644** Hoisting Seine Net

Fishing Industry

1981 (23 Sept.) Phosphorised paper

1166	**641**	14p multicoloured	25	25	☐	☐
1167	**642**	18p multicoloured	50	50	☐	☐
1168	**643**	22p multicoloured	85	85	☐	☐
1169	**644**	25p multicoloured	85	85	☐	☐
Set of 4			2·25	2·50	☐	☐
First Day Cover				2·00	☐	
Presentation Pack			2·50		☐	
PHQ Cards (*set of 4*)			2·25	4·50	☐	☐
Set of 4 Gutter Pairs			5·00		☐	

Nos. 1166/9 were issued on the occasion of the centenary of Royal National Mission to Deep Sea Fishermen.

645 Father Christmas   **646** Jesus Christ

647 Flying Angel   **648** Joseph and Mary arriving at Bethlehem

649 Three Kings approaching Bethlehem

Christmas. Children's Pictures

1981 (18 Nov.) One phosphor band (11½p) or phosphorised paper (others)

1170	**645**	11½p multicoloured	25	20	☐	☐
1171	**646**	14p multicoloured	35	20	☐	☐
1172	**647**	18p multicoloured	50	60	☐	☐
1173	**648**	22p multicoloured	75	75	☐	☐
1174	**649**	25p multicoloured	85	85	☐	☐
Set of 5			2·50	2·50	☐	☐
First Day Cover				2·75	☐	
Presentation Pack			3·00		☐	
PHQ Cards (*set of 5*)			2·25	5·50	☐	☐
Set of 5 Gutter Pairs			5·50		☐	

Collectors Pack 1981

1981 (18 Nov.) Comprises Nos. 1143/74

CP1174a Collectors Pack		17·50	☐

650 Charles Darwin and Giant Tortoises   **651** Darwin and Marine Iguanas

652 Darwin, Cactus Ground Finch and Large Ground Finch   **653** Darwin and Prehistoric Skulls

Death Centenary of Charles Darwin

1982 (10 Feb.) Phosphorised paper

1175	**650**	15½p multicoloured	50	20	☐	☐
1176	**651**	19½p multicoloured	50	60	☐	☐
1177	**652**	26p multicoloured	75	85	☐	☐
1178	**653**	29p multicoloured	95	90	☐	☐
Set of 4			2·50	2·50	☐	☐
First Day Cover				2·75	☐	
Presentation Pack			3·00		☐	
PHQ Cards (*set of 4*)			2·50	6·00	☐	☐
Set of 4 Gutter Pairs			5·25		☐	

654 Boys' Brigade   **655** Girls' Brigade

656 Boy Scout Movement   **657** Girl Guide Movement

Youth Organizations

1982 (24 Mar.) Phosphorised paper

1179	**654**	15½p multicoloured	25	15	☐	☐
1180	**655**	19½p multicoloured	50	50	☐	☐
1181	**656**	26p multicoloured	85	85	☐	☐
1182	**657**	29p multicoloured	1·00	1·10	☐	☐
Set of 4			2·50	2·50	☐	☐

First Day Cover		2·75		☐
Presentation Pack	3·00		☐	
PHQ Cards (*set of* 4)	2·50	6·00	☐	☐
Set of 4 Gutter Pairs	5·50		☐	

Nos. 1179/82 were issued on the occasion of the 75th anniversary of the Boy Scout Movement, the 125th birth anniversary of Lord Baden-Powell and the centenary of the Boys' Brigade (1983).

658 Ballerina

659 Harlequin

660 Hamlet

661 Opera Singer

Europa. British Theatre

1982 (28 Apr.) Phosphorised paper

1183 **658**	15½p multicoloured	25	15	☐	☐
1184 **659**	19½p multicoloured	50	50	☐	☐
1185 **660**	26p multicoloured	1·25	1·00	☐	☐
1186 **661**	29p multicoloured	1·50	1·00	☐	☐
Set of 4		3·25	2·50	☐	☐
First Day Cover			2·75		☐
Presentation Pack		3·00		☐	
PHQ Cards (*set of* 4)		2·50	6·00	☐	☐
Set of 4 Gutter Pairs		8·00		☐	

662 Henry VIII and *Mary Rose*

663 Admiral Blake and *Triumph*

664 Lord Nelson and HMS *Victory*

665 Lord Fisher and HMS *Dreadnought*

666 Viscount Cunningham and HMS *Warspite*

Maritime Heritage

1982 (16 June) Phosphorised paper

1187 **662** 15½p multicoloured	35	25	☐	☐
1188 **663** 19½p multicoloured	50	50	☐	☐
1189 **664** 24p multicoloured	75	85	☐	☐
1190 **665** 26p multicoloured	75	85	☐	☐
1191 **666** 29p multicoloured	1·00	1·00	☐	☐
Set of 5	3·00	3·50	☐	☐
First Day Cover		3·75		☐
Presentation Pack	3·50		☐	
PHQ Cards (*set of* 5)	2·50	6·00	☐	☐
Set of 5 Gutter Pairs	7·00		☐	

667 'Strawberry Thief' (William Morris)

668 Untitled (Steiner and Co)

669 'Cherry Orchard' (Paul Nash)

670 'Chevron' (Andrew Foster)

British Textiles

1982 (23 July) Phosphorised paper

1192 **667** 15½p multicoloured	25	25	☐	☐
1193 **668** 19½p multicoloured	75	75	☐	☐
1194 **669** 26p multicoloured	75	1·00	☐	☐
1195 **670** 29p multicoloured	1·00	1·25	☐	☐
Set of 4	2·50	2·75	☐	☐
First Day Cover		3·00		☐
Presentation Pack	2·75		☐	
PHQ Cards (*set of* 4)	2·50	6·00	☐	☐
Set of 4 Gutter Pairs	5·50		☐	

Nos 1192/5 were issued on the occasion of the 250th birth anniversary of Sir Richard Arkwright (inventor of spinning machine).

671 Development of Communications

672 Modern Technological Aids

Information Technology

1982 (8 Sept.) Phosphorised paper. Perf 14 × 15

1196	**671**	15½p multicoloured	50	25	☐	☐
1197	**672**	26p multicoloured	75	1·00	☐	☐
Set of 2			1·25	1·25	☐	☐
First Day Cover				1·75		☐
Presentation Pack			1·50		☐	
PHQ Cards (*set of 2*)			2·00	5·25	☐	☐
Set of 2 Gutter Pairs			2·75		☐	

673 Austin 'Seven' and 'Metro' **674** Ford 'Model T' and 'Escort'

675 Jaguar 'SS1' and 'XJ6' **676** Rolls-Royce 'Silver Ghost' and 'Silver Spirit'

British Motor Industry

1982 (13 Oct.) Phosphorised paper. Perf 14½ × 14

1198	**673**	15½p multicoloured	50	25	☐	☐
1199	**674**	19½p multicoloured	75	75	☐	☐
1200	**675**	26p multicoloured	75	75	☐	☐
1201	**676**	29p multicoloured	1·00	1·00	☐	☐
Set of 4			2·50	2·50	☐	☐
First Day Cover				2·50		☐
Presentation Pack			3·00		☐	
PHQ Cards (*set of 4*)			2·50	6·00	☐	☐
Set of 4 Gutter Pairs			6·25		☐	

677 'While Shepherds Watched' **678** 'The Holly and the Ivy'

679 'I Saw Three Ships' **680** 'We Three Kings'

681 'Good King Wenceslas'

Christmas. Carols

1982 (17 Nov.) One phosphor band (12½p) or phosphorised paper (others).

1202	**677**	12½p multicoloured	25	20	☐	☐
1203	**678**	15½p multicoloured	50	20	☐	☐
1204	**679**	19½p multicoloured	65	75	☐	☐
1205	**680**	26p multicoloured	75	90	☐	☐
1206	**681**	29p multicoloured	1·00	1·00	☐	☐
Set of 5			3·00	2·75	☐	☐
First Day Cover				2·50		☐
Presentation Pack			3·25		☐	
PHQ Cards (*set of 5*)			2·50	6·00	☐	☐
Set of 5 Gutter Pairs			5·25		☐	

Collectors Pack 1982

1982 (17 Nov.) Comprises Nos. 1175/1206

CP1206a	Collectors Pack		26·00	☐

682 Atlantic Salmon **683** Northern Pike

684 Brown Trout **685** Eurasian Perch

British River Fish

1983 (26 Jan.) Phosphorised paper

1207	**682**	15½p multicoloured	30	25	☐	☐
1208	**683**	19½p multicoloured	60	60	☐	☐
1209	**684**	26p multicoloured	75	85	☐	☐
1210	**685**	29p multicoloured	1·00	1·10	☐	☐
Set of 4			2·50	2·50	☐	☐
First Day Cover				2·50		☐
Presentation Pack			2·75		☐	
PHQ Cards (*set of 4*)			3·00	7·00	☐	☐
Set of 4 Gutter Pairs			5·00		☐	

686 Tropical Island **687** Desert

688 Temperate
Farmland

689 Mountain Range

Commonwealth Day. Geographical Regions

1983 (9 Mar.) Phosphorised paper

1211	**686**	15½p multicoloured	40	25	☐	☐
1212	**687**	19½p multicoloured	75	75	☐	☐
1213	**688**	26p multicoloured	75	75	☐	☐
1214	**689**	29p multicoloured	1·00	1·00	☐	☐
Set of 4			2·50	2·50	☐	
First Day Cover				2·50		☐
Presentation Pack			3·00		☐	
PHQ Cards (*set of* 4)			2·50	6·50	☐	☐
Set of 4 Gutter Pairs			6·00		☐	

690 Humber Bridge

691 Thames Flood Barrier

692 Iolair (oilfield emergency
support vessel)

Europa. Engineering Achievements

1983 (25 May) Phosphorised paper

1215	**690**	16p multicoloured	50	25	☐	☐
1216	**691**	20½p multicoloured	1·00	1·00	☐	☐
1217	**692**	28p multicoloured	1·00	1·00	☐	☐
Set of 3			2·25	2·00	☐	☐
First Day Cover				2·25		☐
Presentation Pack			2·50		☐	
PHQ Cards (*set of* 3)			2·50	5·75	☐	☐
Set of 3 Gutter Pairs			7·00		☐	

693 Musketeer and
Pikeman, The Royal
Scots (1633)

694 Fusilier and Ensign,
The Royal Welch Fusiliers
(mid-18th century)

695 Riflemen, 95th
Rifles (The Royal Green
Jackets) (1805)

696 Sergeant (khaki
service uniform) and
Guardsman full dress),
The Irish Guards (1900).

697 Paratroopers,
The Parachute Regiment (1983)

British Army Uniforms

1983 (6 July) Phosphorised paper

1218	**693**	16p multicoloured	50	10	☐	☐
1219	**694**	20½p multicoloured	50	60	☐	☐
1220	**695**	26p multicoloured	75	90	☐	☐
1221	**696**	28p multicoloured	75	90	☐	☐
1222	**697**	31p multicoloured	75	85	☐	☐
Set of 5			3·00	3·25	☐	☐
First Day Cover				3·25		☐
Presentation Pack			3·50		☐	
PHQ Cards (*set of* 5)			3·50	6·50	☐	☐
Set of 5 Gutter Pairs			7·50		☐	

Nos. 1218/22 were issued on the occasion of the 350th
anniversary of The Royal Scots, the senior line regiment of the
British Army.

698 20th-Century
Garden, Sissinghurst

699 19th-Century
Garden, Biddulph
Grange

700 18th-Century
Garden, Blenheim

701 17th-Century
Garden, Pitmedden

British Gardens

1983 (24 Aug.) Phosphorised paper. Perf 14

1223	**698**	16p multicoloured	50	10	☐	☐
1224	**699**	20½p multicoloured	50	55	☐	☐
1225	**700**	28p multicoloured	75	1·00	☐	☐
1226	**701**	31p multicoloured	1·00	1·00	☐	☐
Set of 4			2·50	2·50	☐	☐
First Day Cover				2·25	☐	
Presentation Pack			3·00		☐	
PHQ Cards (*set of* 4)			3·00	6·25	☐	☐
Set of 4 Gutter Pairs			6·00		☐	

702 Merry-go-round

703 Big Wheel, Helter-skelter and Performing Animals

704 Side-shows

705 Early Produce Fair

British Fairs

1983 (5 Oct.) Phosphorised paper

1227	**702**	16p multicoloured	35	25	☐	☐
1228	**703**	20½p multicoloured	75	75	☐	☐
1229	**704**	28p multicoloured	75	1·00	☐	☐
1230	**705**	31p multicoloured	1·00	1·00	☐	☐
Set of 4			2·50	2·75	☐	☐
First Day Cover				3·00	☐	
Presentation Pack			3·00		☐	
PHQ Cards (*set of* 4)			3·00	6·25	☐	☐
Set of 4 Gutter Pairs			6·00		☐	

Nos. 1227/30 were issued to mark the 850th anniversary of St Bartholomew's Fair, Smithfield, London.

706 'Christmas Post' (Pillar box)

707 'The Three Kings' (chimney-pots)

708 'World at Peace' (Dove and Blackbird)

709 'Light of Christmas' (street lamp)

710 'Christmas Dove' (hedge sculpture)

Christmas

1983 (16 Nov.) One phosphor band (12½p) or phosphorised paper (others)

1231	**706**	12½p multicoloured	25	25	☐	☐
1232	**707**	16p multicoloured	50	25	☐	☐
1233	**708**	20½p multicoloured	75	1·00	☐	☐
1234	**709**	28p multicoloured	75	1·00	☐	☐
1235	**710**	31p multicoloured	1·25	1·25	☐	☐
Set of 5			3·25	3·25	☐	☐
First Day Cover				3·50	☐	
Presentation Pack			3·50		☐	
PHQ Cards (*set of* 5)			3·00	6·25	☐	☐
Set of 5 Gutter Pairs			6·50		☐	

Collectors Pack 1983

1983 (16 Nov.) Comprises Nos. 1207/35

CP1235a	Collectors Pack	32·00	☐

711 Arms of the College of Arms

712 Arms of King Richard III (founder)

713 Arms of the Earl Marshal of England

714 Arms of the City of London

500th Anniversary of College of Arms

1984 (17 Jan.) Phosphorised paper. Perf 14½

1236	**711**	16p multicoloured	50	15	☐	☐
1237	**712**	20½p multicoloured	50	65	☐	☐
1238	**713**	28p multicoloured	1·00	1·10	☐	☐
1239	**714**	31p multicoloured	1·25	1·25	☐	☐
Set of 4			3·00	3·00	☐	☐
First Day Cover				3·00	☐	
Presentation Pack			3·25		☐	
PHQ Cards (*set of* 4)			3·00	6·50	☐	☐
Set of 4 Gutter Pairs			6·25		☐	

715 Highland Cow

716 Chillingham Wild Bull

717 Hereford Bull

718 Welsh Black Bull

719 Irish Moiled Cow

British Cattle

1984 (6 Mar.) Phosphorised paper

1240	**715**	16p multicoloured	35	15	☐	☐
1241	**716**	20½p multicoloured	60	60	☐	☐
1242	**717**	26p multicoloured	80	80	☐	☐
1243	**718**	28p multicoloured	90	90	☐	☐
1244	**719**	31p multicoloured	1·00	1·20	☐	☐
Set of 5			3·50	3·50	☐	☐
First Day Cover				3·50		☐
Presentation Pack			4·00		☐	
PHQ Cards (*set of* 5)			3·00	6·50	☐	☐
Set of 5 Gutter Pairs			7·25		☐	

Nos. 1240/4 marked the centenary of the Highland Cattle Society and the bicentenary of the Royal Highland and Agricultural Society of Scotland.

720 Festival Hall, Liverpool

721 Milburngate Shopping Centre, Durham

722 Bush House, Bristol

723 Commercial Street Housing Scheme, Perth

Urban Renewal

1984 (10 Apr.) Phosphorised paper

1245	**720**	16p multicoloured	30	10	☐	☐
1246	**721**	20½p multicoloured	50	60	☐	☐
1247	**722**	28p multicoloured	1·25	1·25	☐	☐
1248	**723**	31p multicoloured	1·25	1·25	☐	☐

Set of 4	3·00	3·00	☐	☐
First Day Cover		2·50		☐
Presentation Pack	3·00		☐	
PHQ Cards (*set of* 4)	3·00	6·25	☐	☐
Set of 4 Gutter Pairs	6·50		☐	

Nos. 1245/8 marked the opening of the International Gardens Festival, Liverpool, and the 150th anniversaries of the Royal Institute of British Architects and the Chartered Institute of Building.

724 C.E.P.T. 25th Anniversary Logo

725 Abduction of Europa

Nos. 1249/50 and 1251/2 were each printed together, *se-tenant*, in horizontal pairs throughout the sheets.

Europa. 25th Anniversary of C.E.P.T. and 2nd European Parliamentary Elections

1984 (15 May) Phosphorised paper

1249	**724**	16p greenish slate, deep blue and gold	50	25	☐	☐
		a. Horiz. pair. Nos. 1249/50	1·50	1·50	☐	☐
1250	**725**	16p greenish slate, deep blue, black and gold	50	25	☐	☐
1251	**724**	20½p Venetian red, deep magenta and gold	70	40	☐	☐
		a. Horiz. pair. Nos. 1251/2	2·50	2·50	☐	☐
1252	**725**	20½p Venetian red, deep magenta, black and gold	70	40	☐	☐
Set of 4			3·00	3·00	☐	☐
First Day Cover				3·50		☐
Presentation Pack			4·00		☐	
PHQ Cards (*set of* 4)			3·00	6·25	☐	☐
Set of 2 Gutter Blocks of 4			8·00		☐	

726 Lancaster House

London Economic Summit Conference

1984 (5 June) Phosphorised paper

1253	**726**	31p multicoloured	1·25	1·25	☐	☐
First Day Cover				2·25		☐
PHQ Card			1·00	3·50	☐	☐
Gutter Pair			2·50		☐	

727 View of Earth
from 'Apollo 11'

728 Navigational Chart
of English Channel

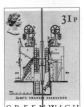

729 Greenwich
Observatory

730 Sir George Airey's
Transit Telescope

Centenary of Greenwich Meridian

1984 (26 June) Phosphorised paper. Perf 14 × 14½

1254	**727**	16p multicoloured	50	25	☐	☐
1255	**728**	20½p multicoloured	75	80	☐	☐
1256	**729**	28p multicoloured	1·00	1·00	☐	☐
1257	**730**	31p multicoloured	1·00	1·10	☐	☐
Set of 4			3·00	3·00	☐	☐
First Day Cover				3·00		☐
Presentation Pack			3·50		☐	
PHQ Cards (*set of* 4)			3·00	6·25	☐	☐
Set of 4 Gutter Pairs			6·50		☐	

731 Bath Mail Coach, 1784

732 Attack on Exeter Mail, 1816

733 Norwich Mail in
Thunderstorm, 1827

734 Holyhead and Liverpool
Mails leaving London, 1828

735 Edinburgh Mail
Snowbound, 1831

T **731/5** were printed together, *se-tenant*, in horizontal strips
of 5 throughout the sheet.

Bicentenary of First Mail Coach Run, Bath and Bristol to London

1984 (31 July) Phosphorised paper

1258	**731**	16p multicoloured	40	35	☐	☐
		a. Horiz strip of 5. Nos. 1258/62	2·50	2·75	☐	☐
1259	**732**	16p multicoloured	40	35	☐	☐
1260	**733**	16p multicoloured	40	35	☐	☐
1261	**734**	16p multicoloured	40	35	☐	☐
1262	**735**	16p multicoloured	40	35	☐	☐
Set of 5			2·50	2·75	☐	☐
First Day Cover				3·00		☐
Presentation Pack			3·00		☐	
Souvenir Book			7·50		☐	
PHQ Cards (*set of* 5)			3·00	6·50	☐	☐
Gutter Block of 10			6·50		☐	

736 Nigerian Clinic

737 Violinist and Acropolis,
Athens

738 Building Project, Sri Lanka

739 British Council Library

50th Anniversary of The British Council

1984 (25 Sept.) Phosphorised paper

1263	**736**	17p multicoloured	50	25	@@
1264	**737**	22p multicoloured	85	1·00	@@
1265	**738**	31p multicoloured	85	1·00	@@
1266	**739**	34p multicoloured	1·00	1·00	@@
Set of 4			3·00	3·00	@@
First Day Cover				3·00	☐
Presentation Pack			3·25		☐
PHQ Cards (*set of* 4)			3·00	6·25	☐ ☐
Set of 4 Gutter Pairs			6·50		☐

740 The Holy Family

741 Arrival in Bethlehem

742 Shepherd and Lamb

743 Virgin and Child

744 Offering of Frankincense

Christmas

1984 (20 Nov.) One phosphor band (13p) or phosphorised paper (others)

1267	**740**	13p multicoloured	25	25	@@
1268	**741**	17p multicoloured	50	50	@@
1269	**742**	22p multicoloured	75	75	@@
1270	**743**	31p multicoloured	1·00	1·00	@@
1271	**744**	34p multicoloured	1·00	1·00	@@
	Set of 5		3·25	3·25	@@
	First Day Cover			3·25	☐
	Presentation Pack		3·75		☐
	PHQ Cards (*set of* 5)		3·00	6·25	@@
	Set of 5 Gutter Pairs		7·00		☐

Collectors Pack 1984

1984 (20 Nov.) Comprises Nos. 1236/71

CP1271a	Collectors Pack	37·00	☐

Post Office Yearbook

1984 Comprises Nos. 1236/71 in hardbound book with slip case

YB1271a	Yearbook	90·00	☐

745 'Flying Scotsman'   **746** 'Golden Arrow'

747 'Cheltenham Flyer'   **748** 'Royal Scot'

749 'Cornish Riviera'

Famous Trains

1985 (22 Jan.) Phosphorised paper

1272	**745**	17p multicoloured	75	25	☐	☐
1273	**746**	22p multicoloured	75	1·00	☐	☐
1274	**747**	29p multicoloured	1·00	1·25	☐	☐
1275	**748**	31p multicoloured	1·25	1·50	☐	☐
1276	**749**	34p multicoloured	2·50	2·50	☐	☐
	Set of 5		6·00	6·00	☐	☐

First Day Cover		6·00		☐
Presentation Pack		6·00		☐
PHQ Cards (*set of* 5)		6·00	15·00	☐ ☐
Set of 5 Gutter Pairs		12·00		☐ ☐

Nos. 1272/6 were issued on the occasion of the 150th anniversary of the Great Western Railway Company.

750 *Bombus terrestris* (Bee)   **751** *Coccinella septempunctata* (ladybird)

752 *Decticus verrucivorus* (bush-cricket)   **753** *Lucanus cervus* (stag beetle)

754 *Anax imperator* (dragonfly)

Insects

1985 (12 Mar.) Phosphorised paper

1277	**750**	17p multicoloured	40	10	☐	☐
1278	**751**	22p multicoloured	60	55	☐	☐
1279	**752**	29p multicoloured	85	90	☐	☐
1280	**753**	31p multicoloured	1·00	1·00	☐	☐
1281	**754**	34p multicoloured	1·00	90	☐	☐
	Set of 5		3·25	3·25	☐	☐
	First Day Cover			3·50		☐
	Presentation Pack		4·50		☐	
	PHQ Cards (*set of* 5)		3·00	7·50	☐	☐
	Set of 5 Gutter Pairs		8·75		☐	

Nos. 1277/81 were issued on the occasion of the centenaries of the Royal Entomological Society of London's Royal Charter and of the Selborne Society.

755 'Water Music', by Handel   **756** 'The Planets', by Holst

757 'The First Cuckoo', by Delius

758 'Sea Pictures', by Elgar

763 Datapost Motorcyclist, City of London

764 Rural Postbus

Europa. European Music Year

1985 (14 May) Phosphorised paper. Perf 14½

1282	**755**	17p multicoloured	55	10	☐	☐
1283	**756**	22p multicoloured	75	90	☐	☐
1284	**757**	31p multicoloured	1·50	1·25	☐	☐
1285	**758**	34p multicoloured	1·50	1·25	☐	☐
Set of 4			4·00	3·25	☐	☐
First Day Cover				4·00		☐
Presentation Pack			4·75		☐	
PHQ Cards (*set of* 4)			3·00	6·50	☐	☐
Set of 4 Gutter Pairs			10·00			☐

Nos. 1282/5 were issued on the occasion of the 300th birth anniversary of Handel.

759 R.N.L.I. Lifeboat and Signal Flags

760 Beachy Head Lighthouse and Chart

765 Parcel Delivery in Winter

766 Town Letter Delivery

350 Years of Royal Mail Public Postal Service

1985 (30 July) Phosphorised paper

1290	**763**	17p multicoloured	50	10	☐	☐
1291	**764**	22p multicoloured	75	70	☐	☐
1292	**765**	31p multicoloured	1·00	1·00	☐	☐
1293	**766**	34p multicoloured	1·50	1·50	☐	☐
Set of 4			3·00	3·00	☐	☐
First Day Cover				3·25		☐
Presentation Pack			3·75		☐	
PHQ Cards (*set of* 4)			3·00	6·50	☐	☐
Set of 4 Gutter Pairs			7·00			☐

767 King Arthur and Merlin

768 The Lady of the Lake

761 'Marecs A' Communications Satellite and Dish Aerials

762 Buoys

Safety at Sea

1985 (18 June) Phosphorised paper. Perf 14

1286	**759**	17p multicoloured	40	25	☐	☐
1287	**760**	22p multicoloured	60	75	☐	☐
1288	**761**	31p multicoloured	1·00	1·00	☐	☐
1289	**762**	34p multicoloured	1·50	1·25	☐	☐
Set of 4			3·00	3·00	☐	☐
First Day Cover				3·00		☐
Presentation Pack			3·75		☐	
PHQ Cards (*set of* 4)			3·00	6·50	☐	☐
Set of 4 Gutter Pairs			7·00			☐

Nos. 1286/9 were issued to mark the bicentenary of the unimmersible lifeboat and the 50th anniversary of Radar.

769 Queen Guinevere and Sir Lancelot

770 Sir Galahad

Arthurian Legends

1985 (3 Sept.) Phosphorised paper

1294	**767**	17p multicoloured	50	25	☐	☐
1295	**768**	22p multicoloured	75	75	☐	☐
1296	**769**	31p multicoloured	1·25	1·25	☐	☐
1297	**770**	34p multicoloured	1·25	1·25	☐	☐
Set of 4			3·50	3·00	☐	☐
First Day Cover				3·50		☐
Presentation Pack			4·00		☐	
PHQ Cards (*set of* 4)			3·00	6·50	☐	☐
Set of 4 Gutter Pairs			7·00			☐

Nos. 1294/7 were issued to mark the 500th anniversary of the printing of Sir Thomas Malory's *Morte d'Arthur*.

771 Peter Sellers (from photo by Bill Brandt)

772 David Niven (from photo by Cornell Lucas)

773 Charlie Chaplin (from photo by Lord Snowdon)

774 Vivien Leigh (from photo by Angus McBean)

775 Alfred Hitchcock (from photo by Howard Coster)

British Film Year

1985 (8 Oct.) Phosphorised paper. Perf 14½

1298	**771**	17p multicoloured	45	25	☐	☐	
1299	**772**	22p multicoloured	60	75	☐	☐	
1300	**773**	29p multicoloured	1·00	1·25	☐	☐	
1301	**774**	31p multicoloured	1·10	1·50	☐	☐	
1302	**775**	34p multicoloured	1·40	1·50	☐	☐	
Set of 5			4·00	4·50	☐	☐	
First Day Cover				5·00		☐	
Presentation Pack			5·50		☐		
Souvenir Book			11·50		☐		
PHQ Cards (*set of* 5)			3·00	8·50	☐	☐	
Set of 5 Gutter Pairs			10·50		☐		

776 Principal Boy

777 Genie

778 Dame

779 Good Fairy

780 Pantomime Cat

Christmas. Pantomime Characters

1985 (19 Nov.) One phosphor band (12p) or phosphorised paper (others)

1303	**776**	12p multicoloured	50	15	☐	☐
1304	**777**	17p multicoloured	50	25	☐	☐
1305	**778**	22p multicoloured	75	1·10	☐	☐
1306	**779**	31p multicoloured	1·25	1·40	☐	☐
1307	**780**	34p multicoloured	1·25	1·40	☐	☐
Set of 5			4·00	4·00	☐	☐
First Day Cover				4·50		☐
Presentation Pack			4·25		☐	
PHQ Cards (*set of* 5)			3·00	6·50	☐	☐
Set of 5 Gutter Pairs			8·00		☐	

Collectors Pack 1985

1985 (19 Nov.) Comprises Nos. 1272/1307

CP1307a	Collectors Pack	35·00	☐

Post Office Yearbook

1985 Comprises Nos. 1272/1307 in hardbound book with slip case

YB1307a	Yearbook	80·00	☐

781 Light Bulb and North Sea Oil Drilling Rig (Energy)

782 Thermometer and Pharmaceutical Laboratory (Health)

783 Garden Hoe and Steel Works (Steel)

784 Loaf of Bread and and Cornfield (Agriculture)

Industry Year

1986 (14 Jan.) Phosphorised paper. Perf 14½ × 14

1308	**781**	17p multicoloured	75	25	☐	☐
1309	**782**	22p multicoloured	50	75	☐	☐
1310	**783**	31p multicoloured	1·25	1·40	☐	☐
1311	**784**	34p multicoloured	1·25	1·40	☐	☐
Set of 4			3·50	3·50	☐	☐
First Day Cover				3·50		☐
Presentation Pack			3·75		☐	
PHQ Cards (*set of* 4)			3·50	6·50	☐	☐
Set of 4 Gutter Pairs			7·00		☐	

785 Dr Edmond Halley as Comet

786 *Giotto* Spacecraft approaching Comet

787 'Twice in a Lifetime'

788 Comet orbiting Sun and Planets

Appearance of Halley's Comet

1986 (18 Feb.) Phosphorised paper

1312	**785**	17p multicoloured	50	25	☐	☐
1313	**786**	22p multicoloured	75	75	☐	☐
1314	**787**	31p multicoloured	1·25	1·25	☐	☐
1315	**788**	34p multicoloured	1·25	1·40	☐	☐
Set of 4			3·50	3·50	☐	☐
First Day Cover				3·50		☐
Presentation Pack			3·75		☐	
PHQ Cards (*set of* 4)			3·50	6·50	☐	☐
Set of 4 Gutter Pairs			7·00		☐	

789 Queen Elizabeth II in 1928, 1942 and 1952

790 Queen Elizabeth II in 1958, 1973 and 1982

Nos. 1316/17 and 1318/19 were each printed together, *se-tenant*, in horizontal pairs throughout the sheets.

60th Birthday of Queen Elizabeth II

1986 (21 Apr.) Phosphorised paper

1316	**789**	17p multicoloured	60	25	☐	☐
		a. Horiz pair.				
		Nos. 1316/17	1·50	1·50	☐	☐
1317	**790**	17p multicoloured	60	25	☐	☐
1318	**789**	34p multicoloured	70	50	☐	☐
		a. Horiz pair.				
		Nos. 1318/19	3·00	4·00	☐	☐
1319	**790**	34p multicoloured	70	50	☐	☐
Set of 4			4·50	5·00	☐	☐
First Day Cover				5·00		☐
Presentation Pack			5·50		☐	
Souvenir Book			8·50		☐	
PHQ Cards (*set of* 4)			5·00	6·50	☐	☐
Set of 2 Gutter Blocks of 4			11·00		☐	

791 Barn Owl

792 Pine Marten

793 Wild Cat

794 Natterjack Toad

Europa. Nature Conservation. Endangered Species

1986 (20 May) Phosphorised paper. Perf 14½ × 14

1320	**791**	17p multicoloured	40	10	☐	☐
1321	**792**	22p multicoloured	80	1·00	☐	☐
1322	**793**	31p multicoloured	1·50	1·25	☐	☐
1323	**794**	34p multicoloured	1·65	1·40	☐	☐
Set of 4			4·00	3·50	☐	☐
First Day Cover				4·00		☐
Presentation Pack			4·00		☐	
PHQ Cards (*set of* 4)			3·50	6·50	☐	☐
Set of 4 Gutter Pairs			10·00		☐	

795 Peasants Working in Fields

796 Freemen working at Town Trades

797 Knight and Retainers

798 Lord at Banquet

900th Anniversary of Domesday Book

1986 (17 June) Phosphorised paper

1324	**795**	17p multicoloured	40	10	☐	☐
1325	**796**	22p multicoloured	85	85	☐	☐
1326	**797**	31p multicoloured	1·25	1·40	☐	☐
1327	**798**	34p multicoloured	1·25	1·40	☐	☐
Set of 4			3·50	3·50	☐	☐
First Day Cover				4·00		☐
Presentation Pack			4·00		☐	
PHQ Cards (*set of* 4)			3·50	6·50	☐	☐
Set of 4 Gutter Pairs			7·00		☐	

799 Athletics

800 Rowing

801 Weightlifting

802 Rifle-shooting

803 Hockey

Thirteenth Commonwealth Games, Edinburgh (Nos. 1328/31) and World Men's Hockey Cup, London (No. 1332)

1986 (15 July) Phosphorised paper

1328	**799**	17p multicoloured	40	25	☐	☐
1329	**800**	22p multicoloured	55	75	☐	☐
1330	**801**	29p multicoloured	75	1·00	☐	☐
1331	**802**	31p multicoloured	1·50	1·75	☐	☐
1332	**803**	34p multicoloured	1·75	1·75	☐	☐
Set of 5			4·00	4·00	☐	☐
First Day Cover				3·50	☐	
Presentation Pack			4·00		☐	
PHQ Cards (*set of* 5)			3·50	7·50	☐	☐
Set of 5 Gutter Pairs			8·75		☐	

No. 1332 also marked the centenary of the Hockey Association.

804 Prince Andrew and Miss Sarah Ferguson

805 Prince Andrew and Miss Sarah Ferguson

Royal Wedding

1986 (22 July) One side band (12p) or phosphorised paper (17p)

1333	**804**	12p multicoloured	50	30	☐	☐
1334	**805**	17p multicoloured	1·00	1·25	☐	☐
Set of 2			1·50	1·50	☐	☐
First Day Cover				2·00		☐
Presentation Pack			1·75		☐	
PHQ Cards (*set of* 2)			2·25	5·00	☐	☐
Set of 2 Gutter Pairs			3·00		☐	

806 Stylised Cross on Ballot Paper

32nd Commonwealth Parliamentary Conference, London

1986 (19 Aug.) Phosphorised paper. Perf 14 × 14½

1335	**806**	34p multicoloured	1·25	1·25	☐	☐
First Day Cover				1·75		☐
PHQ Card			1·00	3·00	☐	☐
Gutter Pair			2·75		☐	

807 Lord Dowding and Hawker Hurricane Mk. I

808 Lord Tedder and Hawker Typhoon 1B

809 Lord Trenchard and de Havilland D.H.9A

810 Sir Arthur Harris and Avro Type 683 Lancaster

811 Lord Portal and de Havilland DH.98 Mosquito

History of the Royal Air Force

1986 (16th Sept.) Phosphorised paper. Perf 14½ × 14

1336	**807**	17p multicoloured	50	10	☐	☐
1337	**808**	22p multicoloured	75	95	☐	☐
1338	**809**	29p multicoloured	1·25	1·25	☐	☐
1339	**810**	31p multicoloured	1·75	1·60	☐	☐
1340	**811**	34p multicoloured	1·75	1·90	☐	☐
Set of 5			5·00	5·50	☐	☐
First Day Cover				5·50		☐
Presentation Pack			5·50		☐	
PHQ Cards (*set of* 5)			4·50	10·00	☐	☐
Set of 5 Gutter Pairs			12·00		☐	

Nos. 1336/40 were issued to celebrate the 50th anniversary of the first R.A.F. Commands.

812 The Glastonbury Thorn

813 The Tanad Valley Plygain

814 The Hebrides Tribute

815 The Dewsbury Church Knell

816 The Hereford Boy Bishop

Christmas. Folk Customs

1986 (18 Nov.–2 Dec.) One phosphor band (12p, 13p) or phosphorised paper (others)

1341	**812**	12p multicoloured (2 Dec.)	50	50	☐	☐
1342		13p multicoloured	25	15	☐	☐
1343	**813**	18p multicoloured	50	15	☐	☐
1344	**814**	22p multicoloured	1·00	1·00	☐	☐
1345	**815**	31p multicoloured	1·25	1·00	☐	☐
1346	**816**	34p multicoloured	1·25	1·10	☐	☐
Set of 6			3·75	3·50	☐	☐
First Day Covers (2)				3·75		☐
Presentation Pack (Nos. 1342/6)			3·75		☐	
PHQ Cards (*set of* 5) (Nos. 1342/6)			3·50	6·50	☐	☐
Set of 6 Gutter Pairs			9·00		☐	

Collectors Pack 1986

1986 (18 Nov.) Comprises Nos. 1308/40, 1342/6

CP1346a	Collectors Pack	37·00	☐

Post Office Yearbook

1986 Comprises Nos. 1308/40, 1342/6 in hardbound book with slip case

YB1346a	Yearbook	70·00	☐

817 North American Blanket Flower

818 Globe Thistle

819 Echeveria

820 Autumn Crocus

Flower Photographs by Alfred Lammer

1987 (20 Jan.) Phosphorised paper. Perf 14½ × 14

1347	**817**	18p multicoloured	40	10	☐	☐
1348	**818**	22p multicoloured	70	85	☐	☐
1349	**819**	31p multicoloured	1·10	1·25	☐	☐
1350	**820**	34p multicoloured	1·10	1·25	☐	☐
Set of 4			3·25	3·25	☐	☐
First Day Cover				3·50		☐
Presentation Pack			4·00		☐	
PHQ Cards (*set of* 4)			3·00	7·00	☐	☐
Set of 4 Gutter Pairs			7·50		☐	☐

821 *The Principia Mathematica*

822 Motion of Bodies in *Ellipses*

823 *Optick Treatise*

824 *The System of the World*

300th Anniversary of The Principia Mathematica by Sir Isaac Newton

1987 (24 Mar.) Phosphorised paper

1351	**821**	18p multicoloured	50	15	☐	☐
1352	**822**	22p multicoloured	75	75	☐	☐
1353	**823**	31p multicoloured	1·25	1·50	☐	☐
1354	**824**	34p multicoloured	1·25	1·25	☐	☐
Set of 4			3·50	3·25	☐	☐
First Day Cover				3·75		☐
Presentation Pack			4·00		☐	
PHQ Cards (*set of* 4)			3·00	6·50	☐	☐
Set of 4 Gutter Pairs			8·00		☐	

825 Willis Faber and Dumas Building, Ipswich

826 Pompidou Centre, Paris

Staatsgalerie, Stuttgart | **828** European Investment Bank, Luxembourg

833 Arms of the Lord Lyon King of Arms | **834** Scottish Heraldic Banner of Prince Charles

opa. British Architects in Europe

87 (12 May) Phosphorised paper

55	**825**	18p multicoloured	50	15	☐	☐
1356	**826**	22p multicoloured	75	75	☐	☐
1357	**827**	31p multicoloured	1·25	1·25	☐	☐
1358	**828**	34p multicoloured	1·75	1·25	☐	☐
	Set of 4		4·00	3·25	☐	☐
	First Day Cover			3·75		☐
	Presentation Pack		4·00		☐	
	PHQ Cards (*set of* 4)		3·00	6·50	☐	☐
	Set of 4 Gutter Pairs		9·50		☐	

835 Arms of Royal Scottish Academy of Painting, Sculpture and Architecture | **836** Arms of Royal Society of Edinburgh

300th Anniversary of Revival of Order of the Thistle

1987 (21 July) Phosphorised paper. Perf 14½

1363	**833**	18p multicoloured	50	10	☐	☐
1364	**834**	22p multicoloured	75	90	☐	☐
1365	**835**	31p multicoloured	1·40	1·40	☐	☐
1366	**836**	34p multicoloured	1·50	1·40	☐	☐
	Set of 4		3·75	3·50	☐	☐
	First Day Cover			3·75		☐
	Presentation Pack		4·00		☐	
	PHQ Cards (*set of* 4)		3·00	6·50	☐	☐
	Set of 4 Gutter Pairs		8·00		☐	

829 Brigade Members with Ashford Litter, 1887 | **830** Bandaging Blitz Victim, 1940

831 Volunteer with fainting Girl, 1965 | **832** Transport of Transplant Organ by Air Wing, 1987

837 Crystal Palace, 'Monarch of the Glen' (Landseer) and Grace Darling | **838** *Great Eastern, Beeton's Book of Household Management* and Prince Albert

839 Albert Memorial, Ballot Box and Disraeli | **840** Diamond Jubilee Emblem, Morse Key and Newspaper Placard for Relief of Mafeking

Centenary of St John Ambulance Brigade

1987 (16 June) Phosphorised paper. Perf 14 × 14½

1359	**829**	18p multicoloured	40	25	☐	☐
1360	**830**	22p multicoloured	60	75	☐	☐
1361	**831**	31p multicoloured	1·25	1·25	☐	☐
1362	**832**	34p multicoloured	1·25	1·25	☐	☐
	Set of 4		3·25	3·25	☐	☐
	First Day Cover			3·75		☐
	Presentation Pack		4·00		☐	
	PHQ Cards (*set of* 4)		3·00	6·50	☐	☐
	Set of 4 Gutter Pairs		7·50		☐	

150th Anniversary of Queen Victoria's Accession

1987 (8 Sept.) Phosphorised paper

1367	**837**	18p multicoloured	50	10	☐	☐
1368	**838**	22p multicoloured	80	75	☐	☐
1369	**839**	31p multicoloured	1·25	1·50	☐	☐
1370	**840**	34p multicoloured	1·35	1·60	☐	☐
	Set of 4		3·50	3·50	☐	☐
	First Day Cover			3·75		☐
	Presentation Pack		4·25		☐	
	PHQ Cards (*set of* 4)		3·00	6·50	☐	☐
	Set of 4 Gutter Pairs		9·00		☐	

841 Pot by Bernard Leach

842 Pot by Elizabeth Fritsch

843 Pot by Lucie Rie

844 Pot by Hans Coper

Studio Pottery

1987 (13 Oct.) Phosphorised paper. Perf 14½ × 14

1371	**841**	18p multicoloured	50	25	☐	☐
1372	**842**	26p multicoloured	70	75	☐	☐
1373	**843**	31p multicoloured	1·25	1·25	☐	☐
1374	**844**	34p multicoloured	1·40	1·50	☐	☐
Set of 4			3·50	3·50	☐	☐
First Day Cover				3·75	☐	
Presentation Pack			3·50		☐	
PHQ Cards (set of 4)			3·00	6·50	☐	☐
Set of 4 Gutter Pairs			8·50		☐	

Nos. 1371/4 also mark the birth centenary of Bernard Leach, the potter.

845 Decorating the Christmas Tree

846 Waiting for Father Christmas

847 Sleeping Child and Father Christmas in Sleigh

848 Child reading

849 Child playing Flute and Snowman

Christmas

1987 (17 Nov.) One phosphor band (13p) or phosphorised paper (others)

1375	**845**	13p multicoloured	30	10	☐	☐
1376	**846**	18p multicoloured	40	20	☐	☐
1377	**847**	26p multicoloured	80	1·00	☐	☐
1378	**848**	31p multicoloured	1·10	1·25	☐	☐
1379	**849**	34p multicoloured	1·25	1·50	☐	☐
Set of 5			3·50	3·75	☐	☐
First Day Cover				3·75		☐
Presentation Pack			3·50		☐	
PHQ Cards (set of 5)			3·00	6·50	☐	☐
Set of 5 Gutter Pairs			8·50		☐	

Collectors Pack 1987

1987 (17 Nov.) Comprises Nos. 1347/79

CP1379a	Collectors Pack	37·00	☐

Post Office Yearbook

1987 Comprises Nos. 1347/79 in hardbound book with slip case

YB1379a	Yearbook	35·00	☐

850 Short-spined Seascorpion ('Bull-rout') (Jonathan Couch)

851 Yellow Waterlily (Major Joshua Swatkin)

852 Whistling ('Bewick's') Swan (Edward Lear)

853 *Morchella esculenta* (James Sowerby)

Bicentenary of Linnean Society. Archive Illustrations

1988 (19 Jan.) Phosphorised paper

1380	**850**	18p multicoloured	55	10	☐	☐
1381	**851**	26p multicoloured	85	1·00	☐	☐
1382	**852**	31p multicoloured	1·10	1·25	☐	☐
1383	**853**	34p multicoloured	1·25	1·40	☐	☐
Set of 4			3·25	3·25	☐	☐
First Day Cover				3·75		☐
Presentation Pack			4·00		☐	
PHQ Cards (set of 4)			3·00	6·50	☐	☐
Set of 4 Gutter Pairs			8·00		☐	

854 Revd William Morgan (Bible translator, 1588)

855 William Salesbury (New Testament translator, 1567)

856 Bishop Richard Davies (New Testament translator, 1567)

857 Bishop Richard Parry (editor of Revised Welsh Bible, 1620)

400th Anniversary of Welsh Bible

1988 (1 Mar.) Phosphorised paper. Perf 14½ × 14

1384	**854**	18p multicoloured	40	10	☐	☐
1385	**855**	26p multicoloured	70	95	☐	☐
1386	**856**	31p multicoloured	1·25	1·25	☐	☐
1387	**857**	34p multicoloured	1·40	1·25	☐	☐
Set of 4			3·25	3·25	☐	☐
First Day Cover				3·75		☐
Presentation Pack			4·00		☐	
PHQ Cards (*set of 4*)			3·00	6·50	☐	☐
Set of 4 Gutter Pairs			8·00		☐	

858 Gymnastics (Centenary of British Amateur Gymnastics Association)

859 Downhill Skiing (Ski Club of Great Britain)

860 Tennis (Centenary of Lawn Tennis Association)

861 Football (Centenary of Football League)

Sports Organizations

1988 (22 Mar.) Phosphorised paper. Perf 14½

1388	**858**	18p multicoloured	40	15	☐	☐
1389	**859**	26p multicoloured	70	80	☐	☐
1390	**860**	31p multicoloured	1·10	1·25	☐	☐
1391	**861**	34p multicoloured	1·25	1·25	☐	☐
Set of 4			3·25	3·25	☐	☐
First Day Cover				3·50		☐
Presentation Pack			4·00		☐	
PHQ Cards (*set of 4*)			2·50	6·00	☐	☐
Set of 4 Gutter Pairs			8·00		☐	

862 *Mallard* and Mailbags on Pick-up Arms

863 Loading Transatlantic Mail on Liner *Queen Elizabeth*

864 Glasgow Tram No. 1173 and Pillar Box

865 Imperial Airways Handley Page H.P.45 *Horatius* and Airmail Van

Europa. Transport and Mail Services in 1930's

1988 (10 May) Phosphorised paper

1392	**862**	18p multicoloured	50	15	☐	☐
1393	**863**	26p multicoloured	1·00	1·00	☐	☐
1394	**864**	31p multicoloured	1·25	1·25	☐	☐
1395	**865**	34p multicoloured	1·60	1·50	☐	☐
Set of 4			4·00	3·50	☐	☐
First Day Cover				3·75		☐
Presentation Pack			4·25		☐	
PHQ Cards (*set of 4*)			2·25	6·00	☐	☐
Set of 4 Gutter Pairs			11·00		☐	

866 Early Settler and Sailing Clipper

867 Queen Elizabeth II with British and Australian Parliament Buildings

868 W. G. Grace (cricketer) and Tennis Racquet

869 Shakespeare, John Lennon (entertainer) and Sydney Landmarks

Nos. 1396/7 and 1398/9 were each printed together, *se-tenant*, in horizontal pairs throughout the sheets, each pair showing a background design of the Australian flag.

Bicentenary of Australian Settlement

1988 (21 June) Phosphorised paper. Perf 14½

1396	**866**	18p multicoloured	30	25	☐	☐
		a. Horiz pair. Nos. 1396/7	1·25	1·50	☐	☐
1397	**867**	18p multicoloured	30	25	☐	☐
1398	**868**	34p multicoloured	60	50	☐	☐
		a. Horiz pair. Nos. 1398/9	2·50	2·50	☐	☐
1399	**869**	34p multicoloured	60	50	☐	☐
Set of 4			3·50	3·50	☐	☐
First Day Cover				3·75		☐
Presentation Pack			4·00		☐	☐
Souvenir Book			15·00		☐	
PHQ Cards (*set of 4*)			2·25	6·00	☐	☐
Set of 2 Gutter Blocks of 4			8·25		☐	

Stamps in similar designs were also issued by Australia. These are included in the Souvenir Book.

870 Spanish Galeasse off The Lizard

871 English Fleet leaving Plymouth

872 Engagement off Isle of Wight

873 Attack of English Fire-ships, Calais

874 Armada in Storm, North Sea

Nos. 1400/4 were printed together, *se-tenant*, in horizontal strips of 5 throughout the sheet, forming a composite design.

400th Anniversary of Spanish Armada

1988 (19 July) Phosphorised paper

1400	**870**	18p multicoloured	30	25	☐	☐
		a. Horiz strip of 5.				
		Nos. 1400/4	3·00	3·00	☐	☐
1401	**871**	18p multicoloured	30	25	☐	☐
1402	**872**	18p multicoloured	30	25	☐	☐
1403	**873**	18p multicoloured	30	25	☐	☐
1404	**874**	18p multicoloured	30	25	☐	☐
Set of 5			3·00	3·00	☐	☐
First Day Cover				3·75		☐
Presentation Pack			3·75		☐	
PHQ Cards (set of 5)			2·75	7·00	☐	☐
Gutter Block of 10			8·00		☐	

875 'The Owl and the pussy-cat'

876 'Edward Lear as a Bird' (self-portrait)

877 'Cat' (from alphabet book)

878 'There was a Young Lady whose Bonnet . . .' (limerick)

Death Centenary of Edward Lear (artist and author)

1988 (6–27 Sept.) Phosphorised paper

1405	**875**	19p black, pale cream and carmine	65	20	☐	☐
1406	**876**	27p black, pale cream and yellow	1·00	1·00	☐	☐
1407	**877**	32p black, pale cream and emerald	1·25	1·40	☐	☐
1408	**878**	35p black, pale cream and blue	1·40	1·40	☐	☐
Set of 4			4·00	3·50		☐
First Day Cover				3·75		☐
Presentation Pack			4·25		☐	
PHQ Cards (set of 4)			2·25	6·00	☐	☐
Set of 4 Gutter Pairs			9·00		☐	
MS1409 122 × 90 mm. Nos. 1405/8			7·00	8·50	☐	☐
First Day Cover (27 Sept.)				8·50		☐

No. **MS**1409 was sold at £1·35, the premium being used for the 'Stamp World London 90' International Stamp Exhibition.

879 Carrickfergus Castle

880 Caernarvon Castle

881 Edinburgh Castle

882 Windsor Castle

1988 (18 Oct.) Ordinary paper

1410	**879**	£1 deep green	4·25	60	☐	☐
1411	**880**	£1·50 maroon	4·50	1·25	☐	☐
1412	**881**	£2 indigo	8·00	1·50	☐	☐
1413	**882**	£5 deep brown	21·00	5·50	☐	☐
Set of 4			35·00	8·00	☐	☐
First Day Cover				35·00		☐
Presentation Pack			35·00		☐	
Set of 4 Gutter pairs			70·00		☐	

For similar designs, but with silhouette of Queen's head see Nos. 1611/14 and 1993/6.

883 Journey to Bethlehem

884 Shepherds and Star

885 Three Wise Men

886 Nativity

887 The Annunciation

Christmas

1988 (15 Nov.) One phosphor band (14p) or phosphorised paper (others)

1414	**883**	14p multicoloured	45	25	☐	☐
1415	**884**	19p multicoloured	50	25	☐	☐
1416	**885**	27p multicoloured	90	1·00	☐	☐
1417	**886**	32p multicoloured	1·10	1·25	☐	☐
1418	**887**	35p multicoloured	1·40	1·25	☐	☐
Set of 5			4·00	3·75	☐	☐
First Day Cover				3·75		☐
Presentation Pack			4·00		☐	
PHQ Cards (*set of* 5)			3·00	6·00	☐	☐
Set of 5 Gutter Pairs			9·50		☐	

Collectors Pack 1988

1988 (15 Nov.) Comprises Nos. 1380/1408, 1414/18

CP1418a	Collectors Pack	35·00	☐

Post Office Yearbook

1988 Comprises Nos. 1380/1404, MS1409, 1414/18 in hardbound book with slip case

YB1418a	Yearbook	37·00	☐

888 Atlantic Puffin

889 Avocet

890 Oystercatcher

891 Northern Gannet

Centenary of Royal Society for the Protection of Birds

1989 (17 Jan.) Phosphorised paper

1419	**888**	19p multicoloured	25	20	☐	☐
1420	**889**	27p multicoloured	1·25	1·25	☐	☐
1421	**890**	32p multicoloured	1·25	1·25	☐	☐
1422	**891**	35p multicoloured	1·25	1·25	☐	☐
Set of 4			3·50	3·50	☐	☐
First Day Cover				4·00		☐
Presentation Pack			4·00		☐	
PHQ Cards (*set of* 4)			3·00	7·00	☐	☐
Set of 4 Gutter Pairs			9·50		☐	

892 Rose

893 Cupid

894 Yachts

895 Fruit

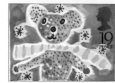

896 Teddy Bear

Nos. 1423/7 were printed together, *se-tenant*, in horizontal strips of five, two such strips forming the booklet pane with twelve half stamp-size labels.

Greetings Booklet Stamps

1989 (31 Jan.) Phosphorised paper

1423	**892**	19p multicoloured	60	50	☐	☐
		a. Booklet pane. Nos. 1423/7 × 2	50·00		☐	
		b. Horiz strip of 5. Nos. 1423/7	25·00	25·00	☐	☐
1424	**893**	19p multicoloured	60	50	☐	☐
1425	**894**	19p multicoloured	60	50	☐	☐
1426	**895**	19p multicoloured	60	50	☐	☐
1427	**896**	19p multicoloured	60	50	☐	☐
Set of 5			25·00	25·00	☐	☐
First Day Cover				25·00		☐

897 Fruit and Vegetables

898 Meat Products

899 Dairy Produce

900 Cereal Products

Food and Farming Year

1989 (7 Mar.) Phosphorised paper. Perf 14 × 14½

1428	**897**	19p multicoloured	45	15	☐	☐
1429	**898**	27p multicoloured	90	85	☐	☐
1430	**899**	32p multicoloured	1·25	1·40	☐	☐
1431	**900**	35p multicoloured	1·40	1·50	☐	☐
Set of 4			3·50	3·50	☐	☐
First Day Cover				3·75	☐	
Presentation Pack			4·00		☐	
PHQ Cards (*set of* 4)			2·25	6·50	☐	☐
Set of 4 Gutter Pairs			8·50		☐	

901 Mortar Board (150th Anniv of Public Education in England)

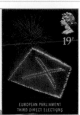

902 Cross on Ballot Paper (3rd Direct Elections to European Parliament)

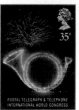

903 Posthorn (26th Postal, Telegraph and Telephone International Congress, Brighton)

904 Globe (Inter - Parliamentry Union Centenary Conference, London)

Nos. 1432/3 and 1434/5 were each printed together, *se- tenant*, in horizontal pairs throughout the sheets.

Anniversaries

1989 (11 Apr.) Phosphorised paper. Perf 14 × 14½

1432	**901**	19p multicoloured	50	25	☐	☐
		a. Horiz pair. Nos. 1432/3	1·50	1·50	☐	☐
1433	**902**	19p multicoloured	50	25	☐	☐
1434	**903**	35p multicoloured	75	50	☐	☐
		a. Horiz pair. Nos. 1434/5	2·50	2·50	☐	☐
1435	**904**	35p multicoloured	75	50	☐	☐
Set of 4			3·50	3·50	☐	☐
First Day Cover				4·50	☐	
Presentation Pack			4·00		☐	
PHQ Cards (*set of* 4)			2·25	6·50	☐	☐
Set of 2 Gutter Strips of 4			9·00		☐	

905 Toy Train and Aeroplanes

906 Building Bricks

907 Dice and Board Games

908 Toy Robot, Boat and Doll's House

Europa. Games and Toys

1989 (16 May) Phosphorised paper

1436	**905**	19p multicoloured	65	25	☐	☐
1437	**906**	27p multicoloured	95	1·00	☐	☐
1438	**907**	32p multicoloured	1·40	1·25	☐	☐
1439	**908**	35p multicoloured	1·50	1·25	☐	☐
Set of 4			4·00	3·50	☐	☐
First Day Cover				3·75	☐	
Presentation Pack			4·25		☐	
PHQ Cards (*set of* 4)			2·25	6·50	☐	☐
Set of 4 Gutter Pairs			10·50		☐	

909 Ironbridge, Shropshire

910 Tin Mine. St Agnes Head, Cornwall

911 Cotton Mills, New Lanark, Strathclyde

912 Pontcysylite Aqueduct, Clwyd

912a

Industrial Archaeology

1989 (4–25 July) Phosphorised paper

1440	**909**	19p multicoloured	60	15	☐	☐
1441	**910**	27p multicoloured	1·00	1·10	☐	☐
1442	**911**	32p multicoloured	1·10	1·25	☐	☐
1443	**912**	35p multicoloured	1·25	1·50	☐	☐
Set of 4			3·50	3·50	☐	☐
First Day Cover				3·75		☐
Presentation Pack			4·00		☐	
PHQ Cards (set of 4)			2·25	6·50	☐	☐
Set of 4 Gutter Pairs			8·50		☐	

MS1444 122 × 90 mm. 912a As
Nos. 1440/3 but designs horizontal 6·00 6·50 ☐ ☐
First Day Cover (25 July) 6·50 ☐

No. **MS**1444 was sold at £1·40, the premium being used for the 'Stamp World London 90' International Stamp Exhibition.

913

914

Booklet Stamps

1989 (22 Aug.)–**92**

(a) Printed in photogravure by Harrison and Sons. Perf 15 × 14

1445	**913**	(2nd) bright blue (1 centre band)	1·00	1·00	☐	☐
1446		(2nd) bright blue (1 side band) (20.3.90)	3·00	3·25	☐	☐
1447	**914**	(1st) black (phosphorised paper)	1·75	1·00	☐	☐
1448		(1st) brownish black (2 bands (20.3.90)	3·25	3·00	☐	☐

(b) Printed in lithography by Walsall. Perf 14

1449	**913**	(2nd) bright blue (1 centre band)	1·00	90	☐	☐
1450	**914**	(1st) black (2 bands)	2·50	2·40	☐	☐

(c) Printed in lithography by Questa. Perf 15 × 14

1451	**913**	(2nd) bright blue (1 centre band) (19.9.89)	1·00	1·00	☐	☐
1451a		(2nd) bright blue (1 side band) (25.2.92)	3·00	3·00	☐	☐
1452	**914**	(1st) black (phosphorised paper) (19.9.89)	2·50	2·50	☐	☐
First Day Cover (Nos. 1445, 1447)			5·00		☐	

For similar stamps showing changed colours see Nos. 1511/16, for those with elliptical perforations Nos. 1664/71 and for self-adhesive versions Nos. 2039/40.
No. 1451a exists with the phosphor band at the left or right of the stamp.

915 Snowflake (×10)

916 *Calliphora erythrocephala* (fly) (×5)

917 Blood Cells (×500)   **918** Microchip (×600)

150th Anniversary of Royal Microscopical Society

1989 (5 Sept.) Phosphorised paper. Perf 14½ × 14

1453	**915**	19p multicoloured	45	25	☐	☐
1454	**916**	27p multicoloured	95	1·00	☐	☐
1455	**917**	32p multicoloured	1·10	1·25	☐	☐
1456	**918**	35p multicoloured	1·25	1·25	☐	☐
Set of 4			3·50	3·50	☐	☐
First Day Cover				3·50		☐
Presentation Pack			4·00		☐	
PHQ Cards (set of 4)			2·25	6·50	☐	☐
Set of 4 Gutter Pairs			8·50		☐	

919 Royal Mail Coach   **920** Escort of Blues and Royals

921 Lord Mayor's Coach   **922** Coach Team passing St Paul's

923 Blues and Royals Drum Horse

Nos. 1457/61 were printed together, *se-tenant*, in horizontal strips of 5 throughout the sheet, forming a composite design.

Lord Mayor's Show, London

1989 (17 Oct.) Phosphorised paper

1457	**919**	20p multicoloured	40	30	☐	☐
		a. Horiz strip of 5.				
		Nos. 1457/61	3·00	3·00	☐	☐
1458	**920**	20p multicoloured	40	30	☐	☐
1459	**921**	20p multicoloured	40	30	☐	☐
1460	**922**	20p multicoloured	40	30	☐	☐
1461	**923**	20p multicoloured	40	30	☐	☐
Set of 5			3·00	3·00	☐	☐
First Day Cover				3·50		☐
Presentation Pack			3·00		☐	
PHQ Cards (*set of 5*)			3·00	6·50	☐	☐
Gutter Strip of 10			8·00		☐	

Nos. 1457/61 commemorate the 800th anniversary of the installation of the first Lord Mayor of London.

924 14th-century Peasants from Stained-glass Window

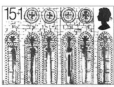

925 Arches and Roundels, West Front

926 Octagon Tower

927 Arcade from West Transept

928 Triple Arch from West Front

Christmas. 800th Anniversary of Ely Cathedral

1989 (14 Nov.) One phosphor band (Nos. 1462/3) or phosphorised paper (others)

1462	**924**	15p gold, silver and blue	40	15	☐	☐
1463	**925**	15p + 1p gold, silver and blue	50	40	☐	☐
1464	**926**	20p + 1p gold, silver and rosine	65	80	☐	☐
1465	**927**	34p + 1p gold, silver and emerald	1·25	1·75	☐	☐
1466	**928**	37p + 1p gold, silver and yellow-olive	1·40	1·90	☐	☐
Set of 5			3·75	4·50	☐	☐
First Day Cover				4·50		☐
Presentation Pack			4·50		☐	
PHQ Cards (*set of 5*)			3·00	6·00	☐	☐
Set of 5 Gutter Pairs			9·00		☐	

Collectors Pack 1989

1989 (14 Nov.) Comprises Nos. 1419/22, 1428/43 and 1453/66

CP1466a	Collectors Pack	38·00	☐

Post Office Yearbook

1989 (14 Nov.) Comprises Nos. 1419/22, 1428/44 and 1453/66 in hardback book with slip case

YB1466a	Yearbook	42·00	☐

929 Queen Victoria and Queen Elizabeth II

150th Anniversary of the Penny Black

1990 (10 Jan.–17 Apr.)

(a) Printed in photogravure by Harrison and Sons (Nos. 1468, 1470, 1472 from booklets only). Perf 15 × 14

1467	**929**	15p bright blue (1 centre band)	80	80	☐	☐
1468		15p bright blue (1 side band) (30 Jan.)	3·75	3·75	☐	☐
1469		20p brownish black and cream (phosphorised paper)	1·00	1·00	☐	☐
1470		20p brownish black and cream (2 bands) (30 Jan.)	2·75	2·75	☐	☐
1471		29p deep mauve (phosphorised paper)	1·75	1·75	☐	☐
1472		29p deep mauve (2 bands) (20 Mar.)	9·00	9·00	☐	☐
1473		34p deep bluish grey (phosphorised paper)	2·00	2·00	☐	☐
1474		37p rosine (phosphorised paper)	2·25	2·25	☐	☐
Set of 5 (Nos. 1467, 1469, 1471, 1473/4)			7·00	7·00	☐	☐
First Day Cover (Nos. 1467, 1469, 1471, 1473/4)				7·00		☐
Presentation Pack (Nos. 1467, 1469, 1471, 1473/4)			9·00		☐	

(b) Litho Walsall (booklets). Perf 14 (30 Jan.)

1475	**929**	15p bright blue (1 centre band)	1·50	1·75	☐	☐
1476		20p brownish black and cream (phosphorised paper)	1·60	1·75	☐	☐

(c) Litho Questa (booklets). Perf 15 × 14 (17 Apr.)

1477	**929**	15p bright blue (1 centre band)	2·25	2·25	☐	☐
1478		20p brownish black (phosphorised paper)	2·00	2·25	☐	☐

No. 1468 exists with the phosphor band at the left or right of the stamp.

For Type 929 redrawn with "1st" face value see No. 2133.

930 Kitten

931 Rabbit

932 Duckling

933 Puppy

150th Anniversary of Royal Society for Prevention of Cruelty to Animals

1990 (23 Jan.) Phosphorised paper. Perf 14 × 14½

1479	**930**	20p multicoloured	75	50	☐	☐
1480	**931**	29p multicoloured	1·25	1·25	☐	☐
1481	**932**	34p multicoloured	1·25	1·50	☐	☐
1482	**933**	37p multicoloured	1·50	1·50	☐	☐
Set of 4			4·50	4·25	☐	☐
First Day Cover				4·25		☐
Presentation Pack			4·50		☐	
PHQ Cards (*set of* 4)			3·00	7·50	☐	☐
Set of 4 Gutter Pairs			9·50		☐	

934 Teddy Bear

935 Dennis the Menace

936 Punch

937 Cheshire Cat

938 The Man in the Moon

939 The Laughing Policeman

940 Clown

941 Mona Lisa

942 Queen of Hearts   **943** Stan Laurel (comedian)

T **934/43** were printed together, *se-tenant*, in booklet panes of 10.

Greetings Booklet Stamps. 'Smiles'

1990 (6 Feb.) Two phosphor bands

1483	**934**	20p multicoloured	70	60	☐	☐
		a. Booklet pane.				
		Nos. 1483/92	30·00		☐	
1484	**935**	20p multicoloured	70	60	☐	☐
1485	**936**	20p multicoloured	70	60	☐	☐
1486	**937**	20p multicoloured	70	60	☐	☐
1487	**938**	20p multicoloured	70	60	☐	☐
1488	**939**	20p multicoloured	70	60	☐	☐
1489	**940**	20p multicoloured	70	60	☐	☐
1490	**941**	20p multicoloured	70	60	☐	☐
1491	**942**	20p multicoloured	70	60	☐	☐
1492	**943**	20p gold and grey-black	70	60	☐	☐
Set of 10			30·00	26·00	☐	☐
First Day Cover				28·00		☐

For these designs with the face value expressed as '1st' see Nos. 1550/9.

944 Alexandra Palace ('Stamp World London 90' Exhibition)

945 Glasgow School of Art

946 British Philatelic Bureau, Edinburgh

947 Templeton Carpet Factory, Glasgow

Europa (Nos. 1493 and 1495) and 'Glasgow 1990 European City of Culture' (Nos. 1494 and 1496)

1990 (6 Mar.) Phosphorised paper

1493	**944**	20p multicoloured	50	25	☐	☐
1494	**945**	20p multicoloured	50	25	☐	☐
1495	**946**	29p multicoloured	1·25	1·75	☐	☐
1496	**947**	37p multicoloured	1·50	1·75	☐	☐
Set of 4			3·50	3·50	☐	☐
First Day Cover				3·50		☐
Presentation Pack			4·25		☐	
PHQ Cards (*set of* 4)			3·00	6·00	☐	☐
Set of 4 Gutter Pairs			10·00		☐	

948 Export Achievement Award

949 Technological Achievement Award

Nos. 1497/8 and 1499/500 were each printed together, *se-tenant*, in horizontal pairs throughout the sheets.

25th Anniversary of Queen's Awards for Export and Technology

1990 (10 Apr.) Phosphorised paper. Perf 14 × 14½

1497	**948**	20p multicoloured		40	30	☐	☐
		a. Horiz pair. Nos. 1497/8	1·40		1·60	☐	☐
1498	**949**	20p multicoloured		40	30	☐	☐
1499	**948**	37p multicoloured		50	50	☐	☐
		a. Horiz pair. Nos. 1499/1500	3·00		3·00	☐	☐
1500	**949**	37p multicoloured		50	50	☐	☐
Set of 4				4·00	4·25	☐	☐
First Day Cover					4·50		☐
Presentation Pack				4·50		☐	
PHQ Cards (*set of* 4)				3·00	6·00	☐	☐
Set of 2 Gutter Strips of 4				8·50		☐	

949a

'Stamp World London 90' International Stamp Exhibition, London

1990 (3 May) Sheet 122 × 90 mm. Phosphorised paper

MS1501	**949a**	20p brownish black and cream	5·50	5·50	☐	☐
First Day Cover				5·75		☐
Souvenir Book (Nos. 1467, 1469, 1471, 1473/4 and **MS**1501				20·00	☐	

No. **MS**1501 was sold at £1, the premium being used for the exhibition.

KEW GARDENS 1840-1990
950 Cycad and Sir Joseph Banks Building

951 Stone Pine and Princess of Wales Conservatory

KEW GARDENS 1840-1990
952 Willow Tree and Palm House

KEW GARDENS 1840-1990
953 Cedar Tree and Pagoda

150th Anniversary of Kew Gardens

1990 (5 June) Phosphorised paper

1502	**950**	20p multicoloured	55	15	☐	☐
1503	**951**	29p multicoloured	75	1·00	☐	☐
1504	**952**	34p multicoloured	1·25	1·60	☐	☐
1505	**953**	37p multicoloured	1·50	1·50	☐	☐
Set of 4			3·50	3·75	☐	☐
First Day Cover				3·75		☐
Presentation Pack			4·00		☐	
PHQ Cards (*set of* 4)			3·00	6·00	☐	☐
Set of 4 Gutter Pairs			9·00		☐	

954 Thomas Hardy and Clyffe Clump, Dorset

150th Birth Anniversary of Thomas Hardy (author)

1990 (10 July) Phosphorised paper

1506	**954**	20p multicoloured	80	75	☐	☐
First Day Cover				1·50		☐
Presentation Pack			1·50		☐	
PHQ Card			1·00	2·25	☐	☐
Gutter Pair			1·75		☐	

955 Queen Elizabeth the Queen Mother

956 Queen Elizabeth

957 Elizabeth, Duchess of York

958 Lady Elizabeth Bowes-Lyon

90th Birthday of Queen Elizabeth the Queen Mother

1990 (2 Aug.) Phosphorised paper

1507	**955**	20p multicoloured	95	25	☐	☐
1508	**956**	29p silver, indigo and grey-blue	1·40	1·50	☐	☐
1509	**957**	34p multicoloured	2·00	2·50	☐	☐
1510	**958**	37p silver, sepia and stone	2·25	2·50	☐	☐
Set of 4			6·00	6·25	☐	☐
First Day Cover				6·25		☐
Presentation Pack			7·00		☐	
PHQ Cards (*set of* 4)			5·50	8·00	☐	☐
Set of 4 Gutter Pairs			15·00		☐	

For these designs with Queen's head and frame in black see Nos. 2280/3.

Booklet Stamps

1990 (7 Aug.)–**92** As Types **913/14**, but colours changed

(a) Photo Harrison. Perf 15 × 14

1511	**913**	(2nd) deep blue (1 centre band)	1·50	1·50	☐	☐
1512	**914**	(1st) bright orange-red (phosphorised paper)	1·50	1·50	☐	☐

(b) Litho Questa. Perf 15 × 14

1513	**913**	(2nd) deep blue (1 centre band)	2·50	2·50	☐	☐
1514	**914**	(1st) bright orange-red (phosphorised paper)	1·00	1·00	☐	☐
1514a		(1st) bright orange-red (2 bands) (25.2.92)	2·25	2·25	☐	☐

(c) Litho Walsall. Perf 14

1515	**913**	(2nd) deep blue (1 centre band)	1·00	1·00	☐	☐
1516	**914**	(1st) bright orange-red (phosphorised paper)	1·25	1·25	☐	☐
		c. Perf 13	2·75	3·00	☐	☐
First Day Cover (Nos. 1515/16)				5·00		☐

For similar stamps with elliptical perforations see Nos. 1664/71.

959 Victoria Cross

960 George Cross

961 Distinguished Service Cross and Distinguished Service Medal

962 Military Cross and Military Medal

963 Distinguished Flying Cross and Distinguished Flying Medal

Gallantry Awards

1990 (11 Sept.) Phosphorised paper

1517	**959**	20p multicoloured	80	75	☐	☐
1518	**960**	20p multicoloured	80	75	☐	☐
1519	**961**	20p multicoloured	80	75	☐	☐
1520	**962**	20p multicoloured	80	75	☐	☐
1521	**963**	20p multicoloured	80	75	☐	☐
Set of 5			3·75	3·50	☐	☐
First Day Cover				3·75		☐
Presentation Pack			4·00		☐	
PHQ Cards (*set of* 5)			3·00	8·00	☐	☐
Set of 5 Gutter Pairs			9·25		☐	

For Type **959** with "all-over" phosphor and perf 14 × 14½ see No. 2666.

964 Armagh Observatory, Jodrell Bank Radio Telescope and La Palma Telescope

965 Newton's Moon and Tides Diagram with Early Telescopes

966 Greenwich Old Observatory and Early Astronomical Equipment

967 Stonehenge, Gyroscope and Navigating by Stars

Astronomy

1990 (16 Oct.) Phosphorised paper. Perf 14 × 14½

1522	**964**	22p multicoloured	65	15	☐	☐
1523	**965**	26p multicoloured	1·00	1·10	☐	☐
1524	**966**	31p multicoloured	1·25	1·40	☐	☐
1525	**967**	37p multicoloured	1·50	1·40	☐	☐
Set of 4			3·75	3·75	☐	☐
First Day Cover				4·00	☐	
Presentation Pack			4·50		☐	
PHQ Cards (set of 4)			3·00	7·00	☐	☐
Set of 4 Gutter Pairs			9·25		☐	

Nos. 1522/5 commemorate the centenary of the British Astronomical Association and the bicentenary of the Armagh Observatory.

968 Building a Snowman

969 Fetching the Christmas Tree

970 Carol Singing

971 Tobogganing

972 Ice-skating

Christmas

1990 (13 Nov.) One phosphor band (17p) or phosphorised paper (others)

1526	**968**	17p multicoloured	50	15	☐	☐
1527	**969**	22p multicoloured	70	20	☐	☐
1528	**970**	26p multicoloured	70	1·10	☐	☐
1529	**971**	31p multicoloured	1·25	1·50	☐	☐
1530	**972**	37p multicoloured	1·25	1·50	☐	☐
Set of 5			4·00	4·00	☐	☐
First Day Cover				4·00	☐	
Presentation Pack			4·50		☐	
PHQ Cards (set of 5)			3·00	7·00	☐	☐
Set of 5 Gutter Pairs			10·00		☐	

Collectors Pack 1990

1990 (13 Nov.) Comprises Nos. 1479/82, 1493/1510 and 1517/30

CP1530a	Collectors Pack	40·00	☐

Post Office Yearbook

1990 Comprises Nos. 1479/82, 1493/1500, 1502/10 and 1517/30 in hardback book with slip case

YB1530a	Yearbook	45·00	☐

973 'King Charles Spaniel'

974 'A Pointer'

975 'Two Hounds in a Landscape'

976 'A Rough Dog'

977 'Fino and Tiny'

Dogs. Paintings by George Stubbs

1991 (8 Jan.) Phosphorised paper. Perf 14 × 14½

1531	**973**	22p multicoloured	50	15	☐	☐
1532	**974**	26p multicoloured	75	1·25	☐	☐
1533	**975**	31p multicoloured	1·00	1·25	☐	☐
1534	**976**	33p multicoloured	1·25	1·25	☐	☐
1535	**977**	37p multicoloured	1·25	1·25	☐	☐
Set of 5			4·50	4·50	☐	☐
First Day Cover				5·00	☐	
Presentation Pack			5·00		☐	
PHQ Cards (set of 5)			3·50	7·00	☐	☐
Set of 5 Gutter Pairs			11·00		☐	

978 Thrush's Nest

979 Shooting Star and Rainbow

980 Magpies and Charm Bracelet

981 Black Cat

982 Common Kingfisher with Key

983 Mallard and Frog

984 Four-leaf Clover in Boot and Match Box

985 Pot of Gold at End of Rainbow

986 Heart-shaped Butterflies

987 Wishing Well and Sixpence

T **978/87** were printed together, *se-tenant*, in booklet panes of 10 stamps and 12 half stamp-size labels, the backgrounds of the stamps forming a composite design.

Greetings Booklet Stamps. 'Good Luck'

1991 (5 Feb.) Two phosphor bands

1536	**978**	(1st) multicoloured	70	60	☐	☐
		a. Booklet pane.				
		Nos. 1536/45	15·00		☐	
1537	**979**	(1st) multicoloured	70	60	☐	☐
1538	**980**	(1st) multicoloured	70	60	☐	☐
1539	**981**	(1st) multicoloured	70	60	☐	☐
1540	**982**	(1st) multicoloured	70	60	☐	☐
1541	**983**	(1st) multicoloured	70	60	☐	☐
1542	**984**	(1st) multicoloured	70	60	☐	☐
1543	**985**	(1st) multicoloured	70	60	☐	☐
1544	**986**	(1st) multicoloured	70	60	☐	☐
1545	**987**	(1st) multicoloured	70	60	☐	☐
Set of 10			15·00	17·00	☐	☐
First Day Cover				19·00		☐

988 Michael Faraday (inventor of electric motor) (Birth Bicentenary)

989 Charles Babbage (computer science pioneer) (Birth Bicentenary)

990 Radar Sweep of East Anglia (50th Anniv of Discovery by Sir Robert Watson-Watt)

991 Gloster Whittle E28/39 Aircraft over East Anglia (50th Anniv of First Flight of Sir Frank Whittle's Jet Engine)

Scientific Achievements

1991 (5 Mar.) Phosphorised paper

1546	**988**	22p multicoloured	60	50	☐	☐
1547	**989**	22p multicoloured	60	50	☐	☐
1548	**990**	31p multicoloured	1·20	1·50	☐	☐
1549	**991**	37p multicoloured	1·35	1·75	☐	☐
Set of 4			3·50	4·00	☐	☐
First Day Cover				4·00		☐
Presentation Pack			4·25		☐	
PHQ Cards (*set of* 4)			3·50	7·00	☐	☐
Set of 4 Gutter Pairs			8·50		☐	

992 Teddy Bear

Nos. 1550/9 were originally printed together, *se-tenant*, in booklet panes of 10 stamps and 12 half stamp-size labels.

Greetings Booklet Stamps. 'Smiles'

1991 (26 Mar.) As Nos. 1483/92, but inscribed '1st' as T **992**. Two phosphor bands. Perf 15 × 14

1550	**992**	(1st) multicoloured	70	60	☐	☐
		a. Booklet pane.				
		Nos. 1550/9	12·00	13·00	☐	☐
1551	**935**	(1st) multicoloured	70	60	☐	☐
1552	**936**	(1st) multicoloured	70	60	☐	☐
1553	**937**	(1st) multicoloured	70	60	☐	☐
1554	**938**	(1st) multicoloured	70	60	☐	☐
1555	**939**	(1st) multicoloured	70	60	☐	☐
1556	**940**	(1st) multicoloured	70	60	☐	☐
1557	**941**	(1st) multicoloured	70	60	☐	☐

1558	942	(1st) multicoloured	70	60	☐	☐
1559	943	(1st) multicoloured	70	60	☐	☐
Set of 10			12·00	13·00	☐	☐
First Day Cover				13·00		☐

The stamps were re-issued in sheets of 10 each with *se-tenant* label on 22 May 2000 in connection with 'customised' stamps available at 'Stamp Show 2000'. The labels show either a pattern of ribbons or a personal photograph.

A similar sheet, but in lithography instead of photogravure, and perforated 14½ × 14, appeared on 3 July 2001 with the labels showing either greetings or a personal photograph. Three further sheets, also in lithography, appeared on 1 October 2002. One contained Nos. 1550/1 each × 10 with greetings labels. Both designs were also available in sheets of 20 with personal photographs.

993 Man looking at Space

994

995 Space looking at Man

996

Nos. 1560/1 and 1562/3 were each printed together, *se-tenant*, in horizontal pairs throughout the sheets, each pair forming a composite design.

Europa. Europe in Space

1991 (23 Apr.) Phosphorised paper

1560	993	22p multicoloured	40	30	☐	☐
		a. Horiz pair. Nos. 1560/1	1·50	1·50	☐	☐
1561	994	22p multicoloured	40	30	☐	☐
1562	995	37p multicoloured	50	40	☐	☐
		a. Horiz pair. Nos. 1562/3	3·50	3·00	☐	☐
1563	996	37p multicoloured	50	40	☐	☐
Set of 4			4·00	3·50	☐	☐
First Day Cover				4·50		☐
Presentation Pack			5·00		☐	
PHQ Cards (set of 4)			3·00	7·00	☐	☐
Set of 2 Gutter Strips of 4			12·00		☐	

997 Fencing

998 Hurdling

999 Diving

1000 Rugby

World Student Games, Sheffield (Nos. 1564/6) and World Cup Rugby Championship, London (No. 1567)

1991 (11 June) Phosphorised paper. Perf 14½ × 14

1564	997	22p multicoloured	60	20	☐	☐
1565	998	26p multicoloured	1·00	1·00	☐	☐
1566	999	31p multicoloured	1·25	1·25	☐	☐
1567	1000	37p multicoloured	1·50	1·50	☐	☐
Set of 4			3·50	3·50	☐	☐
First Day Cover				4·00		☐
Presentation Pack			4·50		☐	
PHQ Cards (set of 4)			3·00	7·00	☐	☐
Set of 4 Gutter Pairs			9·00		☐	

1001 'Silver Jubilee'

1002 'Mme Alfred Carrière'

1003 *Rosa moyesii*

1004 'Harvest Fayre'

1005 'Mutabilis'

9th World Congress of Roses, Belfast

1991 (16 July) Phosphorised paper. Perf 14½ × 14

1568	1001	22p multicoloured	50	20	☐	☐
1569	1002	26p multicoloured	75	1·25	☐	☐
1570	1003	31p multicoloured	1·00	1·25	☐	☐
1571	1004	33p multicoloured	1·25	1·50	☐	☐
1572	1005	37p multicoloured	1·50	1·50	☐	☐
Set of 5			4·50	5·00	☐	☐
First Day Cover				5·00		☐
Presentation Pack			5·00		☐	
PHQ Cards (set of 5)			3·00	9·00	☐	☐
Set of 5 Gutter Pairs			11·00		☐	

1006 Iguanodon

1007 Stegosaurus

1008 Tyrannosaurus

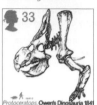

1009 Protoceratops

1010 Triceratops

150th Anniversary of Dinosaurs' Identification by Owen

1991 (20 Aug.) Phosphorised paper. Perf 14½ × 14

1573	**1006**	22p multicoloured	60	20	☐	☐
1574	**1007**	26p multicoloured	1·10	1·25	☐	☐
1575	**1008**	31p multicoloured	1·25	1·25	☐	☐
1576	**1009**	33p multicoloured	1·50	1·50	☐	☐
1577	**1010**	37p multicoloured	1·60	1·50	☐	☐
Set of 5			5·75	5·00	☐	☐
First Day Cover				5·50	☐	
Presentation Pack			6·00		☐	
PHQ Cards (*set of 5*)			3·00	9·00	☐	☐
Set of 5 Gutter Pairs			12·00		☐	

1011 Map of 1816

1012 Map of 1906

1013 Map of 1959

1014 Map of 1991

Bicentenary of Ordnance Survey. Maps of Hamstreet, Kent

1991 (17 Sept.) Phosphorised paper. Perf 14½ × 14

1578	**1011**	24p multicoloured	60	20	☐	☐
1579	**1012**	28p multicoloured	1·00	95	☐	☐
1580	**1013**	33p multicoloured	1·25	1·40	☐	☐
1581	**1014**	39p multicoloured	1·50	1·40	☐	☐
Set of 4			3·50	3·50	☐	☐
First Day Cover				4·25	☐	
Presentation Pack			4·50		☐	
PHQ Cards (*set of 4*)			3·00	7·00	☐	☐
Set of 4 Gutter Pairs			10·00		☐	

1015 Adoration of the Magi

1016 Mary and Baby Jesus in Stable

1017 Holy Family and Angel

1018 The Annunciation

1019 The Flight into Egypt

Christmas. Illuminated Manuscripts from the Bodleian Library, Oxford

1991 (12 Nov.) One phosphor band (18p) or phosphorised paper (others)

1582	**1015**	18p multicoloured	75	10	☐	☐
1583	**1016**	24p multicoloured	90	10	☐	☐
1584	**1017**	28p multicoloured	95	1·25	☐	☐
1585	**1018**	33p multicoloured	1·10	1·50	☐	☐
1586	**1019**	39p multicoloured	1·25	1·75	☐	☐
Set of 5			4·50	4·50	☐	☐
First Day Cover				4·50	☐	
Presentation Pack			4·50		☐	
PHQ Cards (*set of 5*)			3·00	7·50	☐	☐
Set of 5 Gutter Pairs			11·00		☐	

Collectors Pack 1991

1991 (12 Nov.) Comprises Nos. 1531/5, 1546/9 and 1560/86
CP1586a Collectors Pack   40·00   ☐

Post Office Yearbook

1991 Comprises Nos. 1531/5, 1546/9 and 1560/86 in hardback book with slip case
YB1586a Yearbook   45·00   ☐

1020 Fallow Deer in Scottish Forest

1021 Hare on North Yorkshire Moors

1022 Fox in the Fens

1023 Redwing and Home Counties Village

1024 Welsh Mountain Sheep in Snowdonia

The Four Seasons. Wintertime

1992 (14 Jan.) One phosphor band (18p) or phosphorised paper (others)

1587	**1020**	18p multicoloured	55	25	☐	☐
1588	**1021**	24p multicoloured	75	25	☐	☐
1589	**1022**	28p multicoloured	1·00	1·25	☐	☐
1590	**1023**	33p multicoloured	1·25	1·50	☐	☐
1591	**1024**	39p multicoloured	1·40	1·75	☐	☐
Set of 5			4·50	4·50	☐	☐
First Day Cover				4·50		☐
Presentation Pack			4·50		☐	
PHQ Cards (*set of* 5)			3·00	8·00	☐	☐
Set of 5 Gutter Pairs			11·00		☐	

1025 Flower Spray

1026 Double Locket

1027 Key

1028 Model Car and Cigarette Cards

1029 Compass and Map

1030 Pocket Watch

1031 1854 1d. Red Stamp and Pen

1032 Pearl Necklace

1033 Marbles

1034 Bucket, Spade and Starfish

T **1025/34** were printed together, *se-tenant*, in booklet panes of 10 stamps and 12 half stamp-size labels, the backgrounds of the stamps forming a composite design.

Greetings Stamps. 'Memories'

1992 (28 Jan.) Two phosphor bands

1592	**1025**	(1st) multicoloured	70	60	☐	☐
		a. Booklet pane. Nos. 1592/1601	13·00	13·00	☐	☐
1593	**1026**	(1st) multicoloured	70	60	☐	☐
1594	**1027**	(1st) multicoloured	70	60	☐	☐
1595	**1028**	(1st) multicoloured	70	60	☐	☐
1596	**1029**	(1st) multicoloured	70	60	☐	☐
1597	**1030**	(1st) multicoloured	70	60	☐	☐
1598	**1031**	(1st) multicoloured	70	60	☐	☐
1599	**1032**	(1st) multicoloured	70	60	☐	☐
1600	**1033**	(1st) multicoloured	70	60	☐	☐
1601	**1034**	(1st) multicoloured	70	60	☐	☐
Set of 10			13·00	13·00	☐	☐
First Day Cover				13·00		☐
Presentation Pack			17·00		☐	

1035 Queen Elizabeth in Coronation Robes and Parliamentary Emblem

1036 Queen Elizabeth in Garter Robes and Archiepiscopal Arms

1037 Queen Elizabeth with Baby Prince Andrew and Royal Arms

1038 Queen Elizabeth at Trooping the Colour and Service Emblems

1039 Queen Elizabeth and Commonwealth Emblem

Nos. 1602/6 were printed together, *se-tenant*, in horizontal strips of 5 throughout the sheet.

40th Anniversary of Accession

1992 (6 Feb.) Two phosphor bands. Perf 14½ × 14

1602	**1035**	24p multicoloured	50	50	☐	☐
		a. Horiz strip of 5.				
		Nos. 1602/6	6·00	6·50	☐	☐
1603	**1036**	24p multicoloured	50	50	☐	☐
1604	**1037**	24p multicoloured	50	50	☐	☐
1605	**1038**	24p multicoloured	50	50	☐	☐
1606	**1039**	24p multicoloured	50	50	☐	☐
Set of 5			6·00	6·50	☐	☐
First Day Cover				6·00		☐
Presentation Pack			7·00		☐	
PHQ Cards (set of 5)			3·00	7·50	☐	☐
Gutter Block of 10			15·00		☐	

1040 Tennyson in 1888 and 'The Beguiling of Merlin' (Sir Edward Burne-Jones)

1041 Tennyson in 1856 and 'April Love' of Merlin' (Arthur Hughes)

1042 Tennyson in 1864 and 'I am Sick of the Shadows' (John Waterhouse)

1043 Tennyson as a Young Man and 'Mariana' (Dante Gabriel Rossetti)

Death Centenary of Alfred, Lord Tennyson (poet)

1992 (10 Mar.) Phosphorised paper. Perf 14½ 3 14

1607	**1040**	24p multicoloured	60	20	☐	☐
1608	**1041**	28p multicoloured	85	85	☐	☐
1609	**1042**	33p multicoloured	1·40	1·60	☐	☐
1610	**1043**	39p multicoloured	1·50	1·60	☐	☐
Set of 4			4·00	3·75	☐	☐
First Day Cover				4·25		☐
Presentation Pack			4·50		☐	
PHQ Cards (set of 4)			3·00	7·00	☐	☐
Set of 4 Gutter Pairs			10·00		☐	

1044 Carrickfergus Castle

1992 (24 Mar.)–**95**. Designs as Nos. 1410/13, but showing Queen's head in silhouette as T **1044**. Perf 15 × 14 (with one elliptical hole on each vertical side)

1611	**1044**	£1 bottle green and				
		gold†	5·50	1·00	☐	☐
1612	**880**	£1·50 maroon and gold†	6·00	1·20	☐	☐
1613	**881**	£2 indigo and gold†	8·00	1·20	☐	☐
1613a	**1044**	£3 reddish violet and				
		gold†	19·00	3·00	☐	☐
1614	**882**	£5 deep brown and				
		gold†	18·00	3·00	☐	☐
Set of 5			50·00	8·00	☐	☐
First Day Cover (Nos. 1611/13, 1614)				35·00		☐
First Day Cover (22 Aug. 1995) (No. 1613a)				10·00		☐
Presentation Pack (P.O. Pack No. 27)						
(Nos. 1611/13, 1614)			38·00		☐	
Presentation Pack (P.O. Pack No 33)						
(No. 1613a)			30·00		☐	
PHQ Cards (Nos. 1611/14)			15·00	15·00	☐	☐
PHQ Card (No. 1613a)			10·00	25·00	☐	☐
Set of 5 Gutter Pairs			98·00		☐	

†The Queen's head on these stamps is printed in optically variable ink which changes colour from gold to green when viewed from different angles.

PHQ cards for Nos. 1611/13 and 1614 were not issued until 16 February 1993.

Nos. 1611/14 were printed by Harrison. For stamps with different lettering by Enschedé see Nos. 1993/6.

1045 British Olympic Association Logo (Olympic Games, Barcelona)

1046 British Paralympic Association Symbol (Paralympics '92, Barcelona)

1047 *Santa Maria* (500th Anniv of Discovery of America by Columbus)

1048 *Kaisei* (Japanese cadet brigantine) (Grand Regatta Columbus, 1992)

1049 British Pavilion, 'EXPO 92', Seville

Nos. 1615/16 were printed together, *se-tenant*, in horizontal pairs throughout the sheet.

Europa. International Events

1992 (7 Apr.) Phosphorised paper. Perf 14 × 14½

1615	**1045**	24p multicoloured	50	40	☐	☐
		a. Horiz pair.				
		Nos. 1615/16	2·25	1·75	☐	☐
1616	**1046**	24p multicoloured	50	40	☐	☐
1617	**1047**	24p multicoloured	1·00	75	☐	☐
1618	**1048**	39p multicoloured	1·40	1·50	☐	☐
1619	**1049**	39p multicoloured	1·40	1·50	☐	☐
Set of 5			4·50	4·50	☐	☐
First Day Cover				5·00	☐	
Presentation Pack			5·25		☐	
PHQ Cards (*set of 5*)			3·00	7·00	☐	☐
Set of 3 Gutter Pairs and a Gutter						
		Strip of 4	13·00		☐	

1050 Pikeman

1051 Drummer

1052 Musketeer

1053 Standard Bearer

350th Anniversary of the Civil War

1992 (16 June) Phosphorised paper. Perf 14½ × 14

1620	**1050**	24p multicoloured	60	20	☐	☐
1621	**1051**	28p multicoloured	85	85	☐	☐
1622	**1052**	33p multicoloured	1·40	1·50	☐	☐
1623	**1053**	39p multicoloured	1·50	1·75	☐	☐
Set of 4			4·00	4·00	☐	☐
First Day Cover				4·00		☐
Presentation Pack			4·50		☐	
PHQ Cards (*set of 4*)			3·00	7·00	☐	☐
Set of 4 Gutter Pairs			10·50		☐	

1054 *The Yeomen of the Guard*

1055 *The Gondoliers*

1056 *The Mikado*

1057 *The Pirates of Penzance*

1058 *Iolanthe*

150th Birth Anniversary of Sir Arthur Sullivan (composer). Gilbert and Sullivan Operas

1992 (21 July) One phosphor band (18p) or phosphorised paper (others). Perf 14½ × 14

1624	**1054**	18p multicoloured	50	20	☐	☐
1625	**1055**	24p multicoloured	80	20	☐	☐
1626	**1056**	28p multicoloured	95	1·00	☐	☐
1627	**1057**	33p multicoloured	1·50	1·60	☐	☐
1628	**1058**	39p multicoloured	1·60	1·60	☐	☐
Set of 5			4·50	4·25	☐	☐
First Day Cover				4·50		☐
Presentation Pack			4·50		☐	
PHQ Cards (*set of 5*)			3·00	6·25	☐	☐
Set of 5 Gutter Pairs			10·50		☐	

1059 'Acid Rain Kills'

1060 'Ozone Layer'

1061 'Greenhouse Effect'

1062 'Bird of Hope'

Protec3tion of the Environment. Children's Paintings

1992 (15 Sept.) Phosphorised paper. Perf 14 × 14½

1629	**1059**	24p multicoloured	70	25	☐	☐
1630	**1060**	28p multicoloured	1·10	1·25	☐	☐
1631	**1061**	33p multicoloured	1·25	1·50	☐	☐
1632	**1062**	39p multicoloured	1·40	1·50	☐	☐
Set of 4			4·00	4·00	☐	☐
First Day Cover				4·00		☐
Presentation Pack			4·50		☐	
PHQ Cards (set of 4)			3·00	6·25	☐	☐
Set of 4 Gutter Pairs			10·00		☐	

1063 European Star

Single European Market

1992 (13 Oct.) Phosphorised paper

1633	**1063**	24p multicoloured	1·00	1·00	☐	☐
First Day Cover				1·50		☐
Presentation Pack			1·50		☐	
PHQ Card			1·50	4·00	☐	☐
Gutter Pair			2·25		☐	

1064 'Angel Gabriel', St. James's, Pangbourne

1065 'Madonna and Child', St. Mary's, Bibury

1066 'King with Gold', Our Lady and St. Peter, Leatherhead

1067 'Shepherds', All Saints, Porthcawl

1068 'Kings with Frankincense and Myrrh', Our Lady and St. Peter, Leatherhead

Christmas. Stained Glass Windows

1992 (10 Nov.) One phosphor band (18p) or phosphorised paper (others)

1634	**1064**	18p multicoloured	50	15	☐	☐
1635	**1065**	24p multicoloured	75	15	☐	☐
1636	**1066**	28p multicoloured	1·00	1·10	☐	☐
1637	**1067**	33p multicoloured	1·25	1·50	☐	☐
1638	**1068**	39p multicoloured	1·25	1·50	☐	☐
Set of 5			4·25	4·00	☐	☐
First Day Cover				4·50		☐
Presentation Pack			4·50		☐	
PHQ Cards (set of 5)			3·00	7·50	☐	☐
Set of 5 Gutter Pairs			10·00		☐	

Collectors Pack 1992

1992 (10 Nov.) Comprises Nos. 1587/91, 1602/10 and 1615/38

CP1638a	Collectors Pack	45·00	☐

Post Office Yearbook

1992 (11 Nov.) Comprises Nos. 1587/91, 1602/10 and 1615/38 in hardback book with slip case

YB1638a	Yearbook	55·00	☐

1069 Mute Swan Cob and St. Catherine's, Abbotsbury

1070 Cygnet and Decoy

1071 Swans and Cygnet

1072 Eggs in Nest and Tithe Barn, Abbotsbury

1073 Young Swan
and the Fleet

600th Anniversary of Abbotsbury Swannery

1993 (19 Jan.) One phosphor band (18p) or phosphorised
paper (others)

1639 **1069**	18p multicoloured	1·25	25	☐	☐
1640 **1070**	24p multicoloured	1·10	25	☐	☐
1641 **1071**	28p multicoloured	1·40	2·25	☐	☐
1642 **1072**	33p multicoloured	1·75	2·50	☐	☐
1643 **1073**	39p multicoloured	1·90	2·50	☐	☐
Set of 5		6·50	7·50	☐	☐
First Day Cover			7·50		☐
Presentation Pack		7·00		☐	
PHQ Cards (*set of* 5)		4·25	8·50	☐	☐
Set of 5 Gutter Pairs		15·00		☐	

1074 Long John Silver and
Parrot (*Treasure Island*)

1075 Tweedledum and
Tweedledee (*Alice Through
the Looking-Glass*)

1076 William (*William* books)

1077 Mole and Toad (*The
Wind in the Willows*)

1078 Teacher and Wilfrid
('The Bash Street Kids')

1079 Peter Rabbit and Mrs
Rabbit (*The Tale of Peter
Rabbit*)

1080 Snowman
(*The Snowman*) and Father
Christmas (*Father Christmas*)

1081 The Big Friendly Giant
and Sophie (*The BFG*)

1082 Bill Badger and Rupert
Bear

1083 Aladdin and the Genie

T **1074/83** were printed together, *se-tenant*, in booklet panes
of 10 stamps and 20 half stamp-size labels.

Greetings Stamps. 'Gift Giving'

1993 (2 Feb.) Two phosphor bands. Perf 15 × 14 (with one
elliptical hole on each vertical side)

1644 **1074**	(1st) multicoloured	60	50	☐	☐
	a. Booklet pane.				
	Nos. 1644/53	11·00		☐	☐
1645 **1075**	(1st) gold, cream and				
	black	60	50	☐	☐
1646 **1076**	(1st) multicoloured	60	50	☐	☐
1647 **1077**	(1st) multicoloured	60	50	☐	☐
1648 **1078**	(1st) multicoloured	60	50	☐	☐
1649 **1079**	(1st) multicoloured	60	50	☐	☐
1650 **1080**	(1st) multicoloured	60	50	☐	☐
1651 **1081**	(1st) multicoloured	60	50	☐	☐
1652 **1082**	(1st) multicoloured	60	50	☐	☐
1653 **1083**	(1st) multicoloured	60	50	☐	☐
Set of 10		11·00	12·00	☐	☐
First Day Cover			12·00		☐
Presentation Pack		16·00		☐	
PHQ Cards (*set of* 10)		16·00	30·00	☐	☐

1084 Decorated Enamel
Dial

1085 Escapement,
Remontoire and Fusee

1086 Balance, Spring and
Temperature Compensator

1087 Back of Movement

300th Birth Anniversary of John Harrison (inventor of the marine chronometer). Details of 'H4' Clock

1993 (16 Feb.) Phosphorised paper. Perf 14½ × 14

1654 **1084**	24p multicoloured	60	25	☐	☐
1655 **1085**	28p multicoloured	1·00	1·25	☐	☐
1656 **1086**	33p multicoloured	1·40	1·25	☐	☐
1657 **1087**	39p multicoloured	1·50	1·50	☐	☐
Set of 4		4·00	4·00	☐	☐
First Day Cover			4·00		☐

Presentation Pack	4·25		☐
PHQ Cards (*set of* 4)	4·25	7·00	☐ ☐
Set of 4 Gutter Pairs	10·00		☐

1088 Britannia

1993 (2 Mar.) Granite paper. Perf 14 × 14½ (with two elliptical holes on each horizontal side)

1658 **1088**	£10 multicoloured	40·00	12·00	☐ ☐
First Day Cover			25·00	☐
Presentation Pack		45·00		☐
PHQ Card		8·00	60·00	☐ ☐

1089 *Dendrobium hellwigianum*

1090 *Paphiopedilum Maudiae* 'Magnifcum'

1091 *Cymbidium lowianum*

1092 *Vanda* Rothschildiana

1093 *Dendrobium vexillarius* var *albiviride*

14th World Orchid Conference, Glasgow

1993 (16 Mar.) One phosphor band (18p) or phosphorised paper (others)

1659 **1089**	18p multicoloured	45	25	@@
1660 **1090**	24p multicoloured	75	25	@@
1661 **1091**	28p multicoloured	1·00	1·25	@@
1662 **1092**	33p multicoloured	1·25	1·50	@@
1663 **1093**	39p multicoloured	1·60	1·50	@@
Set of 5		4·50	4·50	@@
First Day Cover			4·50	☐
Presentation Pack		5·00		☐
PHQ Cards (*set of* 5)		4·50	7·00	@@
Set of 5 Gutter Pairs		10·00		☐

1993 (6 Apr.)–**2008**. As T **913/14** and **1093a**, but Perf 14 (No. 1665) or 15 × 14 (others) (both with one elliptical hole on each vertical side)

(a) Photo

Harrison (No. 1666)
Questa (Nos. 1664a, 1667a)
Walsall (No. 1665)
Harrison (later De La Rue), Questa or Walsall (No. 1667)
Harrison (later De La Rue), Enschedé, Questa or Walsall (Nos. 1664, 1668, 1669)

1664	**913**	(2nd) bright blue			
		(1 centre band)	1·00	1·00	☐ ☐
		a. Perf 14	1·10	1·10	☐ ☐
1665		(2nd) bright blue			
		(1 side band)	1·10	1·10	☐ ☐
1666	**914**	(1st) bright orange-red			
		(phosphorised paper)	1·50	1·25	☐ ☐
1667		(1st) bright orange-red			
		(2 phosphor bands)	1·10	1·10	☐ ☐
		a. Perf 14	1·50	1·50	☐ ☐
1668		(1st) gold			
		(2 phosphor bands)	1·00	1·00	☐ ☐
1669	**1093a**	(E) deep blue			
		(2 phosphor bands)	1·25	1·25	☐ ☐

(b) Litho Questa or Walsall (No. 1670), Questa Enschedé or Walsall (No. 1671), De La Rue (No. 1672)

1670	**913**	(2nd) bright blue			
		(1 centre band)	90	90	☐ ☐
1671	**914**	(1st) bright orange-red			
		(2 phosphor bands)	1·00	1·00	☐ ☐
1672		(1st) gold			
		(2 phosphor bands)	1·00	1·00	☐ ☐

First Day Covers		
21 Apr. 1997 (1st), 26p (Nos 1668, Y1686)	£3·50	☐
19 Jan. 1999 (E) (No 1669)	£3·50	☐

Nos. 1664, 1667, 1669 and 1670/1 also come from sheets.
No. 1665 exists with the phosphor band at the left or right of the stamp and was only issued in booklets.
No. 1668 was issued by Harrison in booklets and Walsall in sheets and booklets for the Queen's Golden Wedding on 21 April 1997. The gold colour was later adopted for the (1st) class rate, replacing bright orange-red.
For No. 1668 in presentation pack see Pack No. 38 listed below, No. Y1667 etc.
No. 1669 was valid for the basic European airmail rate, initially 30p.
No. 1672 was only issued in £7·40 stamp booklets.

For self-adhesive versions in these colours see Nos. 2039/40 and 2295/8.

1993–2009 As Nos. X841 etc, but perf 14 (No. Y1678) or 15 × 14 (others) (both with one elliptical hole on each vertical side)

(a) Photo

Enschedé:— 20p (Y1679), 29p, 35p (Y1692), 36p, 38p (Y1700), 41p (Y1706), 43p (Y1710)
Harrison:— 20p (Y1681), 25p (Y1683), 26p (Y1686), 35p (Y1693), 41p (Y1707), 43p (Y1711)
Walsall:— 10p (Y1676a), 19p (Y1678), 38p (Y1701a), 43p (Y1711a)
Enschedé or Harrison (later De La Rue):— 4p, 5p, 6p, 10p (Y1676), 25p (Y1684), 31p, 39p (Y1702), £1 (Y1725)
Enschedé, Harrison (later De La Rue) or Questa:— 1p, 2p
Enschedé, Harrison (later De La Rue) or Walsall:— 30p, 37p (Y1697), 42p, 50p, 63p

Harrison (later De La Rue) or Questa:— 19p (Y1677), 20p (Y1680), 26p (Y1685)

De La Rue or Walsall:— 38p (Y1701), 39p (Y1703), 40p (Y1704), 64p, 65p, 68p

De La Rue:— 7p, 8p, 9p, 12p, 14p, 15p, 16p, 17p, 20p (Y1682), 22p, 33p, 34p, 35p (Y1694), 37p (Y1698/9), 41p (Y1708), 43p (Y1712), 44p, 45p, 48p, 49p, 50p, 56p, 62p, 72p, 78p, 81p, 90p, £1 (Y1725b), £1·50, £2, £3, £5 Enschedé or De La Rue:— 35p (Y1695), 40p (Y1705), 46p, 47p, 54p

Y1667	**367**	1p crimson (2 bands)	25	25	☐	☐
Y1668		2p deep green (2 bands)	25	25	☐	☐
Y1669		4p new blue (2 bands)	25	25	☐	☐
Y1670		5p dull red-brown (2 bands)	25	25	☐	☐
Y1671		6p yellow-olive (2 bands)	25	30	☐	☐
Y1672		7p grey (2 bands)	35	35	☐	☐
Y1673		7p bright magenta (2 bands)	25	25	☐	☐
Y1674		8p yellow (2 bands)	35	35	☐	☐
Y1675		9p yellow-orange (2 bands)	15	20	☐	☐
Y1676		10p dull orange (2 bands)	35	35	☐	☐
		a. Perf 14	2·00	2·00	☐	☐
Y1676b		12p greenish blue (2 bands)	20	25	☐	☐
Y1676c		14p rose-red (2 bands)	20	25	☐	☐
Y1676d		15p bright magenta (2 bands)	35	35	☐	☐
Y1676e		16p pale cerise (2 bands)	35	35	☐	☐
Y1676f		17p brown-olive (2 bands)	50	50	☐	☐
Y1677		19p bistre (1 centre band)	75	75	☐	☐
Y1678		19p bistre (1 side band)	2·00	2·00	☐	☐
Y1679		20p turquoise-green (2 bands)	90	90	☐	☐
Y1680		20p bright green (1 centre band)	70	70	☐	☐
Y1681		20p bright green (1 side band)	1·50	1·50	☐	☐
Y1682		20p bright green (2 bands)	75	75	☐	☐
Y1682b		22p drab (2 bands)	50	50	☐	☐
Y1683		25p rose-red (phosphorised paper)	1·10	1·10	☐	☐
Y1684		25p rose-red (2 bands)	1·10	1·10	☐	☐
Y1685		26p red-brown (2 bands)	1·10	1·10	☐	☐
Y1686		26p gold (2 bands)	1·10	1·10	☐	☐
Y1687		29p grey (2 bands)	1·25	1·25	☐	☐
Y1688		30p deep olive-grey (2 bands)	1·10	1·10	☐	☐
Y1689		31p deep mauve (2 bands)	1·20	1·20	☐	☐
Y1690		33p grey-green (2 bands)	1·50	1·50	☐	☐
Y1691		34p yellow-olive (2 bands)	1·25	1·00	☐	☐
Y1692		35p yellow (2 bands)	1·50	1·50	☐	☐
Y1693		35p yellow (phosphorised paper)	7·50	7·50	☐	☐
Y1694		35p sepia (2 bands)	1·10	1·10	☐	☐
Y1695		35p yellow-olive (1 centre band)	50	55	☐	☐
Y1696		36p bright ultramarine (2 bands)	1·50	1·50	☐	☐
Y1697		37p bright mauve (2 bands)	1·40	1·40	☐	☐
Y1698		37p grey-black (2 bands)	1·40	1·40	☐	☐
Y1699		37p brown-olive (1 centre band)	90	90	☐	☐
Y1700		38p rosine (2 bands)	1·50	1·50	☐	☐
Y1701		38p ultramarine (2 bands)	2·00	2·00	☐	☐
		a. Perf 14	7·50	7·50	☐	☐

Y1702		39p bright magenta (2 bands)	1·50	1·50	☐	☐
Y1703		39p grey (2 bands)	1·20	1·20	☐	☐
Y1704		40p deep azure (2 bands)	1·40	1·40	☐	☐
Y1705		40p turquoise-blue (2 bands)	1·30	1·30	☐	☐
Y1706		41p grey-brown (2 bands)	1·75	1·75	☐	☐
Y1707		41p drab (phosphorised paper)	7·50	7·50	☐	☐
Y1708		41p rosine (2 bands)	1·40	1·40	☐	☐
Y1709		42p deep olive-grey (2 bands)	1·40	1·40	☐	☐
Y1710		43p deep olive-brown (2 bands)	1·75	1·75	☐	☐
Y1711		43p sepia (2 bands)	2·50	2·50	☐	☐
		a. Perf 14	2·50	2·50	☐	☐
Y1712		43p emerald (2 bands)	1·40	1·40	☐	☐
Y1713		44p grey-brown (2 bands)	5·00	5·00	☐	☐
Y1714		44p deep bright blue (2 bands)	1·00	1·00	☐	☐
Y1715		45p bright mauve (2 bands)	1·50	1·50	☐	☐
Y1716		46p yellow (2 bands)	1·00	1·00	☐	☐
Y1717		47p turquoise-green (2bands)	1·75	1·75	☐	☐
Y1717a		48p bright mauve (2 bands)	1·00	1·00	☐	☐
Y1718		49p red-brown (2 bands)	1·00	1·00	☐	☐
Y1719		50p ochre (2 bands)	1·75	1·75	☐	☐
Y1719b		50p grey (2 bands)	1·00	1·00	☐	☐
Y1719c		54p red-brown (2 bands)	1·10	1·10	☐	☐
Y1719d		56p yellow-olive (2 bands)	1·10	1·10	☐	☐
Y1719e		62p rosine (2 bands)	1·40	1·40	☐	☐
Y1720		63p light emerald (2 bands)	2·00	2·00	☐	☐
Y1721		64p turquoise-green (2 bands)	2·25	2·25	☐	☐
Y1722		65p greenish blue (2 bands)	2·10	2·10	☐	☐
Y1723		68p grey-brown (2 bands)	2·10	2·10	☐	☐
Y1724		72p rosine (2 bands)	1·50	1·50	☐	☐
Y1724a		78p emerald (2 bands)	1·50	1·50	☐	☐
Y1724b		81p turquoise-green (2 bands)	1·50	1·50	☐	☐
Y1724c		90p ultramarine (2 bands)	2·00	2·00	☐	☐
Y1725		£1 bluish violet (2 bands)	3·25	3·00	☐	☐
Y1725b		£1 magenta (2 bands)	2·00	2·00	☐	☐
Y1726		£1·50 brown-red (2 bands)	4·00	4·00	☐	☐
Y1727		£2 deep blue-green (2 bands)	5·50	5·50	☐	☐
Y1728		£3 deep mauve (2 bands)	8·00	8·00	☐	☐
Y1729		£5 azure (2 bands)	14·00	14·00	☐	☐

(b) Litho Cartor (1p (Y1743n), 16p, 17p, 22p, 50p, 62p, 90p), De La Rue (5p, 48p), Questa or De La Rue (10p), Questa or Walsall (25p, 35p, 41p), Walsall (37p, 60p, 63p), Questa (others)

Y1743	**367**	1p lake (2 bands)	40	40	☐	☐
Y1743n		1p reddish purple (2 bands)	1·00	1·00	☐	☐
Y1743s		5p dull red-brown (2 bands)	70	70	☐	☐
Y1748		6p yellow-olive (2 bands)	12·00	13·00	☐	☐
Y1749		10p dull orange (2 bands)	5·00	5·00	☐	☐
Y1749m		16p pale cerise (2 bands)	70	70	☐	☐
Y1749n		17p bistre (2 bands)	1·00	1·00	☐	☐
Y1750		19p bistre (1 side band)	1·90	1·75	☐	☐
Y1751		20p bright yellow-green (1 centre band)	2·25	2·25	☐	☐
Y1751n		22p olive-brown (2 bands)	2·50	2·50	☐	☐
Y1752		25p red (2 bands)	1·10	1·10	☐	☐
Y1753		26p chestnut (2 bands)	1·00	1·00	☐	☐

Y1754	30p	olive-grey (2 bands)	4·25	4·25	☐	☐
Y1755	35p	yellow (2 bands)	1·60	1·60	☐	☐
Y1756	37p	bright mauve (2 bands)	3·50	3·50	☐	☐
Y1757	41p	drab (2 bands)	1·75	1·75	☐	☐
Y1757f	48p	bright mauve (2 bands)	2·25	2·25	☐	☐
Y1757g	50p	grey (2 bands)	2·25	2·25	☐	☐
Y1758	60p	dull blue-grey (2 bands)	2·50	2·50	☐	☐
Y1758e	62p	rosine (2 bands)	1·75	1·75	☐	☐
Y1759	63p	light emerald (2 bands)	3·50	3·50	☐	☐
Y1760	90p	bright blue (2 bands)	2·25	2·25	☐	☐

(c) Recess Enschedé or De La Rue

Y1800	**367**	£1·50 red	4·50	2·00	☐	☐
Y1801		£2 dull blue	6·00	2·25	☐	☐
Y1802		£3 dull violet	9·00	3·00	☐	☐
Y1803		£5 brown	15·50	5·00	☐	☐
PHQ Card (No. Y1725)			3·00	15·00	☐	☐

PHQ Cards (Nos. 1664, 1668,Y1667/8, Y1670, Y1675/6, Y1676d/e, Y1682, Y1717a,Y1719b, Y1719d, Y1724b, Y1725b, Y1726/9, 2357a/9, 2652/3) **7·00** ☐

Presentation Pack (P.O. Pack No. 30) (contains 19p (Y1677), 25p (Y1683), 29p (Y1687), 36p (Y1696), 38p (Y1700), 41p (Y1706)) **7·00** ☐

Presentation Pack (P.O. Pack No. 34) (contains 1p (Y1667), 2p (Y1668), 4p (Y1669), 5p (Y1670),6p (Y1671), 10p (Y1676), 19p (Y1677), 20p (Y1679), 25p (Y1684), 29p (Y1687), 30p (Y1688), 35p (Y1692), 36p (Y1696), 38p (Y1700), 41p (Y1706), 50p (Y1719), 60p (Y1758), £1 (Y1725)) **30·00** ☐

Presentation Pack (P.O. Pack No. 35) (contains 20p (Y1680), 26p (Y1685), 31p (Y1689), 37p (Y1697), 39p (Y1702), 43p (Y1710), 63p (Y1720)) **9·50** @

Presentation Pack (P.O. Pack No. 38) (contains 1st (1668), 26p (Y1686)) **7·50** @

Presentation Pack (P.O. Pack No. 41) (contains 2nd (1664), 1st (1667), 1p (Y1667), 2p (Y1668), 4p (Y1669), 5p (Y1670), 6p (Y1671), 10p (Y1676), 20p (Y1680), 26p (Y1685), 30p (Y1688), 31p (Y1689), 37p (Y1697), 39p (Y1702), 43p (Y1711), 50p (Y1719), 63p (Y1720), £1 (Y1725)) **16·00** @

Presentation Pack (P.O. Pack No. 43 or 43A) (contains £1·50 (Y1800), £2 (Y1801), £3 (Y1802), £5 (Y1803)) **55·00** ☐

Presentation Pack (P.O. Pack No. 44) contains 7p (Y1672), 19p (Y1677), 38p (Y1701), 44p (Y1713), 64p (Y1721)) **11·00** @

Presentation Pack (P.O. Pack No. 49) (contains 8p (Y1674), 33p (Y1690), 40p (Y1704), 41p (Y1708), 45p (Y1715), 65p (Y1722)) **10·00** ☐

Presentation Pack (P.O. Pack No.57) (contains 2nd (1664), 1st (1667), E (1669), 1p (Y1667), 2p (Y1668), 4p (Y1669), 5p (Y1670), 8p (Y1674), 10p (Y1676), 20p (Y1682), 33p (Y1690), 40p (Y1704), 41p (Y1708), 45p (Y1715), 50p (Y1719), 65p (Y1722), £1(Y1725)) **16·00** ☐

Presentation Pack (P.O. Pack No. 58) (contains 37p (Y1698), 42p (Y1709), 47p (Y1716), 68p (Y1723) **7·50** ☐

Presentation Pack (P.O. Pack No. 62) (contains £1·50 (Y1726), £2 (Y1727), £3 (Y1728), £5(Y1729) **23·00** ☐

Presentation Pack (P.O. Pack No. 67) (contains 7p (No. Y1673), 1st (1668), 35p (Y1694), 39p(Y1703), 40p (Y1705), 43p (Y1712), Worldwide postcard (2357a) **6·00** ☐

Presentation Pack (P.O. Pack No. 71) (contains 1p (Y1667), 2p (Y1668), 5p (Y1670), 9p (Y1675), 10p (Y1676), 20p (Y1682), 35p (Y1695), 40p(Y1705), 42p (Y1709), 46p (Y1716), 47p (Y1717), 50p (Y1719), 68p (Y1723), £1 (Y1725), 2nd (2039), 1st(2295), Worldwide postcard (2357a), Europe (2358), Worldwide (2359) **11·50** ☐

Presentation Pack (P.O. Pack No. 72) (contains 37p (Y1699), 44p (Y1714), 49p (Y1718), 72p (Y1724) **3·50** ☐

Presentation Pack (P.O. Pack No.75) (contains 16p (Y1676e), 48p (Y1717a), 50p (Y1719b), 54p (Y1719c), 78p (Y1724a) **6·75** ☐

Presentation Pack (P.O. Pack No.77) (contains 1p (Y1667), 2p (Y1668), 5p (Y1670), 10p (Y1676), 14p (Y1676c), 16p (Y1676d), 20p (Y1682), 46p (Y1716), 48p (Y1717a), 50p (Y1719b), 54p (Y1719c), 78p (Y1724a), £1 (Y1725b), 2nd (1664), 1st (1668), 2nd Large (2652), 1st Large (2653), Worldwide postcard (2357a), Europe (2358), Worldwide (2359) **20·00** ☐

Presentation Pack (P.O. Pack No.78) (contains 15p (Y1676d), 56p (Y1719d), 81p (Y1724b) **4·00** ☐

Presentation Pack (P.O. Pack No. 84) (contains 17p (Y1676f), 22p (Y1682b), 62p (Y1719e), 90p (Y1724c) **5·25** ☐

For P.O. Pack No. 37 see below No. 1977.
For P.O. Pack No. 74 containing Nos. Y1676b/c see below No. 2657.

First Day Covers

26 Oct. 1993	19p, 25p, 29p, 36p, 38p, 41p (Nos. Y1677, Y1683, Y1687, Y1696, Y1700, Y1706)	6·00	☐
9 Aug. 1994	60p (No. Y1758)	4·00	☐
22 Aug. 1995	£1 (No. Y1725)	3·50	☐
25 June 1996	20p, 26p, 31p, 37p, 39p, 43p, 63p (Nos. Y1680, Y1685, Y1689, Y1697, Y1702, Y1710, Y1720)	8·00	☐
9 Mar. 1999	£1·50, £2, £3, £5 (Nos. Y1800/3)	27·00	☐
20 Apr. 1999	7p, 38p, 44p, 64p (Nos. Y1672, Y1701, Y1713, Y1721)	5·00	☐
25 Apr. 2000	8p, 33p, 40p, 41p, 45p, 65p (Nos. Y1674, Y1690, Y1704, Y1708, Y1715, Y1722)	5·00	☐
4 July 2002	37p, 42p, 47p, 68p, (Nos. Y1698, Y1709, Y1716, Y1723)	4·00	☐
6 May 2003	34p (No. Y1691)	1·20	☐
1 July 2003	£1·50, £2, £3, £5 (Nos. Y1726/9)	21·00	☐
1 April 2004	7p, 35p, 39p, 40p, 43p, World-wide postcard (Nos. Y1673,Y1694, Y1703, Y1705, Y1712, 2357a)	9·00	☐
5 April 2005	9p, 35p, 46p (Nos. Y1675, Y1695, Y1716)	2·20	☐
28 March 2006	37p, 44p, 49p, 72p (Nos. Y1699, Y1714, Y1718, Y1724)	4·25	☐

27 March 2007	16p, 48p, 50p, 54p, 78p (Nos. Y1676e, Y1717a, Y1719b/c, Y1724a)	6·00	☐
1 April 2008	15p, 56p, 81p (Nos. Y1676d, Y1719d, Y1724b)	4·50	☐
31 March 2009	17p, 22p, 62p, 90p, (Nos. Y1676f, Y1682b, Y1719e, Y1724c)	6·00	☐

For Nos. Y1676b/c on first day cover see under Nos. 2650/7.

Nos. Y1725/9 are printed in Iriodin ink which gives a shiny effect to the solid part of the background behind the Queen's head.

Nos. Y1693 and Y1707 were only issued in coils and Nos. Y1676a, Y1678, Y1681, Y1701a, Y1711a and Y1743/60 only in booklets.

No. Y1750 exists with the phosphor band at the left or right of the stamp, but Nos. Y1678 and Y1681 exist with band at right only.

For self-adhesive versions of the 42p and 68p see Nos. 2297/8.

1094 'Family Group' (bronze sculpture) (Henry Moore)

1095 'Kew Gardens' (lithograph) (Edward Bawden)

1096 'St Francis and the Birds' (Stanley Spencer)

1097 'Still Life: Odyssey I' (Ben Nicholson)

Europa. Contemporary Art

1993 (11 May) Phosphorised paper. Perf 14 3 14½

1767	**1094**	24p multicoloured	60	20	☐	☐
1768	**1095**	28p multicoloured	90	1·00	☐	☐
1769	**1096**	33p multicoloured	1·25	1·40	☐	☐
1770	**1097**	39p multicoloured	1·75	1·75	☐	☐
Set of 4			4·00	4·00	☐	☐
First Day Cover				4·50		☐
Presentation Pack			4·50		☐	
PHQ Cards (set of 4)			4·00	7·00	☐	☐
Set of 4 Gutter Pairs			10·00		☐	

1098 Emperor Claudius (from gold coin)

1099 Emperor Hadrian (bronze head)

1100 Goddess Roma (from gemstone)

1101 Christ (Hinton St. Mary mosaic)

Roman Britain

1993 (15 June) Phosphorised paper with two phosphor bands. Perf 14 × 14½

1771	**1098**	24p multicoloured	60	20	☐	☐
1772	**1099**	28p multicoloured	90	1·00	☐	☐
1773	**1100**	33p multicoloured	1·30	1·50	☐	☐
1774	**1101**	39p multicoloured	1·50	1·60	☐	☐
Set of 4			4·00	4·00	☐	☐
First Day Cover				4·00		☐
Presentation Pack			4·50		☐	
PHQ Cards (set of 4)			4·25	7·00	☐	☐
Set of 4 Gutter Pairs			10·00		☐	

1102 Midland Maid and other Narrow Boats, Grand Junction Canal

1103 Yorkshire Maid and other Humber Keels, Stainforth and Keadby Canal

1104 Valley Princess and other Horse-drawn Barges, Brecknock and Abergavenny Canal

1105 Steam Barges including Pride of Scotland and Fishing Boats, Crinan Canal

Inland Waterways

1993 (20 July) Two phosphor bands. Perf 14½ × 14

1775	**1102**	24p multicoloured	50	20	☐	☐
1776	**1103**	28p multicoloured	1·00	1·00	☐	☐
1777	**1104**	33p multicoloured	1·25	1·25	☐	☐
1778	**1105**	39p multicoloured	1·50	1·40	☐	☐
Set of 4			3·75	3·50	☐	☐
First Day Cover				3·75		☐
Presentation Pack			4·50		☐	
PHQ Cards (set of 4)			4·25	7·00	☐	☐
Set of 4 Gutter Pairs			9·00		☐	

Nos. 1775/8 commemorate the bicentenaries of the Acts of Parliament authorising the canals depicted.

1106 Horse Chestnut

1107 Blackberry

1108 Hazel

1109 Rowan

1110 Pear

The Four Seasons. Autumn. Fruits and Leaves

1993 (14 Sept.) One phosphor band (18p) or phosphorised paper (others)

1779 **1106**	18p multicoloured	50	20	☐ ☐
1780 **1107**	24p multicoloured	75	20	☐ ☐
1781 **1108**	28p multicoloured	1·10	1·25	☐ ☐
1782 **1109**	33p multicoloured	1·40	1·50	☐ ☐
1783 **1110**	39p multicoloured	1·50	1·50	☐ ☐
Set of 5		4·75	4·50	☐ ☐
First Day Cover			4·50	☐
Presentation Pack		4·75		☐
PHQ Cards (*set of* 5)		4·50	7·00	☐ ☐
Set of 5 Gutter Pairs		10·50		☐

1111 *The Reigate Squire*

1112 *The Hound of the Baskervilles*

1113 *The Six Napoleons*

1114 *The Greek Interpreter*

1115 *The Final Problem*

T **1111/15** were printed together, *se-tenant*, in horizontal strips of 5 throughout the sheet.

Sherlock Holmes. Centenary of the Publication of The Final Problem

1993 (12 Oct.) Phosphorised paper. Perf 14 × 14½

1784 **1111**	24p multicoloured	50	40	☐ ☐
	a. Horiz strip of 5.			
	Nos. 1784/8	5·00	5·25	☐ ☐
1785 **1112**	24p multicoloured	50	40	☐ ☐
1786 **1113**	24p multicoloured	50	40	☐ ☐
1787 **1114**	24p multicoloured	50	40	☐ ☐
1788 **1115**	24p multicoloured	50	40	☐ ☐
Set of 5		5·00	5·25	☐ ☐
First Day Cover			5·50	☐
Presentation Pack		5·00		☐
PHQ Cards (*set of* 5)		4·50	8·00	☐ ☐
Gutter Strip of 10		11·00		☐

1116

Self-adhesive Booklet Stamp

1993 (19 Oct.) Litho Walsall. Two phosphor bands. Die-cut perf 14 × 15 (with one elliptical hole on each vertical side)

1789 **1116**	(1st) orange-red	1·25	1·40	☐ ☐
First Day Cover			4·50	☐
Presentation Pack				
(booklet pane of 20)		25·00		☐
PHQ Card		4·00	8·00	☐ ☐

For similar 2nd and 1st designs printed in photogravure by Enschedé see Nos. 1976/7.

1117 Bob Cratchit and Tiny Tim

1118 Mr and Mrs Fezziwig

1119 Scrooge

1120 The Prize Turkey

1121 Mr Scrooge's Nephew

Christmas. 150th Anniversary of Publication of A Christmas Carol

1993 (9 Nov.) One phosphor band (19p) or phosphorised paper (others)

1790	**1117**	19p multicoloured	60	15	☐	☐
1791	**1118**	25p multicoloured	90	15	☐	☐
1792	**1119**	30p multicoloured	1·25	1·50	☐	☐
1793	**1120**	35p multicoloured	1·40	1·60	☐	☐
1794	**1121**	41p multicoloured	1·40	1·60	☐	☐
Set of 5			4·50	4·50	☐	☐
First Day Cover				5·00		☐
Presentation Pack			5·00		☐	
PHQ Cards (*set of* 5)			4·50	8·00	☐	☐
Set of 5 Gutter Pairs			11·00		☐	

Collectors Pack 1993

1993 (9 Nov.) Comprises Nos. 1639/43, 1654/7, 1659/63, 1767/88 and 1790/4

CP1794a	Collectors Pack	45·00	☐

Post Office Yearbook

1993 (9 Nov.) Comprises Nos. 1639/43, 1654/7, 1659/63, 1767/88 and 1790/4 in hardback book with slip case

YB1794a	Yearbook	65·00	☐

1122 Class 5 No. 44957 and Class B1 No. 61342 on West Highland Line

1123 Class A1 No. 60149 *Amadis* at Kings Cross

1124 Class 4 No. 43000 on Turntable at Blythe North

1125 Class 4 No. 42455 near Wigan Central

1126 Class Castle No. 7002 *Devizes Castle* on Bridge crossing Worcester and Birmingham Canal

The Age of Steam. Railway Photographs by Colin Gifford

1994 (18 Jan.) One phosphor band (19p) or phosphorised paper with two bands (others). Perf 14½

1795	**1122**	19p deep blue-green, grey-black and black	55	25	☐	☐
1796	**1123**	25p slate-lilac, grey-black and black	90	95	☐	☐
1797	**1124**	30p lake-brown, grey-black and black	1·40	1·50	☐	☐
1798	**1125**	35p deep claret, grey-black and black	1·75	1·80	☐	☐
1799	**1126**	41p indigo, grey-black and black	1·80	1·90	☐	☐
Set of 5			6·00	6·00	☐	☐
First Day Cover				6·00		☐
Presentation Pack			5·75		☐	
PHQ Cards (*set of* 5)			5·75	11·00	☐	☐
Set of 5 Gutter Pairs			12·00		☐	

1127 Dan Dare and the Mekon   **1128** The Three Bears

1129 Rupert Bear   **1130** Alice (*Alice in Wonderland*)

1131 Noggin and the Ice Dragon   **1132** Peter Rabbit posting Letter

1133 Red Riding Hood and Wolf   **1134** Orlando the Marmalade Cat

1135 Biggles   **1136** Paddington Bear on Station

T **1127/36** were printed together, *se-tenant*, in booklet panes of 10 stamps and 20 half stamp-size labels.

Greeting Stamps. 'Messages'

1994 (1 Feb.) Two phosphor bands. Perf 15 × 14 (with one elliptical hole on each vertical side)

1800	**1127**	(1st) multicoloured	60	50	☐	☐
		a. Booklet pane. Nos. 1800/9	13·00		☐	
1801	**1128**	(1st) multicoloured	60	50	☐	☐
1802	**1129**	(1st) multicoloured	60	50	☐	☐
1803	**1130**	(1st) gold, bistre-yellow and black	60	50	☐	☐
1804	**1131**	(1st) multicoloured	60	50	☐	☐
1805	**1132**	(1st) multicoloured	60	50	☐	☐
1806	**1133**	(1st) multicoloured	60	50	☐	☐
1807	**1134**	(1st) multicoloured	60	50	☐	☐
1808	**1135**	(1st) multicoloured	60	50	☐	☐
1809	**1136**	(1st) multicoloured	60	50	☐	☐
Set of 10			13·00	12·00	☐	☐
First Day Cover				12·00		☐
Presentation Pack			18·00		☐	
PHQ Cards (*set of* 10)			16·00	30·00	☐	☐

1137 Castell Y Waun (Chirk Castle), Clwyd, Wales

1138 Ben Arkle, Sutherland, Scotland

1139 Mourne Mountains, County Down, Northern Ireland

1140 Dersingham, Norfolk, England

1141 Dolwyddelan, Gwynedd, Wales

25th Anniversary of Investiture of the Prince of Wales. Paintings by Prince Charles

1994 (1 Mar.) One phosphor band (19p) or phosphorised paper (others)

1810	**1137**	19p multicoloured	55	20	☐	☐
1811	**1138**	25p multicoloured	1·00	20	☐	☐
1812	**1139**	30p multicoloured	1·10	1·50	☐	☐
1813	**1140**	35p multicoloured	1·40	1·75	☐	☐
1814	**1141**	41p multicoloured	1·50	1·75	☐	☐
Set of 5			5·00	5·00	☐	☐
First Day Cover				5·00		☐
Presentation Pack			5·00		☐	
PHQ Cards (*set of* 5)			5·75	11·50	☐	☐
Set of 5 Gutter Pairs			11·00		☐	

1142 Bather at Blackpool

1143 'Where's my Little Lad?'

1144 'Wish You were Here!

1145 Punch and Judy Show

1146 'The Tower Crane' Machine

Centenary of Picture Postcards

1994 (12 Apr.) One side band (19p) or two phosphor bands (others). Perf 14 × 14½

1815	**1142**	19p multicoloured	60	20	☐	☐
1816	**1143**	25p multicoloured	90	20	☐	☐
1817	**1144**	30p multicoloured	1·10	1·50	☐	☐
1818	**1145**	35p multicoloured	1·40	1·75	☐	☐
1819	**1146**	41p multicoloured	1·50	1·75	☐	☐
Set of 5			5·00	5·00	☐	☐
First Day Cover				5·00		☐
Presentation Pack			5·00		☐	
PHQ Cards (*set of* 5)			5·75	11·50	☐	☐
Set of 5 Gutter Pairs			11·00		☐	

1147 British Lion and French Cockerel over Tunnel

1148 Symbolic Hands over Train

Nos. 1820/1 and 1822/3 were printed together, *se-tenant*, in horizontal pairs throughout the sheets.

Opening of Channel Tunnel

1994 (3 May) Phosphorised paper. Perf 14 × 14½

1820 **1147**	25p multicoloured	50	40	☐	☐
	a. Horiz pair.				
	Nos. 1820/1	1·75	2·00	☐	☐
1821 **1148**	25p multicoloured	50	40	☐	☐
1822 **1147**	41p multicoloured	60	50	☐	☐
	a. Horiz pair.				
	Nos. 1822/3	3·25	2·50	☐	☐
1823 **1148**	41p multicoloured	60	50	☐	☐
Set of 4		4·50	4·50	☐	☐
First Day Cover			5·25		☐
Presentation Pack		5·00		☐	
Presentation Pack (UK and					
	French stamps)	25·00		☐	
Souvenir Book		50·00		☐	
PHQ Cards (*set of* 4)		5·75	9·00	☐	☐

Stamps in similar designs were also issued by France and these are included in the joint Presentation Pack and Souvenir Book.

1149 Groundcrew replacing Smoke Canisters on Douglas Boston of 88 Sqn

1150 H.M.S. *Warspite* (battleship) shelling Enemy Positions

1151 Commandos Landing on Gold Beach

1152 Infantry regrouping on Sword Beach

1153 Tank and Infantry advancing, Ouistreham

Nos. 1824/8 were printed together, *se-tenant*, in horizontal strips of 5 throughout the sheet.

50th Anniversary of D-Day

1994 (6 June) Two phosphor bands. Perf 14½ × 14

1824 **1149**	25p multicoloured	50	40	☐	☐
	a. Horiz strip of 5.				
	Nos. 1824/8	4·25	5·00	☐	☐
1825 **1150**	25p multicoloured	50	40	☐	☐
1826 **1151**	25p multicoloured	50	40	☐	☐
1827 **1152**	25p multicoloured	50	40	☐	☐
1828 **1153**	25p multicoloured	50	40	☐	☐
Set of 5		4·25	5·00	☐	☐
First Day Cover			5·50		☐
Presentation Pack		5·50		☐	
PHQ Cards (*set of* 5)		5·00	11·50	☐	☐
Gutter Block of 10		11·00		☐	

1154 The Old Course, St Andrews

1155 The 18th Hole, Muirfield

1156 The 15th Hole ('Luckyslap'), Carnoustie

1157 The 8th Hole ('The Postage Stamp'), Royal Troon

1158 The 9th Hole, Turnberry

Scottish Golf Courses

1994 (5 July) One phosphor band (19p) or phosphorised paper (others). Perf 14½ × 14

1829 **1154**	19p multicoloured	50	20	☐	☐
1830 **1155**	25p multicoloured	75	20	☐	☐
1831 **1156**	30p multicoloured	1·10	1·40	☐	☐
1832 **1157**	35p multicoloured	1·25	1·40	☐	☐
1833 **1158**	41p multicoloured	1·40	1·40	☐	☐
Set of 5		4·50	4·25	☐	☐
First Day Cover			4·75		☐
Presentation Pack		4·75		☐	
PHQ Cards (*set of* 5)		5·75	11·50	☐	☐
Set of 5 Gutter Pairs		11·50		☐	

Nos. 1829/33 commemorate the 250th anniversary of golf's first set of rules produced by the Honourable Company of Edinburgh Golfers.

1159 Royal Welsh Show, Llanelwedd

1160 All England Tennis Championships, Wimbledon

1161 Cowes Week

1162 Test Match, Lord's

1163 Braemar Gathering

The Four Seasons. Summertime. Events

1994 (2 Aug.) One phosphor band (19p) or phosphorised paper (others)

1834	**1159**	19p multicoloured	50	20	☐	☐
1835	**1160**	25p multicoloured	75	20	☐	☐
1836	**1161**	30p multicoloured	1·10	1·25	☐	☐
1837	**1162**	35p multicoloured	1·25	1·60	☐	☐
1838	**1163**	41p multicoloured	1·40	1·60	☐	☐
Set of 5			4·50	4·25	☐	☐
First Day Cover				4·75		☐
Presentation Pack			4·75		☐	
PHQ Cards (set of 5)			5·75	11·50	☐	☐
Set of 5 Gutter Pairs			11·50		☐	

1164 Ultrasonic Imaging

1165 Scanning Electron Microscopy

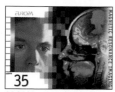
1166 Magnetic Resonance Imaging

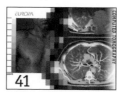
1167 Computed Tomography

Europa. Medical Discoveries

1994 (27 Sept.) Phosphorised paper. Perf 14 × 14½

1839	**1164**	25p multicoloured	75	25	☐	☐
1840	**1165**	30p multicoloured	1·00	1·25	☐	☐
1841	**1166**	35p multicoloured	1·50	1·75	☐	☐
1842	**1167**	41p multicoloured	1·75	1·75	☐	☐

Set of 4	4·50	4·50	☐ ☐
First Day Cover		4·75	☐
Presentation Pack	4·75		☐
PHQ Cards (set of 4)	5·75	10·00	☐ ☐
Set of 4 Gutter Pairs	11·00		☐

1168 Virgin Mary and Joseph

1169 Three Wise Men

1170 Virgin and Child

1171 Shepherds

1172 Angels

Christmas. Children's Nativity Plays

1994 (1 Nov.) One phosphor band (19p) or phosphorised paper (others)

1843	**1168**	19p multicoloured	50	15	☐	☐
1844	**1169**	25p multicoloured	75	15	☐	☐
1845	**1170**	30p multicoloured	1·00	1·50	☐	☐
1846	**1171**	35p multicoloured	1·25	1·50	☐	☐
1847	**1172**	41p multicoloured	1·50	1·75	☐	☐
Set of 5			4·50	4·75	☐	☐
First Day Cover				4·75		☐
Presentation Pack			4·75		☐	
PHQ Cards (set of 5)			5·75	11·50	☐	☐
Set of 5 Gutter Pairs			10·50		☐	

Collectors Pack 1994

1994 (14 Nov.) Comprises Nos. 1795/1847

CP1847a	Collectors Pack	55·00	☐

Post Office Yearbook

1994 (14 Nov.) Comprises Nos. 1795/9 and 1810/47 in hardback book with slip case

YB1847a	Yearbook	55·00	☐

1173 Sophie (black cat)

1174 Puskas (Siamese) and Tigger (tabby)

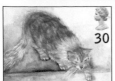

1175 Chloe (ginger cat)

1176 Kikko (tortoiseshell) and Rosie (Abyssinian)

1177 Fred (black and white cat)

Cats

1995 (17 Jan.) One phosphor band (19p) or two phosphor bands (others). Perf 14½ × 14

1848	**1173**	19p multicoloured	75	20	☐	☐
1849	**1174**	25p multicoloured	75	25	☐	☐
1850	**1175**	30p multicoloured	1·00	1·50	☐	☐
1851	**1176**	35p multicoloured	1·25	1·50	☐	☐
1852	**1177**	41p multicoloured	1·50	1·50	☐	☐
Set of 5			4·75	4·75	☐	☐
First Day Cover				4·75	☐	
Presentation Pack			5·50		☐	
PHQ Cards (*set of* 5)			6·00	11·50	☐	☐
Set of 5 Gutter Pairs			11·00		☐	

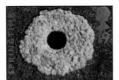

1178 Dandelions

1179 Sweet Chestnut Leaves

1180 Garlic Leaves

1181 Hazel Leaves

1182 Spring Grass

The Four Seasons. Springtime. Plant Sculptures by Andy Goldsworthy

1995 (14 Mar.) One phosphor band (19p) or two phosphor bands (others)

1853	**1178**	19p multicoloured	75	15	☐	☐
1854	**1179**	25p multicoloured	75	15	☐	☐
1855	**1180**	30p multicoloured	1·00	1·50	☐	☐
1856	**1181**	35p multicoloured	1·25	1·50	☐	☐
1857	**1182**	41p multicoloured	1·50	1·75	☐	☐
Set of 5			4·75	4·75	☐	☐

First Day Cover		4·75		☐
Presentation Pack		5·00		☐
PHQ Cards (*set of* 5)		6·00	11·50	☐ ☐
Set of 5 Gutter Pairs		11·50		☐

1183 'La Danse a la Campagne' (Renoir)

1184 'Troilus and Criseyde' (Peter Brookes)

1185 'The Kiss' (Rodin)

1186 'Girls on the Town' (Beryl Cook)

1187 'Jazz' (Andrew Mockett)

1188 'Girls performing a Kathal Dance' (Aurangzeb period)

1189 'Alice Keppel with her Daughter' (Alice Hughes)

1190 'Children Playing' (L. S. Lowry)

1191 'Circus Clowns' (Emily Firmin and Justin Mitchell)

1192 Decoration from 'All the Love Poems of Shakespeare' (Eric Gill)

T **1183/92** were printed together, *se-tenant*, in booklet panes of 10 stamps and 20 half stamp-size labels.

Greetings Stamp. 'Greetings in Art'

1995 (21 Mar.) Two phosphor bands. Perf 14½ × 14 (with one elliptical hole on each vertical side)

1858	**1183**	(1st) multicoloured	60	50	☐	☐
		a. Booklet pane. Nos. 1858/67	11·00	11·00	☐	☐
1859	**1184**	(1st) multicoloured	60	50	☐	☐
1860	**1185**	(1st) multicoloured	60	50	☐	☐
1861	**1186**	(1st) multicoloured	60	50	☐	☐
1862	**1187**	(1st) multicoloured	60	50	☐	☐
1863	**1188**	(1st) multicoloured	60	50	☐	☐
1864	**1189**	(1st) purple-brown and silver	60	50	☐	☐

1865	**1190**	(1st) multicoloured	60	50	☐	☐
1866	**1191**	(1st) multicoloured	60	50	☐	☐
1867	**1192**	(1st) black, greenish yellow and silver	60	50	☐	☐
Set of 10			11·50	11·00	☐	☐
First Day Cover				11·50		☐
Presentation Pack			12·00		☐	
PHQ Cards (*set of* 10)			16·00	30·00	☐	☐

The National Trust *Celebrating 100 Years* **19**

1193 Fireplace Decoration, Attingham Park, Shropshire

The National Trust *Protecting Land* **25**

1194 Oak Seedling

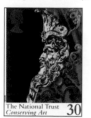

The National Trust *Conserving Art* **30**

1195 Carved Table Leg, Attingham Park

The National Trust *Saving Coast* **35**

1196 St. David's Head, Dyfed, Wales

The National Trust *Repairing Buildings* **41**

1197 Elizabethan Window, Little Moreton Hall, Cheshire

Centenary of The National Trust

1995 (11 Apr.) One phosphor band (19p), two phosphor bands (25p, 35p) or phosphorised paper (30p, 41p)

1868	**1193**	19p multicoloured	60	20	☐	☐
1869	**1194**	25p multicoloured	80	20	☐	☐
1870	**1195**	30p multicoloured	1·00	1·50	☐	☐
1871	**1196**	35p multicoloured	1·25	1·50	☐	☐
1872	**1197**	41p multicoloured	1·40	1·75	☐	☐
Set of 5			4·50	4·75	☐	☐
First Day Cover				4·75		☐
Presentation Pack			4·75		☐	
PHQ Cards (*set of* 5)			6·00	11·50	☐	☐
Set of 5 Gutter Pairs			11·00		☐	

1198 British Troops and French Civilians celebrating

1199 Symbolic Hands and Red Cross

1200 St. Paul's Cathedral and Searchlights

1201 Symbolic Hand releasing Peace Dove

1202 Symbolic Hands

Europa. Peace and Freedom

1995 (2 May) One phosphor band (Nos. 1873/4) or two phosphor bands (others). Perf 14½ × 14

1873	**1198**	19p silver, bistre-brown and grey-black	70	40	☐	☐
1874	**1199**	19p multicoloured	70	40	☐	☐
1875	**1200**	25p silver, blue and grey-black	1·00	1·00	☐	☐
1876	**1201**	25p multicoloured	1·00	1·00	☐	☐
1877	**1202**	30p multicoloured	1·25	2·25	☐	☐
Set of 5			4·25	4·25	☐	☐
First Day Cover				4·75		☐
Presentation Pack			5·00		☐	
PHQ Cards (*set of* 5)			6·00	11·50	☐	☐
Set of 5 Gutter Pairs			10·50		☐	

Nos. 1873 and 1875 commemorate the 50th anniversary of the end of the Second World War, No. 1874 the 125th anniversary of the British Red Cross Society and Nos. 1876/7 the 50th anniversary of the United Nations.
Nos. 1876/7 include the 'EUROPA' emblem.
For No. 1875 with the face value expressed as '1st' see No. **MS**2547.

1203 *The Time Machine*

1204 *The First Men in the Moon*

1205 *The War of the Worlds*

1206 *The Shape of Things to Come*

Science Fiction. Novels by H. G. Wells

1995 (6 June) Two phosphor bands. Perf 14½ × 14

1878	**1203**	25p multicoloured	75	25	☐	☐
1879	**1204**	30p multicoloured	1·25	1·50	☐	☐
1880	**1205**	35p multicoloured	1·25	1·60	☐	☐
1881	**1206**	41p multicoloured	1·50	1·60	☐	☐
Set of 4			4·25	4·50	☐	☐
First Day Cover				4·75	☐	
Presentation Pack			5·00		☐	
PHQ Cards (*set of* 4)			6·00	11·50	☐	☐
Set of 4 Gutter Pairs			10·00		☐	

Nos. 1878/81 commemorate the centenary of publication of Wells's *The Time Machine*.

1207 The Swan, 1595

1208 The Rose, 1592

1209 The Globe, 1599

1210 The Hope, 1613

1211 The Globe, 1614

T **1207/11** were printed together, *se-tenant*, in horizontal strips of 5 throughout the sheet, the backgrounds forming a composite design.

Reconstruction of Shakespeare's Globe Theatre

1995 (8 Aug.) Two phosphor bands. Perf 14½

1882	**1207**	25p multicoloured	50	40	☐	☐
		a. Horiz strip of 5.				
		Nos. 1882/6	4·50	4·75	☐	☐
1883	**1208**	25p multicoloured	50	40	☐	☐
1884	**1209**	25p multicoloured	50	40	☐	☐
1885	**1210**	25p multicoloured	50	40	☐	☐
1886	**1211**	25p multicoloured	50	40	☐	☐
Set of 5			4·50	4·75	☐	☐
First Day Cover				5·50	☐	
Presentation Pack			5·00		☐	
PHQ Cards (*set of* 5)			6·00	11·50	☐	☐
Gutter Strip of 10			10·50		☐	

1212 Sir Rowland Hill and Uniform Penny Postage Petition

1213 Hill and Penny Black

1214 Guglielmo Marconi and Early Wireless

1215 Marconi and Sinking of *Titanic* (liner)

Pioneers of Communications

1995 (5 Sept.) One phosphor band (19p) or phosphorised paper (others). Perf 14½ × 14

1887	**1212**	19p silver, red and black	75	30	☐	☐
1888	**1213**	25p silver, brown and black	1·00	50	☐	☐
1889	**1214**	41p silver, grey-green and black	1·50	1·75	☐	☐
1890	**1215**	60p silver, deep ultramarine and black	1·75	2·25	☐	☐
Set of 4			4·50	4·50	☐	☐
First Day Cover				4·75	☐	
Presentation Pack			5·00		☐	
PHQ Cards (*set of* 4)			5·75	11·50	☐	☐
Set of 4 Gutter Pairs			11·00		☐	

Nos. 1887/8 mark the birth bicentenary of Sir Rowland Hill and Nos. 1889/90 the centenary of the first radio transmissions.

1216 Harold Wagstaff

1217 Gus Risman

1218 Jim Sullivan

1219 Billy Batten

1220 Brian Bevan

Centenary of Rugby League

1995 (3 Oct.) One phosphor band (19p) or two phosphor bands (others). Perf 14 × 14½

1891	**1216**	19p multicoloured	75	25	☐	☐
1892	**1217**	25p multicoloured	75	30	☐	☐
1893	**1218**	30p multicoloured	1·00	1·50	☐	☐
1894	**1219**	35p multicoloured	1·00	1·60	☐	☐
1895	**1220**	41p multicoloured	1·50	1·60	☐	☐
Set of 5			4·75	4·75	☐	☐
First Day Cover				4·75		☐
Presentation Pack			5·50		☐	
PHQ Cards (*set of* 5)			6·00	11·50	☐	☐
Set of 5 Gutter Pairs			11·00		☐	

1221 European Robin in Mouth of Pillar Box

1222 European Robin on Railings and Holly

1223 European Robin on Snow-covered Milk Bottles

1224 European Robin on Road Sign

1225 European Robin on Door Knob and Christmas Wreath

Christmas. Christmas Robins

1995 (30 Oct.) One phosphor band (19p) or two phosphor bands (others)

1896	**1221**	19p multicoloured	60	20	☐	☐
1897	**1222**	25p multicoloured	85	30	☐	☐
1898	**1223**	30p multicoloured	1·25	1·50	☐	☐
1899	**1224**	41p multicoloured	1·60	1·75	☐	☐
1900	**1225**	60p multicoloured	1·75	1·90	☐	☐
Set of 5			5·50	5·50	☐	☐
First Day Cover				5·50		☐
Presentation Pack			5·75		☐	
PHQ Cards (*set of* 5)			6·00	11·50	☐	☐
Set of 5 Gutter Pairs			12·00		☐	

The 19p value was re-issued on 3 October 2000 in sheets of 20 each with *se-tenant* label, in connection with 'customised' stamps available from the Philatelic Bureau. The labels show either Christmas greetings or a personal photograph.

Collectors Pack 1995

1995 (30 Oct.) Comprises Nos. 1848/1900

CP1900a	Collectors Pack	55·00	☐

Post Office Yearbook

1995 (30 Oct.) Comprises Nos. 1848/57 and 1868/1900 in hardback book with slip case

YB1900a	Yearbook	55·00	☐

1226 Opening Lines of 'To a Mouse' and Fieldmouse

1227 'O my Luve's like a red, red rose' and Wild Rose

1228 'Scots, wha hae wi Wallace bled' and Sir William Wallace

1229 'Auld Lang Syne' and Highland Dancers

Death Bicentenary of Robert Burns (Scottish poet)

1996 (25 Jan.) One phosphor band (19p) or two phosphor bands (others). Perf 14½

1901	**1226**	19p cream, bistre-brown and black	75	25	☐	☐
1902	**1227**	25p multicoloured	1·00	30	☐	☐
1903	**1228**	41p multicoloured	1·50	2·00	☐	☐
1904	**1229**	60p multicoloured	1·75	2·50	☐	☐
Set of 4			4·50	4·50	☐	☐
First Day Cover				4·75		☐
Presentation Pack			5·00		☐	
PHQ Cards (*set of* 4)			6·00	11·50	☐	☐
Set of 4 Gutter Pairs			10·50		☐	

1230 'MORE! LOVE' (Mel Calman)

1231 'Sincerely' (Charles Barsotti)

1232 'Do you have something for the HUMAN CONDITION? (Mel Calman)

1233 'MENTAL FLOSS' (Leo Cullum)

1234 '4.55 P.M.' (Charles Barsotti)

1235 'Dear lottery prize winner (Larry)

1236 'I'm writing to you because...' (Mel Calman)

1237 'FETCH THIS, FETCH THAT' (Charles Barsotti)

1238 'My day starts before I'm ready for it' (Mel Calman)

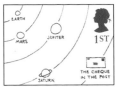

1239 'THE CHEQUE IN THE POST' (Jack Ziegler)

T **1230/9** were printed together, *se-tenant*, in booklet panes of 10 stamps and 20 half stamp size labels.

Greetings Stamps. Cartoons

1996 (26 Feb.–11 Nov.) 'All-over' phosphor. Perf 14½ × 14 (with one elliptical hole on each vertical side)

1905	**1230**	(1st) black and bright mauve	50	40	☐	☐
		a. Booklet pane. Nos. 1905/14	10·00		☐	
		p. Two phosphor bands	1·00	60	☐	☐
		pa. Booklet pane. Nos. 1905p/14p (11 Nov.)	38·00		☐	
1906	**1231**	(1st) black and blue-green	50	40	☐	☐
		p. Two phosphor bands	1·00	60	☐	☐
1907	**1232**	(1st) black and new blue	50	40	☐	☐
		p. Two phosphor bands	1·00	60	☐	☐
1908	**1233**	(1st) black and bright violet	50	40	☐	☐
		p. Two phosphor bands	1·00	60	☐	☐
1909	**1234**	(1st) black and vermilion	50	40	☐	☐
		p. Two phosphor bands	1·00	60	☐	☐
1910	**1235**	(1st) black and new blue	50	40	☐	☐
		p. Two phosphor bands	1·00	60	☐	☐
1911	**1236**	(1st) black and vermilion	50	40	☐	☐
		p. Two phosphor bands	1·00	60	☐	☐
1912	**1237**	(1st) black and bright violet	50	40	☐	☐
		p. Two phosphor bands	1·00	60	☐	☐
1913	**1238**	(1st) black and blue-green	50	40	☐	☐
		p. Two phosphor bands	1·00	60	☐	☐
1914	**1239**	(1st) black and bright mauve	50	40	☐	☐
		p. Two phosphor bands	1·00	60	☐	☐
Set of 10 (Nos. 1905/14)			10·00	11·00	☐	☐
Set of 10 (Nos. 1905p/14p)			38·00	36·00	☐	☐
First Day Cover (Nos. 1905/14)				11·00		☐
Presentation Pack (Nos. 1905/14)			16·00		☐	
PHQ Cards (*set of* 10)			16·00	30·00	☐	☐

Nos. 1905/14 were re-issued on 18 December 2001 in sheets of 10, each stamp with a *se-tenant* label showing cartoon titles. They were again issued on 29 July 2003 in sheets of 20 containing two of each design, each stamp accompanied by a half stamp size label showing a crossword grid or personal photograph. Such sheets are perforated without elliptical holes.

1240 'Muscovy Duck'

1241 'Lapwing'

1242 'White-fronted Goose'

1243 'Bittern'

1244 'Whooper Swan'

50th Anniversary of the Wildfowl and Wetlands Trust. Bird Paintings by C. F. Tunnicliffe

1996 (12 Mar.) One phosphor band (19p) or phosphorised paper (others). Perf 14 × 14½

1915	**1240**	19p multicoloured	70	25	☐	☐
1916	**1241**	25p multicoloured	90	30	☐	☐
1917	**1242**	30p multicoloured	1·00	1·25	☐	☐
1918	**1243**	35p multicoloured	1·10	1·50	☐	☐
1919	**1244**	41p multicoloured	1·50	1·60	☐	☐
Set of 5			4·75	4·50	☐	☐
First Day Cover				5·75		☐
Presentation Pack			5·00		☐	
PHQ Cards (*set of* 5)			6·00	11·50	☐	☐
Set of 5 Gutter Pairs			10·50		☐	

1245 The Odeon, Harrogate

1246 Laurence Olivier and Vivien Leigh in Lady Hamilton (film)

1247 Old Cinema Ticket

1248 Pathé News Still

1249 Cinema Sign, The Odeon, Manchester

Centenary of Cinema

1996 (16 Apr.) One phosphor band (19p) or two phosphor bands (others). Perf 14 × 14½

1920	**1245**	19p multicoloured	50	25	☐	☐
1921	**1246**	25p multicoloured	70	30	☐	☐
1922	**1247**	30p multicoloured	1·00	1·75	☐	☐
1923	**1248**	35p black, red and silver	1·25	2·00	☐	☐
1924	**1249**	41p multicoloured	1·50	2·25	☐	☐
Set of 5			4·75	4·75	☐	☐
First Day Cover				5·75		☐
Presentation Pack			5·50		☐	
PHQ Cards (*set of 5*)			6·00	11·50	☐	☐
Set of 5 Gutter Pairs			11·00		☐	

1250 Dixie Dean

1251 Bobby Moore

1252 Duncan Edwards

1253 Billy Wright

1254 Danny Blanchflower

European Football Championship

1996 (14 May) One phosphor band (19p) or two phosphor bands (others). Perf 14½ × 14

1925	**1250**	19p multicoloured	50	20	☐	☐
1926	**1251**	25p multicoloured	75	20	☐	☐
1927	**1252**	35p multicoloured	1·25	1·75	☐	☐
1928	**1253**	41p multicoloured	1·50	1·75	☐	☐
1929	**1254**	60p multicoloured	1·75	2·00	☐	☐
Set of 5			5·50	5·75	☐	☐
First Day Cover				5·75		☐
Presentation Pack			5·75		☐	
PHQ Cards (*set of 5*)			6·00	11·50	☐	☐
Set of 5 Gutter Pairs			12·00		☐	

1255 Athlete on Starting Blocks

1256 Throwing the Javelin

1257 Basketball

1258 Swimming

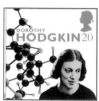

1259 Athlete celebrating and Olympic Rings

T **1255/9** were printed together, *se-tenant*, in horizontal strips of 5 throughout the sheet.

Olympic and Paralympic Games, Atlanta

1996 (9 July) Two phosphor bands. Perf 14½ × 14

1930	**1255**	26p multicoloured	50	40	☐	☐
		a. Horiz strip of 5.				
		Nos. 1930/4	4·50	4·50	☐	☐
1931	**1256**	26p multicoloured	50	40	☐	☐
1932	**1257**	26p multicoloured	50	40	☐	☐
1933	**1258**	26p multicoloured	50	40	☐	☐
1934	**1259**	26p multicoloured	50	40	☐	☐
Set of 5			4·50	4·50	☐	☐
First Day Cover				5·00		☐
Presentation Pack			4·50		☐	
PHQ Cards (*set of 5*)			6·00	11·50	☐	☐
Gutter Strip of 10			11·00		☐	

For these designs with the face value expressed as '1st' see **MS**2554.

1260 Prof. Dorothy Hodgkin (scientist)

1261 Dame Margot Fonteyn (ballerina)

1262 Dame Elisabeth Frink (sculptress)

1263 Dame Daphne du Maurier (novelist)

)**1264** Dame Marea Hartman (sports administrator)

Europa. Famous Women

1996 (6 Aug.) One phosphor band (20p) or two phosphor bands (others). Perf 14½

1935	**1260**	20p dull blue-green, brownish grey and black	60	25	☐	☐
1936	**1261**	26p dull mauve, brownish grey and black	75	25	☐	☐
1937	**1262**	31p bronze, brownish grey and black	1·10	1·10	☐	☐
1938	**1263**	37p silver, brownish grey and black	1·25	1·40	☐	☐
1939	**1264**	43p gold, brownish grey and black	1·50	1·50	☐	☐

Set of 5	4·75	4·50	☐ ☐
First Day Cover		5·00	☐
Presentation Pack	4·75		☐
PHQ Cards (*set of* 5)	6·00	11·50	☐ ☐
Set of 5 Gutter Pairs	12·00		☐

Nos. 1936/7 include the 'EUROPA' emblem.

1265 *Muffin the Mule*   **1266** *Sooty*

1267 *Stingray*   **1268** *The Clangers*

1269 *Dangermouse*

50th Anniversary of Children's Television

1996 (3 Sept.)–**97** One phosphor band (20p) or two phosphor bands (others). Perf 14½ × 14

1940	**1265**	20p multicoloured	55	20	☐	☐
		a. Perf 15 × 14 (23.9.97)	2·00	2·00	☐	☐
1941	**1266**	26p multicoloured	80	20	☐	☐
1942	**1267**	31p multicoloured	1·00	1·50	☐	☐
1943	**1268**	37p multicoloured	1·40	1·75	☐	☐
1944	**1269**	43p multicoloured	1·60	2·00	☐	☐

Set of 5	4·75	4·75	☐ ☐
First Day Cover		4·75	☐
Presentation Pack	4·75		☐
PHQ Cards (*set of* 5)	6·00	11·50	☐ ☐
Set of 5 Gutter Pairs	10·50		☐

No. 1940a comes from stamp booklets.

1270 Triumph TR3   **1271** MG TD

1272 Austin-Healey 100   **1273** Jaguar XK120

1274 Morgan Plus 4

Classic Sports Cars

1996 (1 Oct.) One phosphor band (20p) or two phosphor bands (others). Perf 14½

1945	**1270**	20p multicoloured	55	20	☐	☐
1946	**1271**	26p multicoloured	1·10	20	☐	☐
1947	**1272**	37p multicoloured	1·40	1·90	☐	☐
1948	**1273**	43p multicoloured	1·60	1·90	☐	☐
1949	**1274**	63p multicoloured	1·75	2·00	☐	☐

Set of 5	5·75	6·00	☐ ☐
First Day Cover		6·00	☐
Presentation Pack	6·00		☐
PHQ Cards (*set of* 5)	6·00	11·50	☐ ☐
Set of 5 Gutter Pairs	13·00		☐

1275 The Three Kings   **1276** The Annunciation

1277 The Journey to Bethlehem   **1278** The Nativity

1279 The Shepherds

Christmas

1996 (28 Oct.) One phosphor band (2nd) or two phosphor bands (others)

1950	**1275**	(2nd) multicoloured	75	20	☐	☐
1951	**1276**	(1st) multicoloured	1·00	35	☐	☐
1952	**1277**	31p multicoloured	1·25	1·75	☐	☐
1953	**1278**	43p multicoloured	1·25	1·75	☐	☐
1954	**1279**	63p multicoloured	1·50	2·00	☐	☐
Set of 5			5·50	5·50	☐	☐
First Day Cover				6·00		☐
Presentation Pack			5·75		☐	
PHQ Cards (*set of* 5)			6·00	11·50	☐	☐
Set of 5 Gutter Pairs			13·00		☐	

Collectors Pack 1996

1996 (28 Oct.) Comprises Nos. 1901/4 and 1915/54

CP1954a	Collectors Pack	60·00	☐

Post Office Yearbook

1996 (28 Oct.) Comprises Nos. 1901/4 and 1915/54 in hardback book with slip case

YB1954a	Yearbook	60·00	☐

1280 *Gentiana acaulis* (Georg Ehret)

1281 *Magnolia grandiflora* (Ehret)

1282 *Camellia japonica* (Alfred Chandler)

1283 *Tulipa* (Ehret)

1284 *Fuchsia* 'Princess of Wales' (Augusta Sowerby)

1285 *Tulipa gesneriana* (Ehret)

1286 *Gazania splendens* (Charlotte Sowerby)

1287 *Iris latifolia* (Ehret)

1288 *Hippeastrum rutilum* (Pierre-Joseph Redoute)

1289 *Passiflora coerulea* (Ehret)

T **1280/9** were printed together, *se-tenant*, in booklet panes of 10 stamps and 20 half stamp-size labels.

Greeting Stamps. 19th-century Flower Paintings

1997 (6 Jan.) Two phosphor bands. Perf 14½ × 14 (with one elliptical hole on each vertical side)

1955	**1280**	(1st) multicoloured	50	40	☐	☐
		a. Booklet pane.				
		Nos. 1955/64	11·00		☐	
1956	**1281**	(1st) multicoloured	50	40	☐	☐
1957	**1282**	(1st) multicoloured	50	40	☐	☐
1958	**1283**	(1st) multicoloured	50	40	☐	☐
1959	**1284**	(1st) multicoloured	50	40	☐	☐
1960	**1285**	(1st) multicoloured	50	40	☐	☐
1961	**1286**	(1st) multicoloured	50	40	☐	☐
1962	**1287**	(1st) multicoloured	50	40	☐	☐
1963	**1288**	(1st) multicoloured	50	40	☐	☐
1964	**1289**	(1st) multicoloured	50	40	☐	☐
Set of 10			11·00	11·00	☐	☐
First Day Cover				11·50		☐
Presentation Pack			16·00		☐	
PHQ Cards (*set of* 10)			16·00	30·00	☐	☐

Nos. 1955/64 were re-issued on 21 January 2003 in *se-tenant* sheets of 20, each accompanied by a label showing flowers or personal photograph. Such sheets are perforated without elliptical holes.

For Nos. 1955, 1958 and 1962 perf 15 × 14 see Nos. 2463/5.

1290 'King Henry VIII'

1291 'Catherine of Aragon'

1292 'Anne Boleyn'

1293 'Jane Seymour'

1294 'Anne of Cleves'

1295 'Catherine Howard'

1296 'Catherine Parr'

T **1290/6** were printed together, *se-tenant*, in horizontal strips of 6 throughout the sheet.

450th Death Anniversary of King Henry VIII

1997 (21 Jan.) Two phosphor bands. Perf 15 (No. 1965) or 14 × 15 (others)

1965	**1290**	26p multicoloured	50	40	☐	☐
1966	**1291**	26p multicoloured	50	40	☐	☐
		a. Horiz strip of 6.				
		Nos. 1966/71	8·00	8·50	☐	☐
1967	**1292**	26p multicoloured	50	40	☐	☐
1968	**1293**	26p multicoloured	50	40	☐	☐
1969	**1294**	26p multicoloured	50	40	☐	☐
1970	**1295**	26p multicoloured	50	40	☐	☐
1971	**1296**	26p multicoloured	50	40	☐	☐
Set of 7			8·00	8·50	☐	☐
First Day Cover				9·50		☐
Presentation Pack			10·00		☐	
PHQ Cards (*set of* 7)			10·00	18·00	☐	☐
Gutter Pair and Gutter Block of 12			17·00		☐	

1297 St. Columba in Boat

1298 St. Columba on Iona

1299 St. Augustine with King Ethelbert

1300 St. Augustine with Model of Cathedral

Religious Anniversaries

1997 (11 Mar.) Two phosphor bands. Perf 14½

1972	**1297**	26p multicoloured	75	35	☐	☐
1973	**1298**	37p multicoloured	1·10	1·50	☐	☐
1974	**1299**	43p multicoloured	1·50	1·50	☐	☐
1975	**1300**	63p multicoloured	2·00	2·10	☐	☐
Set of 4			4·75	5·00	☐	☐
First Day Cover				5·75		☐
Presentation Pack			5·25		☐	
PHQ Cards (*set of* 4)			5·75	11·50	☐	☐
Set of 4 Gutter Pairs			11·50		☐	

Nos. 1972/3 commemorate the 1400th death anniversary of St Columba and Nos. 1974/5 the 1400th anniversary of the arrival of St Augustine of Canterbury in Kent.

1301

1302

Self-adhesive Coil Stamps

1997 (18 Mar.) Photo Enschedé. One centre phosphor band (2nd) or two phosphor bands (1st). Perf 14 × 15 die-cut (with one elliptical hole on each vertical side)

1976	**1301**	(2nd) bright blue	2·75	2·50	☐	☐
1977	**1302**	(1st) bright orange-red	2·75	2·75	☐	☐
Set of 2			5·00	4·75	☐	☐
First Day Cover				5·50		☐
Presentation Pack			7·00		☐	

Nos. 1976/7, which were priced at 20p and 26p, were each sold in rolls of 100 with the stamps separate on the backing paper.

> Machin stamps printed in gold were issued on 21 April 1997 for the Royal Golden Wedding. These are listed as definitives under Nos. 1668 (1st) and Y1686 26p.

1303 *Dracula*

1304 *Frankenstein*

1305 *Dr Jekyll and Mr Hyde*

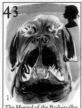

1306 *The Hound of the Baskervilles*

Europa. Tales and Legends. Horror Stories

1997 (13 May) Two phosphor bands. Perf 14 × 15

1980	**1303**	26p multicoloured	1·00	40	☐ ☐
1981	**1304**	31p multicoloured	1·10	1·50	☐ ☐
1982	**1305**	37p multicoloured	1·30	1·75	☐ ☐
1983	**1306**	43p multicoloured	2·00	1·95	☐ ☐
Set of 4			5·00	5·50	☐ ☐
First Day Cover				5·50	☐
Presentation Pack			5·25		☐
PHQ Cards (*set of* 4)			5·75	11·50	☐ ☐
Set of 4 Gutter Pairs			12·00		☐

Nos. 1980/3 commemorate the birth bicentenary of Mary Shelley (creator of Frankenstein) with the 26p and 31p values incorporating the 'EUROPA' emblem.

1307 Reginald Mitchell and Supermarine Spitfire MkIIA

1308 Roy Chadwick and Avro Lancaster MkI

1309 Ronald Bishop and de Havilland Mosquito B MkXVI

1310 George Carter and Gloster Meteor T Mk7

1311 Sir Sidney Camm and Hawker Hunter FGA Mk9

British Aircraft Designers

1997 (10 June) One phosphor band (20p) or two phosphor bands (others)

1984	**1307**	20p multicoloured	75	40	☐ ☐
1985	**1308**	26p multicoloured	1·10	1·25	☐ ☐
1986	**1309**	37p multicoloured	1·40	1·25	☐ ☐
1987	**1310**	43p multicoloured	1·50	1·60	☐ ☐
1988	**1311**	63p multicoloured	2·00	2·00	☐ ☐
Set of 5			6·00	6·50	☐ ☐
First Day Cover				6·50	☐

Presentation Pack		6·50	☐
PHQ Cards		6·00	13·00	☐ ☐
Set of 5 Gutter Pairs		15·00	☐

1312 Carriage Horse and Coachman

1313 Lifeguards Horse and Trooper

1314 Household Cavalry Drum Horse and Drummer

1315 Duke of Edinburgh's Horse and Groom

'All The Queen's Horses'. 50th Anniv of the British Horse Society

1997 (8 July) One phosphor band (20p) or two phosphor bands (others). Perf 14½

1989	**1312**	20p multicoloured	80	45	☐ ☐
1990	**1313**	26p multicoloured	1·10	1·50	☐ ☐
1991	**1314**	43p multicoloured	1·50	1·50	☐ ☐
1992	**1315**	63p multicoloured	2·00	2·00	☐ ☐
Set of 4			5·00	5·25	☐ ☐
First Day Cover				5·75	☐
Presentation Pack			5·50		☐
PHQ Cards (*set of* 4)			5·75	11·50	☐ ☐
Set of 4 Gutter Pairs			12·00		☐

CASTLE

Harrison printing (Nos. 1611/14)

CASTLE

Enschedé printing (Nos. 1993/6)

Differences between Harrison and Enschedé printings:

Harrison – 'C' has top serif and tail of letter points to right. 'A' has flat top. 'S' has top and bottom serifs.

Enschedé – 'C' has no top serif and tail of letter points upwards. 'A' has pointed top. 'S' has no serifs.

1997 (29 July) Designs as Nos. 1611/14 with Queen's head in silhouette as T 1044, but re-engraved as above. Perf 15 × 14 (with one elliptical hole on each vertical side)

1993	**880**	£1·50 deep claret and gold†	12·00	6·00	☐ ☐
1994	**881**	£2 indigo and gold†	14·00	2·25	☐ ☐
1995	**1044**	£3 violet and gold†	30·00	3·50	☐ ☐
1996	**882**	£5 deep brown and gold†	36·00	10·00	☐ ☐
Set of 4			75·00	18·00	☐ ☐
Set of 4 Gutter Pairs			£175		☐
Presentation Pack (P.O Pack No. 40)			£150		☐

† The Queen's head on these stamps is printed in optically variable ink which changes colour from gold to green when viewed from different angles.

1316 Haroldswick, Shetland

1317 Painswick, Gloucestershire

Enid Blyton's *Malory Towers*
1324 *Malory Towers*

1318 Beddgelert, Gwynedd

1319 Ballyroney, County Down

Sub-Post Offices

1997 (12 Aug.) One phosphor band (20p) or two phosphor bands (others). Perf 14½

1997	**1316**	20p multicoloured	75	50	☐	☐
1998	**1317**	26p multicoloured	1·00	1·00	☐	☐
1999	**1318**	43p multicoloured	1·50	1·50	☐	☐
2000	**1319**	63p multicoloured	2·25	2·25	☐	☐
Set of 4			5·50	5·00	☐	☐
First Day Cover				5·75		☐
Presentation Pack			5·00		☐	
PHQ Cards (*set of* 4)			5·75	11·50	☐	☐
Set of 4 Gutter Pairs			12·00		☐	

Nos. 1997/2000 also mark the centenary of the National Federation of Sub-Postmasters.

Enid Blyton's *Noddy*
1320 *Noddy*

Enid Blyton's *Famous Five*
1321 *Famous Five*

Enid Blyton's *Secret Seven*
1322 *Secret Seven*

Enid Blyton's *Faraway Tree*
1323 *Faraway Tree*

Birth Centenary of Enid Blyton (children's author)

1997 (9 Sept.) One phosphor band (20p) or two phosphor bands (others). Perf 14 × 14½

2001	**1320**	20p multicoloured	50	45	☐	☐
2002	**1321**	26p multicoloured	1·00	1·25	☐	☐
2003	**1322**	37p multicoloured	1·25	1·25	☐	☐
2004	**1323**	43p multicoloured	1·50	2·00	☐	☐
2005	**1324**	63p multicoloured	1·75	2·00	☐	☐
Set of 5			5·50	6·00	☐	☐
First Day Cover				6·00		☐
Presentation Pack			5·75		☐	
PHQ Cards (*set of* 5)			6·00	13·00	☐	☐
Set of 5 Gutter Pairs			12·00		☐	

1325 Children and Father Christmas pulling Cracker

1326 Father Christmas with Traditional Cracker

1327 Father Christmas riding Cracker

1328 Father Christmas on Snowball

1329 Father Christmas and Chimney

Christmas. 150th Anniversary of the Christmas Cracker

1997 (27 Oct.) One phosphor band (2nd) or two phosphor bands (others)

2006	**1325**	(2nd) multicoloured	75	20	☐	☐
2007	**1326**	(1st) multicoloured	90	30	☐	☐
2008	**1327**	31p multicoloured	1·00	1·50	☐	☐
2009	**1328**	43p multicoloured	1·25	1·75	☐	☐
2010	**1329**	63p multicoloured	1·60	2·00	☐	☐
Set of 5			5·50	5·00	☐	☐
First Day Cover				6·00		☐

Presentation Pack		5·75	☐
PHQ Cards (*set of 5*)		6·00 13·00	☐ ☐
Set of 5 Gutter Pairs		12·00	☐

The 1st value was re-issued on 3 October 2000, in sheets of 10 in photogravure, each stamp with a *se-tenant* label, in connection with 'customised' service available from the Philatelic Bureau. On 1 October 2002 in sheet size of 20 in lithography the 1st value was again issued but perforated 14½ × 14. The labels show either Christmas greetings or a personal photograph.

1330 Wedding Photograph, 1947

1331 Queen Elizabeth II and Prince Philip, 1997

Royal Golden Wedding

1997 (13 Nov.) One phosphor band (20p) or two phosphor bands (others). Perf 15

2011	**1330**	20p gold, yellow-brown and grey-black	85	45	☐	☐
2012	**1331**	26p multicoloured	1·10	70	☐	☐
2013	**1330**	43p gold, bluish green and grey-black	1·90	2·25	☐	☐
2014	**1331**	63p multicoloured	2·50	3·00	☐	☐
Set of 4			5·75	5·75	☐	☐
First Day Cover				8·25	☐	
Presentation Pack			6·25		☐	
Souvenir Book (contains Nos. 1668, 1989/92 and 2011/14)			50·00		☐	
PHQ Cards (*set of* 4)			5·75	11·50	☐	☐
Set of 4 Gutter Pairs			12·00		☐	

Collectors Pack 1997

1997 (13 Nov.) Comprises Nos. 1965/75, 1980/92 and 1997/2014

CP2014a	Collectors Pack	65·00	☐

Post Office Yearbook

1997 (13 Nov.) Comprises Nos. 1965/75, 1980/92 and 1997/2014 in hardback book with slip case

YB2014a	Yearbook	65·00	☐

1332 Common Doormouse

1333 Lady's Slipper Orchid

1334 Song Thrush

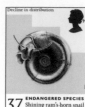
1335 Shining Ram's-horn Snail

1336 Mole Cricket

1337 Devil's Bolete

Endangered Species

1998 (20 Jan.) One side phosphor band (20p) or two phosphor bands (others). Perf 14 × 14½

2015	**1332**	20p multicoloured	60	40	☐	☐
2016	**1333**	26p multicoloured	75	40	☐	☐
2017	**1334**	31p multicoloured	1·00	2·00	☐	☐
2018	**1335**	37p multicoloured	1·25	1·25	☐	☐
2019	**1336**	43p multicoloured	1·40	1·75	☐	☐
2020	**1337**	63p multicoloured	1·90	2·25	☐	☐
Set of 6			6·25	6·50	☐	☐
First Day Cover				6·50	☐	
Presentation Pack			6·75		☐	
PHQ Cards (*Set of* 6)			6·00	14·00	☐	☐
Set of 6 Gutter Pairs			15·00		☐	

1338 Diana, Princess of Wales (photo by Lord Snowdon)

1339 At British Lung Foundation Function, April 1997 (photo by John Stillwell)

1340 Wearing Tiara, 1991 (photo by Lord Snowdon)

1341 On Visit to Birmingham, October 1995 (photo by Tim Graham)

1342 In Evening Dress, 1987 (photo by Terence Donovan)

T **1338/42** were printed together, *se-tenant*, in horizontal strips of 5 throughout the sheet.

Diana, Princess of Wales Commemoration

1998 (3 Feb.) Two phosphor bands

2021	**1338**	26p multicoloured	50	40	□	□
		a. Horiz strip of 5.				
		Nos. 2021/5	4·50	4·50	□	□
2022	**1339**	26p multicoloured	50	40	□	□
2023	**1340**	26p multicoloured	50	40	□	□
2024	**1341**	26p multicoloured	50	40	□	□
2025	**1342**	26p multicoloured	50	40	□	□
Set of 5			4·50	4·50	□	□
First Day Cover				5·50		□
Presentation Pack			16·00			□
Presentation Pack (Welsh)			£150			□
Gutter Strip of 10			10·00			□

1343 Lion of England and Griffin of Edward III

1344 Falcon of Plantagenet and Bull of Clarence

1345 Lion of Mortimer and Yale of Beaufort

1346 Greyhound of Richmond and Dragon of Wales

1347 Unicorn of Scotland and Horse of Hanover

T **1343/7** were printed together, *se-tenant*, in horizontal strips of 5 throughout the sheet.

650th Anniversary of the Order of the Garter. The Queen's Beasts

1998 (24 Feb.) Two phosphor bands

2026	**1343**	26p multicoloured	90	90	□	□
		a. Horiz strip of 5.				
		Nos. 2026/30	4·50	4·50	□	□
2027	**1344**	26p multicoloured	90	90	□	□
2028	**1345**	26p multicoloured	90	90	□	□

2029	**1346**	26p multicoloured	90	90	□	□
2030	**1347**	26p multicoloured	90	90	□	□
Set of 5			4·00	4·00	□	□
First Day Cover				5·25		□
Presentation Pack			5·00			□
PHQ Cards (set of 5)			6·00	13·00	□	□
Gutter Block of 10			10·00			□

The phosphor bands on Nos. 2026/30 are only half the height of the stamps and do not cover the silver parts of the designs.

1348

Booklet Stamps

1998 (10 Mar.) Design as T **157** (issued 1952–54), but with face values in decimal currency as T **1348**. One side phosphor band (20p) or two phosphor bands (others). Perf 14 (with one elliptical hole on each vertical side)

2031	**1348**	20p light green	70	75	□	□
2032		26p red-brown	90	95	□	□
2033		37p light purple	2·75	2·75	□	□
Set of 3			4·00	4·00	□	□

For further Wilding designs see Nos. 2258/9, **MS**2326, **MS**2367 and 2378/80.

1349 St. John's Point Lighthouse, County Down

1350 Smalls Lighthouse, Pembrokeshire

1351 Needles Rock Lighthouse, Isle of Wight, c 1900

1352 Bell Rock Lighthouse, Arbroath, mid-19th-century

1353 Eddystone Lighthouse, Plymouth, 1698

Lighthouses

1998 (24 Mar.) One side phosphor band (20p) or two phosphor bands (others). Perf 14½ × 14

2034 **1349**	20p multicoloured	50	40	☐	☐
2035 **1350**	26p multicoloured	75	50	☐	☐
2036 **1351**	37p multicoloured	1·10	1·50	☐	☐
2037 **1352**	43p multicoloured	1·50	1·75	☐	☐
2038 **1353**	63p multicoloured	2·10	2·50	☐	☐
Set of 5		5·50	6·00	☐	☐
First Day Cover			6·00		☐
Presentation Pack		6·00		☐	
PHQ Cards (*set of 5*)		6·00	13·00	☐	☐
Set of 5 Gutter Pairs		13·50		☐	

Nos. 2034/8 commemorate the 300th anniversary of the first Eddystone Lighthouse and the final year of manned lighthouses.

Self-adhesive stamps

1998 (6 Apr.) Photo Enschedé, Questa or Walsall. Designs as T 913/14. One centre phosphor band (2nd) or two phosphor bands (1st). Perf 15 × 14 die-cut (with one elliptical hole on each vertical side)

2039	(2nd) bright blue	1·00	1·00	☐	☐
	b. Perf 14½ × 14 die-cut	£150		☐	☐
2040	(1st) bright orange-red	1·50	1·50	☐	☐
	b. Perf 14½ × 14 die-cut	£150		☐	☐
Set of 2		2·50	2·50	☐	☐

Nos. 2039/40 were initially priced at 20p and 26p, and were available in coils of 200 (Enschedé), sheets of 100 (Enschedé, Questa or Walsall) or self-adhesive booklets (Questa or Walsall).
See also Nos. 2295/8.

1354 Tommy Cooper

1355 Eric Morecambe

1356 Joyce Grenfell

1357 Les Dawson

1358 Peter Cook

Comedians

1998 (23 Apr.) One phosphor band (20p) or two phosphor bands (others). Perf 14½ × 14

2041 **1354**	20p multicoloured	50	50	☐	☐
2042 **1355**	26p multicoloured	75	85	☐	☐
2043 **1356**	37p multicoloured	1·25	1·25	☐	☐
2044 **1357**	43p multicoloured	1·50	1·50	☐	☐

2045 **1358**	63p multicoloured	1·75	2·10	☐	☐
Set of 5		5·25	5·50	☐	☐
First Day Cover			6·00		☐
Presentation Pack		6·00		☐	
PHQ Cards (*set of 5*)		6·00	13·00	☐	☐
Set of 5 Gutter Pairs		13·50		☐	

1359 Hands forming Heart

1360 Adult and Child holding Hands

1361 Hands forming Cradle

1362 Hands taking Pulse

50th Anniversary of National Health Service

1998 (23 June) One side phosphor band (20p) or two phosphor bands (others). Perf 14 × 14½

2046 **1359**	20p multicoloured	50	50	☐	☐
2047 **1360**	26p multicoloured	90	90	☐	☐
2048 **1361**	43p multicoloured	1·50	1·50	☐	☐
2049 **1362**	63p multicoloured	2·10	2·10	☐	☐
Set of 4		4·50	4·50	☐	☐
First Day Cover			5·75		☐
Presentation Pack		5·50		☐	
PHQ Cards (*set of 4*)		5·75	11·50	☐	☐
Set of 4 Gutter Pairs		11·00		☐	

1363 *The Hobbit* (J.R.R. Tolkien)

1364 *The Lion, The Witch and the Wardrobe* (C. S. Lewis)

1365 *The Phoenix and the Carpet* (E. Nesbit)

1366 *The Borrowers* (Mary Norton)

1367 *Through the Looking Glass* (Lewis Carroll)

Famous Children's Fantasy Novels

1998 (21 July) One phosphor band (20p) or two phosphor bands (others)

2050	**1363**	20p multicoloured	50	45	☐	☐
2051	**1364**	26p multicoloured	75	55	☐	☐
2052	**1365**	37p multicoloured	1·25	1·50	☐	☐
2053	**1366**	43p multicoloured	1·50	1·50	☐	☐
2054	**1367**	63p multicoloured	2·10	2·00	☐	☐
Set of 5			5·75	5·75	☐	☐
First Day Cover				5·75		☐
Presentation Pack			6·00		☐	
PHQ Cards (*set of* 5)			6·00	13·00	☐	☐
Set of 5 Gutter Pairs			13·00		☐	

Nos. 2050/4 commemorate the birth centenary of C. S. Lewis and the death centenary of Lewis Carroll.

1368 Woman in Yellow Feathered Costume

1369 Woman in Blue Costume and Headdress

1370 Group of Children in White and Gold Robes

1371 Child in 'Tree' Costume

Europa. Festivals. Notting Hill Carnival

1998 (25 Aug.) One centre phosphor band (20p) or two phosphor bands (others). Perf 14 × 14½

2055	**1368**	20p multicoloured	75	45	☐	☐
2056	**1369**	26p multicoloured	95	55	☐	☐
2057	**1370**	43p multicoloured	1·50	2·00	☐	☐
2058	**1371**	63p multicoloured	2·00	2·75	☐	☐
Set of 4			4·75	4·75	☐	☐
First Day Cover				5·75		☐
Presentation Pack			5·25		☐	
PHQ Cards (*set of* 4)			5·75	11·50	☐	☐
Set of 4 Gutter Pairs			12·50		☐	

Nos. 2055/6 include the 'EUROPA' emblem.

1372 Sir Malcolm Campbell's *Bluebird*, 1925

1373 Sir Henry Segrave's *Sunbeam*, 1926

1374 John G. Parry Thomas's *Babs*, 1926

1375 John R. Cobb's *Railton Mobil Special*, 1947

1376 Donald Campbell's *Bluebird CN7*, 1964

British Land Speed Record Holders

1998 (29 Sept.–13 Oct.) One phosphor band (20p) or two phosphor bands (others). Perf 15 × 14

2059	**1372**	20p multicoloured (centre band)	50	25	☐	☐
		a. Perf 14½ × 13½ (side band) (13 Oct.)	1·40	1·20	☐	☐
2060	**1373**	26p multicoloured	75	30	☐	☐
2061	**1374**	30p multicoloured	1·25	1·50	☐	☐
2062	**1375**	43p multicoloured	1·50	1·60	☐	☐
2063	**1376**	63p multicoloured	2·00	2·40	☐	☐
Set of 5			5·50	5·50	☐	☐
First Day Cover				6·00		☐
Presentation Pack			6·25		☐	
PHQ Cards (*set of* 5)			6·00	13·00	☐	☐
Set of 5 Gutter Pairs			13·00		☐	

No. 2059a, which occurs with the phosphor band at the left or right of the stamp, comes from stamp booklets. There are minor differences of design between No. 2059 and No. 2059a, which also omits the copyright symbol and date.

Nos. 2059/63 commemorate the 50th death anniversary of Sir Malcolm Campbell.

1377 Angel with Hands raised in Blessing

1378 Angel praying

1379 Angel playing Flute

1380 Angel playing Lute

1381 Angel praying

Christmas. Angels

1998 (2 Nov.) One phosphor band (20p) or two phosphor bands (others)

2064	**1377**	20p multicoloured	50	50	☐ ☐
2065	**1378**	26p multicoloured	75	60	☐ ☐
2066	**1379**	30p multicoloured	1·25	1·50	☐ ☐
2067	**1380**	43p multicoloured	1·50	1·60	☐ ☐
2068	**1381**	63p multicoloured	2·00	2·25	☐ ☐
Set of 5			5·75	5·75	☐ ☐
First Day Cover				6·00	☐
Presentation Pack			6·50		☐
PHQ Cards (*set of* 5)			6·00	13·00	☐ ☐
Set of 5 Gutter Pairs			13·00		☐

Collectors Pack 1998

1998 (2 Nov.) Comprises Nos. 2015/30, 2034/8 and 2041/68

CP2068a	Collectors Pack	95·00	☐

Post Office Yearbook

1998 (2 Nov.) Comprises Nos. 2015/30, 2034/8 and 2041/68 in hardback book with slip case

YB2068a	Yearbook	85·00	☐

1382 Greenwich Meridian and Clock (John Harrison's Chronometer)

1383 Industrial Worker and Blast Furnace (James Watt's discovery of steam power)

1384 Early Photos of Leaves (Henry Fox-Talbot's photographic experiments)

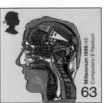

1385 Computer inside Human Head (Alan Turing's work on computers)

Millennium Series. The Inventors' Tale

1999 (12 Jan.–21 Sept.) One centre phosphor band (20p) or two phosphor bands (others). Perf 14 × 14½

2069	**1382**	20p multicoloured	75	70	☐ ☐
2070	**1383**	26p multicoloured	95	1·00	☐ ☐
2071	**1384**	43p multicoloured	1·50	1·60	☐ ☐
2072	**1385**	63p multicoloured	2·25	2·40	☐ ☐
		a. Perf 13½ × 14			
		(21 Sept.)	3·50	3·50	☐ ☐
Set of 4			5·25	5·25	☐ ☐
First Day Cover				14·00	☐
Presentation Pack			7·50		☐
PHQ Cards (*set of* 4)			8·50	13·00	☐ ☐
Set of 4 Gutter Pairs			13·00		☐

1386 Airliner hugging Globe (International air travel)

1387 Woman on Bicycle (Development of the bicycle)

1388 Victorian Railway Station (Growth of public transport)

1389 Captain Cook and Maori (Captain James Cook's voyages)

Millennium Series. The Travellers' Tale

1999 (2 Feb.) One centre phosphor band (20p) or two phosphor bands (others). Perf 14 × 14½

2073	**1386**	20p multicoloured	75	70	☐ ☐
2074	**1387**	26p multicoloured	95	1·00	☐ ☐
2075	**1388**	43p grey-black, stone and bronze	1·50	1·60	☐ ☐
2076	**1389**	63p multicoloured	2·25	2·40	☐ ☐
Set of 4			5·25	5·25	☐ ☐
First Day Cover				8·00	☐
Presentation Pack			7·50		☐
PHQ Cards (*set of* 4)			8·50	13·00	☐ ☐
Set of 4 Gutter Pairs			13·00		☐

1390

1999 (16 Feb.)

(a) Embossed and litho Walsall. Self-adhesive.
Die-cut perf 14 × 15

2077	**1390**	(1st) grey (face value) (Queen's head in colourless relief) (phosphor background around head)	3·00	2·50	☐	☐

(b) Recess Enschedé. Perf 14 × 14½

2078	**1390**	(1st) grey-black (2 phosphor bands)	3·00	2·50	☐	☐

(c) Typo Harrison. Perf 14 × 15

2079	**1390**	(1st) black (2 phosphor bands)	3·00	2·50	☐	☐
Set of 3			8·00	7·00	☐	☐

Nos. 2077/9 were only issued in £7·54 stamp booklets.

1391 Vaccinating Child (pattern in cow markings) (Jenner's development of smallpox vaccine)

1392 Patient on Trolley (nursing care)

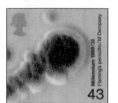

1393 Penicillin Mould (Fleming's discovery of Penicillin)

1394 Sculpture of Test-tube Baby (development of in vitro fertilization)

Millennium Series. The Patients' Tale

1999 (2 Mar.) One centre phosphor band (20p) or two phosphor bands (others). Perf 13½ × 14

2080	**1391**	20p multicoloured	75	70	☐	☐
2081	**1392**	26p multicoloured	95	1·00	☐	☐
2082	**1393**	43p multicoloured	1·50	1·60	☐	☐
2083	**1394**	63p multicoloured	2·25	2·40	☐	☐
Set of 4			5·25	5·25	☐	☐
First Day Cover				8·00		☐
Presentation Pack			7·50		☐	
PHQ Cards (*set of* 4)			8·50	13·00	☐	☐
Set of 4 Gutter Pairs			13·00		☐	

1395 Dove and Norman Settler (medieval migration to Scotland)

1396 Pilgrim Fathers and Red Indian (17th-century migration to America)

1397 Sailing Ship and Aspects of Settlement (19th-century migration to Australia)

1398 Hummingbird and Superimposed Stylised Face (20th-century migration to Great Britain)

Millennium Series. The Settlers' Tale

1999 (6 Apr.) One centre phosphor band (20p) or two phosphor bands (others). Perf 14 × 14½

2084	**1395**	20p multicoloured	75	70	☐	☐
2085	**1396**	26p multicoloured	95	1·00	☐	☐
2086	**1397**	43p multicoloured	2·00	1·75	☐	☐
2087	**1398**	63p multicoloured	3·00	3·00	☐	☐
Set of 4			5·75	5·75	☐	☐
First Day Cover				8·00		☐
Presentation Pack			7·50		☐	
PHQ Cards (*set of* 4)			8·50	13·00	☐	☐
Set of 4 Gutter Pairs			13·00		☐	

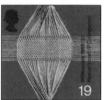

1399 Woven Threads (wollen industry)

1400 Salts Mill, Saltaire (worsted cloth industry)

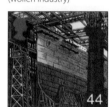

1401 Hull on Slipway (shipbuilding)

1402 Lloyd's Building (City of London finance centre)

Millennium Series. The Workers' Tale

1999 (4 May) One centre phosphor band (19p) or two phosphor bands (others). Perf 14 × 14½

2088	**1399**	19p multicoloured	75	70	☐	☐
2089	**1400**	26p multicoloured	95	1·00	☐	☐
2090	**1401**	44p multicoloured	1·75	1·60	☐	☐
2091	**1402**	64p multicoloured	2·25	2·40	☐	☐
Set of 4			5·25	5·25	☐	☐
First Day Cover				8·00		☐
Presentation Pack			7·50		☐	
PHQ Cards (*set of* 4)			8·50	13·00	☐	☐
Set of 4 Gutter Pairs			13·00		☐	

1403 Freddie Mercury
(lead singer of Queen)
('Popular Music')

1404 Bobby Moore with
World Cup, 1966 ('Sport')

1411 Generations of School
Children ('Right to Education')

1412 'MAGNA CARTA'
('Human Rights')

Millennium Series. The Citizens' Tale

1999 (6 July) One centre phosphor band (19p) or two
phosphor bands (others). Perf 14 × 14½

2098	**1409**	19p multicoloured	75	70	☐	☐
2099	**1410**	26p multicoloured	95	1·00	☐	☐
2100	**1411**	44p multicoloured	1·75	1·60	☐	☐
2101	**1412**	64p multicoloured	2·50	2·40	☐	☐
Set of 4			5·75	5·25	☐	
First Day Cover				8·00	☐	
Presentation Pack			7·50		☐	
PHQ Cards (*set of* 4)			8·50	13·00	☐	☐
Set of 4 Gutter Pairs			13·00		☐	

1405 Dalek from *Dr Who*
(science-fiction series)
('Television')

1406 Charlie Chaplin
(film star) ('Cinema')

Millennium Series. The Entertainers' Tale

1999 (1 June) One centre phosphor band (19p) or two
phosphor bands (others). Perf 14 × 14½

2092	**1403**	19p multicoloured	75	70	☐	☐
2093	**1404**	26p multicoloured	95	1·00	☐	☐
2094	**1405**	44p multicoloured	1·50	1·60	☐	☐
2095	**1406**	64p multicoloured	2·25	2·40	☐	☐
Set of 4			5·25	5·25	☐	☐
First Day Cover				8·00	☐	
Presentation Pack			7·50		☐	
PHQ Cards (*set of* 4)			8·50	13·00	☐	☐
Set of 4 Gutter Pairs			13·00		☐	

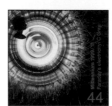

1413 Molecular Structures
('DNA decoding')

1414 Galapagos Finch and
Fossilized Skeleton ('Darwin's
theory of evolution')

1407 Prince Edward and
Miss Sophie Rhys-Jones (from
photos by John Swannell)

1408 Prince Edward and
Miss Sophie Rhys-Jones (from
photos by John Swannell)

Royal Wedding

1999 (15 June) Two phosphor bands

2096	**1407**	26p multicoloured	85	85	☐	☐
2097	**1408**	64p multicoloured	2·50	2·50	☐	☐
Set of 2			3·00	3·00	☐	☐
First Day Cover				4·75	☐	
Presentation Pack			4·00		☐	
PHQ Cards (*set of* 2)			8·50	6·75	☐	☐
Set of 2 Gutter Pairs			7·00		☐	

1415 Rotation of Polarized
Light by Magnetism
(Faraday's work on electricity)

1416 Saturn (development
of astronomical telescopes)

Millennium Series. The Scientists' Tale

1999 (3 Aug.–21 Sept.) One centre phosphor band (19p) or
two phosphor bands (others). Perf 13½ × 14 (19p, 64p) or
14 × 14½ (26p, 44p)

2102	**1413**	19p multicoloured	75	70	☐	☐
2103	**1414**	26p multicoloured	1·50	1·00	☐	☐
		b. Perf 14½ × 14				
		(21 Sept.)	2·50	2·50	☐	☐
2104	**1415**	44p multicoloured	1·50	1·60	☐	☐
		a. Perf 14½ × 14				
		(21 Sept.)	2·75	2·75	☐	☐
2105	**1416**	64p multicoloured	2·25	2·40	☐	☐
Set of 4			5·25	5·25	☐	☐
First Day Cover				8·00	☐	
Presentation Pack			7·50		☐	
PHQ Cards (*set of* 4)			8·50	13·00	☐	☐
Set of 4 Gutter Pairs			13·00		☐	

Nos. 2103b and 2104a come from stamp booklets.

1409 Suffragette behind
Prison Window ('Equal
Rights for Women')

1410 Water Tap
('Right to Health')

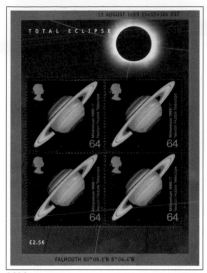

1416a

Solar Eclipse

1999 (11 Aug.) Sheet 89 × 121 mm. Two phosphor bands. Perf 14 × 14½

MS2106 1416a 64p × 4 multicoloured	22·00	22·00	☐	☐
First Day Cover		22·00	☐	

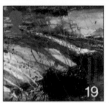 

1417 Upland Landscape (Strip farming)

1418 Horse-drawn Rotary Seed Drill (Mechanical farming)

 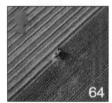

1419 Man peeling Potato (Food imports)

1420 Aerial View of Combine Harvester (Satellite agriculture)

Millennium Series. The Farmers' Tale

1999 (7 Sept.) One centre phosphor band (19p) or two phosphor bands (others). Perf 14 × 14½

2107	**1417**	19p multicoloured	75	70	☐	☐
2108	**1418**	26p multicoloured	95	1·00	☐	☐
2109	**1419**	44p multicoloured	2·00	1·60	☐	☐
2110	**1420**	64p multicoloured	2·50	2·40	☐	☐
Set of 4			5·75	5·25	☐	☐
First Day Cover				8·00		☐
Presentation Pack			7·50		☐	
PHQ Cards (*set of* 4)			8·50	13·00	☐	☐
Set of 4 Gutter Pairs			13·00		☐	

No. 2107 includes the 'EUROPA' emblem.

1421 Robert the Bruce (Battle of Bannockburn, 1314)

1422 Cavalier and Horse (English Civil War)

1423 War Graves Cemetery, The Somme (World Wars)

1424 Soldiers with Boy (Peace-keeping)

Millennium Series. The Soldiers' Tale

1999 (5 Oct.) One centre phosphor band (19p) or two phosphor bands (others). Perf 14 × 14½

2111	**1421**	19p black, stone and silver	75	70	☐	☐
2112	**1422**	26p multicoloured	95	1·00	☐	☐
2113	**1423**	44p grey-black, black and silver	2·00	1·60	☐	☐
2114	**1424**	64p multicoloured	2·50	2·40	☐	☐
Set of 4			5·75	5·25	☐	☐
First Day Cover				8·00		☐
Presentation Pack			7·50		☐	
PHQ Cards (*set of* 4)			8·50	13·00	☐	☐
Set of 4 Gutter Pairs			13·00		☐	

1425 'Hark the herald angels sing' and Hymn book (John Wesley)

1426 King James I and Bible (Authorised Version of Bible)

1427 St. Andrews Cathedral, Fife ('Pilgrimage')

1428 Nativity ('First Christmas')

Millennium Series. The Christians' Tale

1999 (2 Nov.) One centre phosphor band (19p) or two phosphor bands (others). Perf 14 × 14½

2115	**1425**	19p multicoloured	75	70	☐	☐
2116	**1426**	26p multicoloured	95	1·00	☐	☐
2117	**1427**	44p multicoloured	1·50	1·60	☐	☐
2118	**1428**	64p multicoloured	2·25	2·40	☐	☐

Set of 4	5·25	5·25	☐	☐
First Day Cover		8·00		☐
Presentation Pack	7·50		☐	
PHQ Cards (*set of* 4)	8·50	13·00	☐	☐
Set of 4 Gutter Pairs	13·00		☐	

1429 'World of the Stage' (Allen Jones)

1430 'World of Music' (Bridget Riley)

1431 'World of Literature' (Lisa Milroy)

1432 'New Worlds' (Sir Howard Hodgkin)

Millennium Series. The Artists' Tale

1999 (7 Dec.) One centre phosphor band (19p) or two phosphor bands (others). Perf 14 × 14½

2119	**1429**	19p multicoloured	75	70	☐ ☐
2120	**1430**	26p multicoloured	95	1·00	☐ ☐
2121	**1431**	44p multicoloured	1·50	1·60	☐ ☐
2122	**1432**	64p multicoloured	2·25	2·40	☐ ☐
Set of 4			5·25	5·25	☐ ☐
First Day Cover				8·00	☐
Presentation Pack			7·50		☐
PHQ Cards (*set of* 4)			8·50	13·00	☐ ☐
Set of 4 Gutter Pairs			13·00		☐

Collectors Pack 1999

1999 (7 Dec.) Comprises Nos. 2069/76, 2080/105 and 2107/22

CP2122a	Collectors Pack	£135	☐

Post Office Yearbook

1999 (7 Dec.) Comprises Nos. 2069/76, 2080/105 and 2107/22 in hardback book with slip case

YB2122a	Yearbook	£135	☐

1433a

Millennium Series. 'Millennium Timekeeper'

1999 (14 Dec.) Sheet 120 × 89 mm. Multicoloured. Two phosphor bands. Perf 14 × 14½

MS2123	**1433a**	64p Clock face and map of North America; 64p Clock face and map of Asia; 64p Clock face and map of Middle East; 64p Clock face and map of Europe	26·00	26·00	☐	☐
First Day Cover				26·00		☐
Presentation Pack			30·00		☐	
PHQ Cards (*set of* 5)			22·00	32·00	☐	☐

No. **MS**2123 also exists overprinted 'EARLS COURT, LONDON 22–28 MAY 2000 THE STAMP SHOW 2000' from Exhibition Premium Passes, costing £10, available from 1 March 2000.

1437 Queen Elizabeth II

New Millennium

2000 (6 Jan.) Photo De La Rue, Questa or Walsall (No. 2124); Questa or Walsall (No. 2124d). Two phosphor bands. Perf 15 × 14 (with one elliptical hole on each vertical side)

2124	**1437**	(1st) olive-brown	1·00	1·00	☐	☐
		d. Perf 14	1·00	1·00	☐	☐
First Day Cover				3·00		
Presentation Pack			9·00		☐	
PHQ Card (23 May)			5·00	16·00	☐	☐

No. 2124 comes from sheets or stamp booklets and No. 2124d from booklets only.

 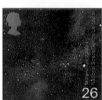

1438 Barn Owl (World Owl Trust, Muncaster)

1439 Night Sky (National Space Science Centre, Leicester)

1440 River Goyt and Textile Mills (Torrs Walkaway, New Mills)

1441 Cape Gannets (Seabird Centre, North Berwick)

Millennium Projects (1st series). 'Above and Beyond'

2000 (18 Jan.–26 May) One centre phosphor band (19p) or two phosphor bands (others). Perf 14 × 14½ (1st, 44p) or 13½ × 14 (others)

2125	**1438**	19p multicoloured	1·25	70	☐	☐
2126	**1439**	26p multicoloured	95	1·00	☐	☐
2126a		(1st) multicoloured (26 May)	5·25	4·50	☐	☐
2127	**1440**	44p multicoloured	1·50	1·75	☐	☐
2128	**1441**	64p multicoloured	2·50	2·50	☐	☐
Set of 4 (ex No. 2126a)			5·75	5·75	☐	☐
First Day Cover				8·00	☐	
Presentation Pack			7·00		☐	
PHQ Cards (*set of* 4)			8·50	13·00	☐	☐
Set of 4 Gutter Pairs			13·00		☐	

No. 2126a was only issued in £2·70 and £6·83 stamp booklets.

1442 Millennium Beacon (Beacons across the Land)

1443 Garratt Steam Locomotive No. 143 pulling Train (Rheilffordd Eryri, Welsh Highland Railway)

1444 Lightning (Dynamic Earth Centre, Edinburgh)

1445 Multicoloured Lights (Lighting Croydon's Skyline)

Millennium Projects (2nd series). 'Fire and Light'

2000 (1 Feb.) One centre phosphor band (19p) or two phosphor bands (others). Perf 14 × 14½

2129	**1442**	19p multicoloured	75	70	☐	☐
2130	**1443**	26p multicoloured	1·25	1·00	☐	☐
2131	**1444**	44p multicoloured	1·50	1·50	☐	☐
2132	**1445**	64p multicoloured	2·25	2·50	☐	☐
Set of 4			5·50	5·50	☐	☐
First Day Cover				8·00	☐	
Presentation Pack			7·00		☐	
PHQ Cards (*set of* 4)			8·50	13·00	☐	☐
Set of 4 Gutter Pairs			13·00		☐	

1446 Queen Victoria and Queen Elizabeth II

2000 (15 Feb.) Design T **929**, but redrawn with '1st' face value as T **1446**. Two phosphor bands. Perf 14 (with one elliptical hole on each vertical side)

2133	**1446**	(1st) brownish black and cream	1·50	1·25	☐	☐

No. 2133 was only issued in stamp booklets.

1447 Beach Pebbles (Turning the Tide, Durham Coast)

1448 Frog's Legs and Water Lilies (National Pondlife Centre, Merseyside)

1449 Cliff Boardwalk (Parc Ardfordirol, Llanelli Coast)

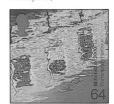

1450 Reflections in Water (Portsmouth Harbour Development)

Millennium Projects (3rd series). 'Water and Coast'

2000 (7 Mar.) One centre phosphor band (19p) or two phosphor bands (others). Perf 14 × 14½

2134	**1447**	19p multicoloured	75	70	☐	☐
2135	**1448**	26p multicoloured	1·25	1·00	☐	☐
2136	**1449**	44p black, grey and silver	1·50	1·50	☐	☐
2137	**1450**	64p multicoloured	2·25	2·50	☐	☐
Set of 4			5·50	5·50	☐	☐
First Day Cover				8·00	☐	
Presentation Pack			7·00		☐	
PHQ Cards (*set of* 4)			8·50	13·00	☐	☐
Set of 4 Gutter Pairs			13·00		☐	

1451 Reed Beds, River Braid (ECOS, Ballymena)

1452 South American Leaf-cutter Ants ('Web of Life' Exhibition, London Zoo)

1453 Solar Sensors (Earth Centre, Doncaster)

1454 Hydroponic Leaves (Project SUZY, Teesside)

Millennium Projects (4th series). 'Life and Earth'

2000 (4 Apr.) One centre phosphor band (2nd) or two phosphor bands (others). Perf 14 × 14½

2138	**1451**	(2nd) multicoloured	75	70	☐	☐
2139	**1452**	(1st) multicoloured	1·25	1·00	☐	☐
2140	**1453**	44p multicoloured	1·50	1·50	☐	☐
2141	**1454**	64p multicoloured	2·25	1·50	☐	☐
	Set of 4		5·50	5·50	☐	☐
	First Day Cover			8·00		☐
	Presentation Pack		7·00		☐	
	PHQ Cards (*set of 4*)		8·50	13·00	☐	☐
	Set of 4 Gutter Pairs		13·00		☐	

1455 Pottery Glaze (Ceramic Mesuem, stoke-on-trent)

1456 Bankside Galleries (Tate Modern, London)

1457 Road Marking (Cycle Network Artworks)

1458 People of Salford (Lowry Centre, Salford)

Millennium Projects (5th series). 'Art and Craft'

2000 (2 May) One centre phosphor band (2nd) or two phosphor bands (others). Perf 14 × 14½

2142	**1455**	(2nd) multicoloured	75	70	☐	☐
2143	**1456**	(1st) multicoloured	1·25	1·00	☐	☐
2144	**1457**	45p multicoloured	1·50	1·50	☐	☐
2145	**1458**	65p multicoloured	2·25	2·50	☐	☐
	Set of 4		5·50	5·50	☐	☐
	First Day Cover			8·00		☐
	Presentation Pack		7·50		☐	
	PHQ Cards (*set of 4*)		8·50	13·00	☐	☐
	Set of 4 Gutter Pairs		13·00		☐	

'Stamp Show 2000' International Stamp Exhibition, London. Jeffrey Matthews Colour Palette

2000 (22 May) Sheet, 124 × 70 mm, containing stamps as T **367** with two labels. Phosphorised paper. Perf 15 × 14 (with one elliptical hole on each vertical side)

MS2146	4p new blue; 5p dull red-brown; 6p yellow-olive; 10p dull orange; 31p dp mauve; 39p brt magenta; 64p turq-green; £1 bluish violet	30·00	30·00	☐	☐
First Day Cover			30·00		☐
Exhibition Card (wallet, sold at £4.99, containing one mint sheet and one cancelled on postcard)		75·00		☐	

The £1 value is printed in Iriodin ink which gives a shiny effect to the solid part of the background behind the Queen's head.

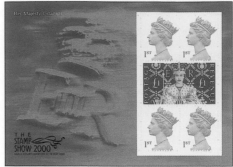

1459

'Stamp Show 2000' International Stamp Exhibition, London. 'Her Majesty's Stamps'

2000 (23 May) Sheet 121 × 89 mm. Phosphorised paper. Perf 15 × 14 (with one elliptical hole on each vertical side of stamps as T **1437**)

MS2147	**1459**	(1st) olive-brown (Type **1437**) × 4; £1 slate-green (as Type **163**)	21·00	21·00	☐	☐
	First Day Cover			22·00		☐
	Presentation Pack		£100		☐	
	PHQ Cards (*set of 2*)		22·00	32·00	☐	☐

The £1 value is an adaptation of the 1953 Coronation 1s. 3d. stamp. It is shown on one of the PHQ cards with the other depicting the complete miniature sheet.

See also No. 2380 for T **163** from £7·46 stamp booklet.

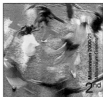

1460 Children playing (Millenium Greens Project)

1461 Millennium Bridge, Gateshead

1462 Daisies (Mile End Park, London)

1463 African Hut and Thatched Cottage ('On the Meridian Line' Project)

Millennium Projects (6th series). 'People and Places'

2000 (6 June) One centre phosphor band (2nd) or two phosphor bands (others). Perf 14 × 14½

2148	**1460**	(2nd) multicoloured	75	70	☐	☐
2149	**1461**	(1st) multicoloured	1·25	1·00	☐	☐
2150	**1462**	45p multicoloured	1·50	1·50	☐	☐
2151	**1463**	65p multicoloured	2·25	2·50	☐	☐
	Set of 4		5·50	5·50	☐	☐

First Day Cover		8·00	☐
Presentation Pack	7·50		☐
PHQ Cards (set of 4)	8·50	13·00	☐ ☐
Set of 4 Gutter Pairs	13·00		☐

1464 Raising the Stone (Strangford Stone, Killyleagh)

1465 Horse's Hooves (Trans Pennine Trail, Derbyshire)

1466 Cyclist (Kingdom of Fife Cycle Ways, Scotland)

1467 Bluebell Wood (Groundwork's 'Changing Places' Project)

Millennium Projects (7th series). 'Stone and Soil'

2000 (4 July) One centre phosphor band (2nd) or two phosphor bands (others). Perf 14 × 14½

2152	**1464**	(2nd) brownish black, grey-black and silver	75	70	☐ ☐
2153	**1465**	(1st) multicoloured	1·25	1·00	☐ ☐
2154	**1466**	45p multicoloured	1·50	1·75	☐ ☐
2155	**1467**	65p multicoloured	2·50	2·50	☐ ☐
Set of 4			5·50	5·75	☐ ☐
First Day Cover				8·00	☐
Presentation Pack			7·50		☐
PHQ Cards (set of 4)			8·50	13·00	☐ ☐
Set of 4 Gutter Pairs			13·00		☐

1468 Tree Roots ('Yews for the Millennium' Project)

1469 Sunflower ('Eden' Project, St. Austell)

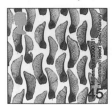

1470 Sycamore Seeds (Millennium Seed Bank, Wakehurst Place, Surrey)

1471 Forest, Doire Dach ('Forest for Scotland')

Millennium Projects (8th series). 'Tree and Leaf'

2000 (1 Aug.) One centre phosphor band (2nd) or two phosphor bands (others). Perf 14 × 14½

2156	**1468**	(2nd) multicoloured	75	70	☐ ☐
2157	**1469**	(1st) multicoloured	1·25	1·00	☐ ☐
2158	**1470**	45p multicoloured	1·50	1·60	☐ ☐
2159	**1471**	65p multicoloured	2·50	2·50	☐ ☐
Set of 4			5·50	5·50	☐ ☐
First Day Cover				8·00	☐
Presentation Pack			7·50		☐
PHQ Cards (set of 4)			8·50	13·00	☐ ☐
Set of 4 Gutter Pairs			13·00		☐

1472 Queen Elizabeth the Queen Mother

1472a Royal Family on Queen Mother's 100th Birthday (from photo by J. Swannell)

Queen Elizabeth the Queen Mother's 100th Birthday

2000 (4 Aug.) Phosphorised paper plus two phosphor bands. Perf 14½

2160	**1472**	27p multicoloured	2·50	2·75	☐ ☐
MS2161		121 × 89 mm. **1472a** 27p Queen Elizabeth II; 27p Prince William; 27p Queen Elizabeth the Queen Mother; 27p Prince Charles	11·00	11·00	☐ ☐
First Day Cover (**MS**2161)				12·00	☐
Presentation Pack (**MS**2161)			38·00		☐
PHQ Cards (set of 5)			11·00	24·00	☐ ☐

No. 2160 was only issued in stamp booklets and in No. **MS**2161.

The complete miniature sheet is shown on one of the PHQ cards with the others depicting individual stamps.

1473 Head of Gigantiops destructor (Ant) (Wildscreen at Bristol)

1474 Gathering Water Lilies on Broads (Norfolk and Norwich Project)

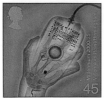

1475 X-ray of Hand holding Computer Mouse (Millennium Point, Birmingham

1476 Tartan Wool Holder (Scottish Cultural Resources Access Network)

Millennium Projects (9th series). 'Mind and Matter'

2000 (5 Sept.) One centre phosphor band (2nd) or two phosphor bands (others). Perf 14 × 14½

2162	**1473**	(2nd) multicoloured	75	70	□	□
2163	**1474**	(1st) multicoloured	1·25	1·00	□	□
2164	**1475**	45p multicoloured	1·50	1·75	□	□
2165	**1476**	65p multicoloured	2·25	2·50	□	□
Set of 4			5·50	5·75	□	□
First Day Cover				8·00	□	
Presentation Pack			7·50		□	
PHQ Cards (set of 4)			8·50	13·00	□	□
Set of 4 Gutter Pairs			13·00		□	

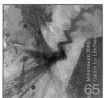

1477 Acrobatic Performers (Millennium Dome)

1478 Football Players (Hampden Park, Glasgow)

1479 Bather (Bath Spa Project)

1480 Hen's Egg under Magnification (Centre for Life, Newcastle)

Millennium Projects (10th series). 'Body and Bone'

2000 (3 Oct.) One centre phosphor band (2nd) or two phosphor bands (others). Perf 14 × 14½ (2nd) or 13½ × 14 (others)

2166	**1477**	(2nd) black, slate-blue and silver	75	70	□	□
2167	**1478**	(1st) multicoloured	1·25	1·00	□	□
2168	**1479**	45p multicoloured	1·50	1·50	□	□

2169	**1480**	65p multicoloured	2·25	2·50	□	□
Set of 4			5·50	5·75	□	□
First Day Cover				8·00	□	
Presentation Pack			7·50		□	
PHQ Cards (set of 4)			8·50	13·00	□	□
Set of 4 Gutter Pairs			13·00		□	

1481 Virgin and Child Stained Glass Window, St. Edmundsbury Cathedral (Suffolk Cathedral Millennium Project)

1482 Floodlit Church of St. Peter and St. Paul, Overstowey (Church Floodlighting Trust)

1483 12th-cent. Latin Gradual (St. Patrick Centre, Downpatrick)

1484 Chapter House Ceiling, York Minster (York Millennium Mystery Plays)

Millennium Projects (11th series). 'Spirit and Faith'

2000 (7 Nov.) One centre phosphor band (2nd) or two phosphor bands (others). Perf 14 × 14½

2170	**1481**	(2nd) multicoloured	75	70	□	□
2171	**1482**	(1st) multicoloured	1·25	1·00	□	□
2172	**1483**	45p multicoloured	1·50	1·50	□	□
2173	**1484**	65p multicoloured	2·25	2·50	□	□
Set of 4			5·50	5·50	□	□
First Day Cover				8·00	□	
Presentation Pack			7·50		□	
PHQ Cards (set of 4)			8·50	13·00	□	□
Set of 4 Gutter Pairs			13·00		□	

Post Office Yearbook

2000 (7 Nov.) Comprises Nos. **MS**2125/6, 2127/32, 2134/45, 2148/59 and **MS**2161/81 in hardback book with slip case

YB2181a	Yearbook	£120	□

The last two issues in the Millennium Projects Series were supplied for insertion into the above at a later date.

1485 Church Bells (Ringing in the Millennium)

1486 Eye (Year of the Artist)

1487 Top of Harp (Canolfan Mileniwn, Cardiff)

1488 Figure within Latticework (TS2K Creative Enterprise Centres, London)

Millennium Projects (12th series). 'Sound and Vision'

2000 (5 Dec.) One centre phosphor band (2nd) or two phosphor bands (others). Perf 14 × 14½

2174	**1485**	(2nd) multicoloured	75	70	☐	☐
2175	**1486**	(1st) multicoloured	1·25	1·00	☐	☐
2176	**1487**	45p multicoloured	1·50	1·50	☐	☐
2177	**1488**	65p multicoloured	2·25	2·50	☐	☐
Set of 4			5·50	5·50	☐	☐
First Day Cover				8·00		☐
Presentation Pack			7·50		☐	
PHQ Cards (set of 4)			8·50	13·00	☐	☐
Set of 4 Gutter Pairs			13·00		☐	

Collectors Pack 2000

2000 (5 Dec.) Comprises Nos. **MS**2125/6, 2127/32, 2134/45, 2148/59 and **MS**2161/81

CP2181a	Collectors Pack	£120	☐

1489 'Flower' ('Nurture Children')

1490 'Tiger' ('Listen to Children')

1491 'Owl' ('Teach Children')

1492 'Butterfly' ('Ensure Children's Freedom')

New Millennium. Rights of the Child. Face Paintings

2001 (16 Jan.) One centre phosphor band (2nd) or two phosphor bands (others). Perf 14 × 14½

2178	**1489**	(2nd) multicoloured	75	75	☐	☐
2179	**1490**	(1st) multicoloured	1·00	1·10	☐	☐
2180	**1491**	45p multicoloured	1·60	1·75	☐	☐
2181	**1492**	65p multicoloured	2·40	2·50	☐	☐
Set of 4			5·75	5·75	☐	☐
First Day Cover				7·50		☐
Presentation Pack			7·50		☐	
PHQ Cards (set of 4)			8·50	13·00	☐	☐
Set of 4 Gutter Pairs			14·00		☐	

1493 'Love'   **1494** 'THANKS'

 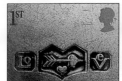

1495 'abc' (New Baby)   **1496** 'WELCOME'

1497 'Cheers'

'Occasions' Greetings Stamps

2001 (6 Feb.) Two phosphor bands. Perf 14½ × 14

2182	**1493**	(1st) multicoloured	1·10	1·10	☐	☐
2183	**1494**	(1st) multicoloured	1·10	1·10	☐	☐
2184	**1495**	(1st) multicoloured	1·10	1·10	☐	☐
2185	**1496**	(1st) multicoloured	1·10	1·10	☐	☐
2186	**1497**	(1st) multicoloured	1·10	1·10	☐	☐
Set of 5			5·00	5·00	☐	☐
First Day Cover				6·50		☐
Presentation Pack (13 Feb.)			7·00		☐	
PHQ Cards (set of 5)			8·50	13·00	☐	☐
Set of 5 Gutter Pairs			13·00		☐	

The silver-grey backgrounds are printed in Iriodin ink which gives a shiny effect.

Further packs of Nos. 2182/6 were sold from 3 July 2001. These comprised the listed stamps in blocks of ten (from sheets) with an insert describing the occasion (*Price* £10 *per pack*). Nos. 2182/6 were printed in photogravure. They were subsequently re-issued on 1 May, as sheets of 20, printed in lithography instead of photogravure with each stamp accompanied by a half stamp-size label showing either postal symbols or a personal photograph.

1498 Dog and Owner on Bench   **1499** Dog in Bath

1500 Boxer at Dog Show   **1501** Cat in Handbag

1502 Cat on Gate

1503 Dog in Car

1504 Cat at Window

1505 Dog behind Fence

1506 Cat watching Bird

1507 Cat in Washbasin

T **1498/1507** were printed together in sheetlets of 10 (5 × 2), with the surplus self-adhesive paper around each stamp retained. The booklet pane has vertical roulettes between rows 2/3 and 4/5.

Cats and Dogs

2001 (13 Feb.) Self-adhesive. Two phosphor bands. Die-cut perf 15 × 14

2187	**1498**	(1st) black, grey and silver	60	50	☐	☐
		a. Sheetlet.				
		Nos. 2187/96	15·00	13·00	☐	☐
		b. Booklet pane.				
		Nos.2187/96 plus				
		Nos. 2040 × 2	30·00		☐	
2188	**1499**	(1st) black, grey and silver	60	50	☐	☐
2189	**1500**	(1st) black, grey and silver	60	50	☐	☐
2190	**1501**	(1st) black, grey and silver	60	50	☐	☐
2191	**1502**	(1st) black, grey and silver	60	50	☐	☐
2192	**1503**	(1st) black, grey and silver	60	50	☐	☐
2193	**1504**	(1st) black, grey and silver	60	50	☐	☐
2194	**1505**	(1st) black, grey and silver	60	60	☐	☐
2195	**1506**	(1st) black, grey and silver	60	60	☐	☐
2196	**1507**	(1st) black, grey and silver	60	60	☐	☐
Set of 10			15·00	13·00	☐	☐
First Day Cover				15·00		☐
Presentation Pack			20·00		☐	
PHQ Cards (set of 10)			18·00	32·00	☐	☐

1508 'RAIN'

1509 'FAIR'

1510 'STORMY'

1511 'VERY DRY'

Nos. 2197/200 show the four quadrants of a barometer dial which are combined on the miniature sheet.

The Weather

2001 (13 Mar.) One side phosphor band (19p) or two phosphor bands (others). Perf 14½

2197	**1508**	19p multicoloured	70	75	☐	☐
2198	**1509**	27p multicoloured	85	1·00	☐	☐
2199	**1510**	45p multicoloured	1·50	1·50	☐	☐
2200	**1511**	65p multicoloured	2·40	2·50	☐	☐
Set of 4			5·00	5·50	☐	☐
First Day Cover				7·00		☐
Presentation Pack			12·50		☐	
Set of 4 Gutter Pairs			14·00		☐	
MS2201	105 × 105 mm.					
		Nos. 2197/200	15·00	15·00	☐	☐
First Day Cover				15·00		☐
PHQ Cards (set of 5)			8·50	20·00	☐	☐

The reddish violet on both the 27p and the miniature sheet is printed in thermochromic ink which changes from reddish violet to light blue when exposed to heat.

The PHQ cards depict the four values and the miniature sheet.

1512 *Vanguard* Class Submarine, 1992

1513 *Swiftsure* Class Submarine, 1973

1514 *Unity* Class Submarine, 1939

1515 'Holland' Type Submarine, 1901

1516 White Ensign

1517 Union Jack

1518 Jolly Roger flown by H.M.S. *Proteus* (submarine)

1519 Flag of Chief of Defence Staff

Centenary of Royal Navy Submarine Service

2001 (10 Apr.–22 Oct.) One centre phosphor band (2nd) or two phosphor bands (others).

(a) Submarines. PVA gum. Perf 15 × 14

2202	**1512**	(2nd) multicoloured	70	75	☐	☐
		a. Perf 15½ × 15				
		(22 Oct.)	3·75	3·00	☐	☐
2203	**1513**	(1st) multicoloured	85	90	☐	☐
		a. Perf 15½ × 15				
		(22 Oct.)	3·75	3·00	☐	☐
2204	**1514**	45p multicoloured	1·75	1·60	☐	☐
		a. Perf 15½ × 15				
		(22 Oct.)	3·75	3·00	☐	☐
2205	**1515**	65p multicoloured	2·40	2·50	☐	☐
		a. Perf 15½ × 15				
		(22 Oct.)	3·75	3·00	☐	☐
Set of 4			5·25	5·25	☐	☐
First Day Cover				7·50		☐
Presentation Pack			22·00		☐	
PHQ Cards (*set of* 4)			8·50	14·00	☐	☐
Set of 4 Gutter Pairs			13·50		☐	

(b) Flags. Sheet 92 × 97 mm. PVA gum. Perf 14½

MS2206	**1516**	(1st) multicoloured;				
	1517	(1st) multicoloured;				
	1518	(1st) multicoloured;				
	1519	(1st) multicoloured				
		(22 Oct.)	9·00	9·00	☐	☐
First Day Cover				11·00		☐
Presentation Pack			20·00		☐	
PHQ Cards (*set of* 5)			20·00	25·00	☐	☐

(c) Self-adhesive. Die-cut perf 15½ × 14 (No. 2207) or 14½ (others)

2207	**1513**	(1st) multicoloured				
		(17 Apr.)	45·00	40·00	☐	☐
2208	**1516**	(1st) multicoloured				
		(22 Oct.)	15·00	15·00	☐	☐
2209	**1518**	(1st) multicoloured				
		(22 Oct.)	15·00	15·00	☐	☐

Nos. 2202a/5a only come from stamp booklets.
The five PHQ cards depict the four designs and the complete miniature sheet.
Nos. 2207/9 only come from two different £1.62 booklets.
Type **1516** was re-issued on 21 June 2005 in sheets of 20, printed in lithography instead of photogravure, with half stamp-size *se-tenant* labels showing signal flags.
Designs as Type **1517** were issued on 27 July 2004 in sheets of 20 printed in lithography instead of photogravure with each vertical row of stamps alternated with half stamp-size labels.

1520 Leyland X2 Open-top, London General B Type, Leyland Titan TD1 and AEC Regent 1

1521 AEC Regent 1, Daimler COG5, Utility Guy Arab Mk II and AEC Regent III RT Type

1522 AEC Regent III RT Type, Bristol KSW5G Open-Top, AEC Routemaster and Bristol Lodekka FSF6G

1523 Bristol Lodekka FSF6G, Leyland Titan PD3/4, Leyland Atlantean PDR1/1 and Daimler Fleetline CRG6LX-33

1524 Daimler Fleetline CRG6LX-33, MCW Metrobus DR102/43, Leyland Olympian ONLXB/1R and Dennis Trident

T **1520/4** were printed together, *se-tenant*, in horizontal strips of 5 throughout the sheet. The illustrations of the first bus on No. 2210 and the last bus on No. 2214 continue onto the sheet margins.

150th Anniversary of First Double-decker Bus

2001 (15 May) 'All-over' phosphor. Perf 14½ × 14

2210	**1520**	(1st) multicoloured	60	50	☐	☐
		a. Horiz strip of 5.				
		Nos. 2210/14	6·00	6·00	☐	☐
2211	**1521**	(1st) multicoloured	60	50	☐	☐
2212	**1522**	(1st) multicoloured	60	50	☐	☐
2213	**1523**	(1st) multicoloured	60	60	☐	☐
2214	**1524**	(1st) multicoloured	60	60	☐	☐
Set of 5			6·00	6·00	☐	☐
First Day Cover				6·50		☐
Presentation Pack			9·00		☐	
PHQ Cards (*set of* 5)			20·00	32·00	☐	☐
Gutter Strip of 10			12·00		☐	
MS2215 120 × 105 mm. Nos. 2210/14			10·50	10·50	☐	☐
First Day Cover				15·00		☐

In No. **MS**2215 the illustrations of the AEC Regent III RT Type and the Daimler Fleetline CRG6LX-33 appear twice.

1525 Toque Hat by Pip Hackett

1526 Butterfly Hat by Dai Rees

1527 Top Hat by Stephen Jones

1528 Spiral Hat by Philip Treacy

Fashion Hats

2001 (19 June) 'All-over' phosphor. Perf 14½

2216	**1525**	(1st) multicoloured	85	90	☐	☐
2217	**1526**	(E) multicoloured	1·10	1·25	☐	☐
2218	**1527**	45p multicoloured	1·60	1·60	☐	☐
2219	**1528**	65p multicoloured	2·50	2·50	☐	☐
Set of 4			5·50	5·50	☐	☐
First Day Cover				7·25		☐
Presentation Pack			7·50		☐	
PHQ Cards (*set of* 4)			8·50	14·00	☐	☐
Set of 4 Gutter Pairs			13·00		☐	

1529 Common Frog   **1530** Great Diving Beetle

1531 Three-spined Stickleback   **1532** Southern Hawker Dragonfly

Europa. Pond Life

2001 (10 July) Two phosphor bands

2220	**1529**	(1st) multicoloured	1·00	1·00	☐	☐
2221	**1530**	(E) multicoloured	1·25	1·25	☐	☐
2222	**1531**	45p multicoloured	1·50	1·50	☐	☐
2223	**1532**	65p multicoloured	2·00	2·25	☐	☐
Set of 4			5·50	5·75	☐	☐
First Day Cover				11·00		☐
Presentation Pack			7·50		☐	
PHQ Cards (*set of* 4)			8·50	14·00	☐	☐
Set of 4 Gutter Pairs			13·00		☐	

The 1st and E values incorporate the 'EUROPA' emblem. The bluish silver on all four values is in Iriodin ink and was used as a background for those parts of the design below the water line.

1533 Policeman   **1534** Clown

1535 Mr. Punch   **1536** Judy

1537 Beadle   **1538** Crocodile

Nos. 2224/9 were printed together, *se-tenant*, in horizontal strips of 6 throughout the sheet.

Punch and Judy Show Puppets

2001 (4 Sept.) Two phosphor bands

		(a) PVA gum. Perf 14 × 15				
2224	**1533**	(1st) multicoloured	60	50	☐	☐
		a. Horiz strip of 6.				
		Nos. 2224/9	5·50	5·50	☐	☐
2225	**1534**	(1st) multicoloured	60	50	☐	☐
2226	**1535**	(1st) multicoloured	60	50	☐	☐
2227	**1536**	(1st) multicoloured	60	50	☐	☐
2228	**1537**	(1st) multicoloured	60	50	☐	☐
2229	**1538**	(1st) multicoloured	60	50	☐	☐
Set of 6			5·50	5·50	☐	☐
First Day Cover				7·00		☐
Presentation Pack			7·50		☐	
PHQ Cards (*set of* 6)			8·50	18·00	☐	☐
Gutter Block of 12			13·00		☐	
		(b) Self-adhesive. Die-cut perf 14 × 15½				
2230	1535	(1st) multicoloured	17·00	17·00	☐	☐
2231	1536	(1st) multicoloured	17·00	17·00	☐	☐

Nos. 2230/1 were only issued in £1.62 stamp booklets.

1539 Carbon 60 Molecule (Chemistry)   **1540** Globe (Economic Sciences)

1541 Embossed Dove (Peace)   **1542** Crosses (Physiology or Medicine)

1543 Poem 'The Addressing of Cats' by T.S. Eliot in Open Book (Literature)

1544 Hologram of Boron Molecule (Physics)

Centenary of Nobel Prizes

2001 (2 Oct.) One side phosphor band (2nd) or phosphor frame (others). Perf 14½

2232	**1539**	(2nd) black, silver and grey-black	75	65	☐	☐
2233	**1540**	(1st) multicoloured	1·00	90	☐	☐
2234	**1541**	(E) black, silver and bright green	1·00	1·25	☐	☐
2235	**1542**	40p multicoloured	1·25	1·25	☐	☐
2236	**1543**	45p multicoloured	1·50	1·75	☐	☐
2237	**1544**	65p black and silver	2·25	2·50	☐	☐
Set of 6			8·50	7·50	☐	☐
First Day Cover				9·50		☐
Presentation Pack			40·00		☐	
PHQ Cards (*set of* 6)			10·00	18·00	☐	☐
Set of 6 Gutter Pairs			16·00		☐	

The grey-black on No. 2232 is printed in thermochromic ink which temporarily changes to pale grey when exposed to heat.

The centre of No. 2235 is coated with a eucalyptus scent.

1545 Robins with Snowman

1546 Robins on Bird Table

1547 Robins skating on Bird Bath

1548 Robins with Christmas Pudding

1549 Robins in Paper Chain Nest

Christmas. Robins

2001 (6 Nov.) Self-adhesive. One centre phosphor band (2nd) or two phosphor bands (others). Die-cut perf 14½

2238	**1545**	(2nd) multicoloured	75	70	☐	☐
2239	**1546**	(1st) multicoloured	1·00	1·00	☐	☐
2240	**1547**	(E) multicoloured	1·00	1·10	☐	☐
2241	**1548**	45p multicoloured	1·50	1·50	☐	☐
2242	**1549**	65p multicoloured	2·00	2·25	☐	☐
Set of 5			6·00	6·00	☐	☐
First Day Cover				9·50		☐
Presentation Pack			8·00		☐	
PHQ Cards (*set of* 5)			11·00	16·00	☐	☐

The 1st value was re-issued on 30 September 2003, in sheets of 20, in lithography instead of photogravure, each stamp *se-tenant* with a Christmas label or a personal photograph. The sheet contained die-cut perforated stamps and labels. The 2nd and 1st class stamps were issued again on 1 November 2005 in sheets of 20 containing ten 1st class and ten 2nd class stamps, each stamp accompanied by a *se-tenant* label showing a snowman.

Collectors Pack 2001

2001 (6 Nov.) Comprises Nos. 2178/2200, 2202/**MS**2206, 2210/14, 2216/29 and 2232/42

CP2242a	Collectors Pack	£120	☐

Post Office Yearbook

2001 (6 Nov.) Comprises Nos. 2178/96, **MS**2201/6, **MS**2215/29 and 2232/42 in hardback book with slip case

YB2242a	Yearbook	£110	☐

1550 'How the Whale got his Throat'

1551 'How the Camel got his Hump'

1552 'How the Rhinoceros got his Skin'

1553 'How the Leopard got his Spots'

1554 'The Elephant's Child'

1555 'The Sing-Song of Old Man Kangaroo'

1556 'The Beginning of the Armadillos'

1557 'The Crab that played with the Sea'

1558 'The Cat that walked by Himself'

1559 'The Butterfly that stamped'

T **1550/9** were printed together in sheetlets of 10 (5 × 2), with the surplus self-adhesive paper around each stamp retained.

Centenary of Publication of Rudyard Kipling's Just So Stories

2002 (15 Jan.) Self-adhesive. Two phosphor bands. Die-cut perf 15 × 14

2243	**1550**	(1st) multicoloured	50	45	☐	☐
		a. Sheetlet.				
		Nos. 2243/52	10·00	10·00	☐	☐
2244	**1551**	(1st) multicoloured	50	45	☐	☐
2245	**1552**	(1st) multicoloured	50	45	☐	☐
2246	**1553**	(1st) multicoloured	50	45	☐	☐
2247	**1554**	(1st) multicoloured	50	45	☐	☐
2248	**1555**	(1st) multicoloured	50	45	☐	☐
2249	**1556**	(1st) multicoloured	50	45	☐	☐
2250	**1557**	(1st) multicoloured	50	45	☐	☐
2251	**1558**	(1st) multicoloured	50	45	☐	☐
2252	**1559**	(1st) multicoloured	50	45	☐	☐
Set of 10			10·00	10·00	☐	☐
First Day Cover				11·00		☐
Presentation Pack			15·00		☐	
PHQ Cards (*set of* 10)			14·00	38·00	☐	☐

1560 Queen Elizabeth II, 1952 (Dorothy Wilding)

1561 Queen Elizabeth II, 1968 (Cecil Beaton)

1562 Queen Elizabeth II, 1978 (Lord Snowdon)

1563 Queen Elizabeth II, 1984 (Yousef Karsh)

1564 Queen Elizabeth II, 1996 (Tim Graham)

1565

Golden Jubilee. Studio portraits of Queen Elizabeth II by photographers named

2002 (6 Feb.) One centre phosphor band (2nd) or two phosphor bands (others). W **1565**. Perf 14½ × 14

2253	**1560**	(2nd) multicoloured	75	55	☐	☐
2254	**1561**	(1st) multicoloured	1·00	80	☐	☐
2255	**1562**	(E) multicoloured	1·50	1·50	☐	☐
2256	**1563**	45p multicoloured	1·75	2·00	☐	☐
2257	**1564**	65p multicoloured	2·75	3·00	☐	☐
Set of 5			7·00	7·00	☐	☐
First Day Cover				9·00		
Presentation Pack			8·50		☐	
PHQ Cards (*set of* 5)			4·50	14·00	☐	☐
Set of 5 Gutter Pairs			16·00		☐	

Stamps from sheets had the watermark sideways: those from stamp booklets had the watermark upright.

1566

Booklet Stamps

2002 (6 Feb.) Designs as 1952-54 issue, but with service indicator as T **1566**. One centre phosphor band (2nd) or two phosphor bands (1st). W **1565**. Uncoated paper. Perf 15 × 14 (with one elliptical hole on each vertical side)

2258	**1566**	(2nd) carmine-red	1·20	1·00	☐	☐
2259	**154**	(1st) green	1·25	1·25	☐	☐
Set of 2			2·40	2·25	☐	☐

Nos. 2258/9 were only issued in £7.29 stamp booklets.
See also Nos. 2031/3, MS2326, MS2367 and 2378/80.

1567 Rabbits ('a new baby')

1568 'LOVE'

1569 Aircraft Sky-writing 'hello'

1570 Bear pulling Potted Topiary Tree (Moving Home)

1571 Flowers ('best wishes')

'Occasions' Greetings Stamps

2002 (5 Mar.)-**03** Two phosphor bands

(a) Litho. PVA gum. Perf 15 × 14

2260 **1567**	(1st) multicoloured	1·10	1·10	☐ ☐
2261 **1568**	(1st) multicoloured	1·10	1·10	☐ ☐
2262 **1569**	(1st) multicoloured	1·10	1·10	☐ ☐
2263 **1570**	(1st) multicoloured	1·10	1·10	☐ ☐
2264 **1571**	(1st) multicoloured	1·10	1·10	☐ ☐
Set of 5		5·00	5·00	☐ ☐
First Day Cover			6·75	☐
Presentation Pack		7·50		☐
PHQ Cards (set of 5)		4·50	14·00	☐ ☐
Set of 5 Gutter Pairs		11·00		☐

(b) Photo. Self-adhesive. Die-cut perf 15 × 14

2264a **1569**	(1st) multicoloured			
	(4.3.03)	6·00	6·00	☐ ☐

Nos. 2260/4 were re-issued on 23 April 2002 in sheets of 20 perforated 14½ × 14, either of one design or *se-tenant*, with each stamp accompanied by a half stamp-size label showing either greetings or a personal photograph.

No. 2262 was also issued in sheets of 20 with *se-tenant* labels in connection with the Hong Kong Stamp Expo on 30 January 2004. It was issued in sheets of 20 perforated 14 with *se-tenant* labels on 21 April 2005 for Pacific Explorer 2005 World Stamp Expo, on 25 May 2006 for Washington 2006 International Stamp Exhibition, on 14 November 2006 for Belgica 2006 International Stamp Exhibition and on 5 August 2008 for Beijing 2008 Olympic Expo.

No. 2264a was only issued in £1·62 stamp booklets in which the surplus self-adhesive paper around each stamp was removed.

1572 Studland Bay, Dorset

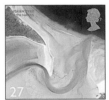

1573 Luskentyre, South Harris

1574 Cliffs, Dover, Kent

1575 Padstow Harbour, Cornwall

1576 Broadstairs, Kent

1577 St. Abb's Head, Scottish Borders

1578 Dunster Beach, Somerset

1579 Newquay Beach, Cornwall

1580 Portrush, County Antrim

1581 Sand-spit, Conwy

T **1572/81** were printed together, *se-tenant*, in blocks of 10 (5 × 2) throughout the sheet.

British Coastlines

2002 (19 Mar.) Two phosphor bands. Perf 14½

2265 **1572**	27p multicoloured	60	50	☐ ☐
	a. Block of 10.			
	Nos. 2265/74	8·75	8·75	☐ ☐
2266 **1573**	27p multicoloured	60	50	☐ ☐
2267 **1574**	27p multicoloured	60	50	☐ ☐
2268 **1575**	27p multicoloured	60	50	☐ ☐
2269 **1576**	27p multicoloured	60	50	☐ ☐
2270 **1577**	27p multicoloured	60	50	☐ ☐
2271 **1578**	27p multicoloured	60	50	☐ ☐
2272 **1579**	27p multicoloured	60	50	☐ ☐
2273 **1580**	27p multicoloured	60	50	☐ ☐
2274 **1581**	27p multicoloured	60	50	☐ ☐
Set of 10		8·75	8·75	☐
First Day Cover			11·50	☐
Presentation Pack		10·50		☐
PHQ Cards (set of 10)		9·25	28·00	☐ ☐
Gutter Block of 20		18·00		☐

1582 Slack Wire Act

1583 Lion Tamer

1584 Trick Tri-cyclists   **1585** Krazy Kar

1586 Equestrienne

1588 Airbus A340-600 (2002)   **1589** Concorde (1976)

1590 Trident (1964)   **1591** VC 10 (1964)

1592 Comet (1952)

Europa. Circus

2002 (10 Apr.) One centre phosphor band (2nd) or two phosphor bands (others). Perf 14½

2275	**1582**	(2nd) multicoloured	50	60	☐	☐
2276	**1583**	(1st) multicoloured	75	85	☐	☐
2277	**1584**	(E) multicoloured	1·00	1·25	☐	☐
2278	**1585**	45p multicoloured	1·75	1·50	☐	☐
2279	**1586**	65p multicoloured	2·75	2·25	☐	☐
Set of 5			6·00	6·00	☐	☐
First Day Cover				8·00		☐
Presentation Pack			7·50		☐	
PHQ Cards (*set of* 5)			4·50	14·00	☐	☐
Set of 5 Gutter Pairs			14·00		☐	

The 1st and E values incorporate the "EUROPA" emblem. Due to the funeral of the Queen Mother, the actual issue of Nos. 2275/9 was delayed from 9 April which is the date that appears on first day covers.

1587 Queen Elizabeth the Queen Mother

Queen Elizabeth the Queen Mother Commemoration

2002 (25 Apr.) Vert designs as T **955/8** with changed face values and showing both the Queen's head and frame in black as in T **1587**. Two phosphor bands. Perf 14 × 15

2280	**1587**	(1st) multicoloured	1·00	85	☐	☐
2281	**956**	(E) black and indigo	1·25	1·10	☐	☐
2282	**957**	45p multicoloured	1·50	1·50	☐	☐
2283	**958**	65p black, stone and sepia	2·00	2·25	☐	☐
Set of 4			5·50	5·50	☐	☐
First Day Cover				8·00		☐
Presentation Pack			7·00		☐	
Set of 4 Gutter Pairs			14·00		☐	

50th Anniversary of Passenger Jet Aviation. Airliners

2002 (2 May) One centre phosphor band (2nd) or two phosphor bands (others). Perf 14½

(a) Photo De La Rue. PVA gum						
2284	**1588**	(2nd) multicoloured	75	55	☐	☐
2285	**1589**	(1st) multicoloured	1·00	80	☐	☐
2286	**1590**	(E) multicoloured	1·25	1·25	☐	☐
2287	**1591**	45p multicoloured	1·50	1·50	☐	☐
2288	**1592**	65p multicoloured	2·00	2·25	☐	☐
Set of 5			6·00	6·00	☐	☐
First Day Cover				8·00		☐
Presentation Pack			8·00		☐	
Set of 5 Gutter Pairs			14·00		☐	
MS2289	120 × 105 mm. Nos. 2284/8		10·00	10·00	☐	☐
First Day Cover				12·00		☐
PHQ Cards (*set of* 6)			5·25	25·00	☐	☐

(b) Photo Questa. Self-adhesive						
2290	**1589**	(1st) multicoloured	7·00	7·00	☐	☐

The complete miniature sheet is shown on one of the PHQ cards with the others depicting individual stamps.

No. 2290 was only issued in £1.62 stamp booklets.

1593 Crowned Lion with Shield of St. George

1594 Top Left Quarter of English Flag, and Football **1595** Top Right Quarter of English Flag, and Football

1596 Bottom Left Quarter of English Flag, and Football **1597** Bottom Right Quarter of English Flag, and Football

World Cup Football Championship, Japan and Korea

2002 (21 May) Two phosphor bands. Perf 14½ × 14

	(a) PVA gum				
2291 **1593**	(1st) deep turquoise-blue, scarlet-vermilion and silver	2·50	2·50	☐	☐
MS2292	145 × 74 mm. No. 2291; **1594** (1st) multicoloured; **1595** (1st) multi-coloured; **1596** (1st) multicoloured; **1597** (1st) multicoloured	6·00	6·00	☐	☐
First Day Cover (**MS**2292)			9·00		☐
Presentation Pack (**MS**2292)		7·00		☐	
PHQ Cards (*set of* 6)		5·25	15·00	☐	☐
Gutter Pair (No. 2291)		12·00		☐	

	(b) Self-adhesive. Die-cut perf 15 × 14				
2293 **1594**	(1st) multicoloured	6·00	6·00	☐	☐
2294 **1595**	(1st) multicoloured	6·00	6·00	☐	☐

The complete miniature sheet is shown on one of the PHQ cards with the others depicting individual stamps from **MS**2292 and No. 2291.

Nos. 2293/4 were only issued in £1.62 stamp booklets. Stamps as Type **1597** were also issued in sheets of 20, *se-tenant* with half stamp-sized labels, printed in lithography instead of photogravure. The labels show either match scenes or personal photographs.

Stamps as Type **1593** but with 'WORLD CUP 2002' inscription omitted were issued on 17 May 2007 in sheets of 20 with *se-tenant* labels showing scenes from Wembley Stadium.

Self-adhesive Stamps

2002 (5 June–4 July) Self-adhesive. Photo Questa, Walsall or Enschedé (No. 2295) or Walsall (others). Two phosphor bands. Perf 15 × 14 die-cut (with one elliptical hole on each vertical side)

2295	**914**	(1st) gold	1·00	1·00	☐	☐
2296	**1093a**	(E) deep blue (4 July)	2·00	2·00	☐	☐
2297	**367a**	42p deep olive-grey (4 July)	3·00	3·00	☐	☐
2298		68p grey-brown (4 July)	4·00	4·00	☐	☐
Set of 4			9·00	9·00	☐	☐
PHQ Card (No. 2295)			60	3·50	☐	☐

Further printings of No. 2295 in sheets of 100 appeared on 4 July 2002 produced by Enschedé and on 18 March 2003 printed by Walsall.

1598 Swimming

1599 Running

1600 Cycling

1601 Long Jumping

1602 Wheelchair Racing

17th Commonwealth Games, Manchester

2002 (16 July) One side phosphor band (2nd) or two phosphor bands (others). Perf 14½

2299	**1598**	(2nd) multicoloured	75	55	☐	☐
2300	**1599**	(1st) multicoloured	1·00	80	☐	☐
2301	**1600**	(E) multicoloured	1·25	1·25	☐	☐
2302	**1601**	47p multicoloured	1·50	1·50	☐	☐
2303	**1602**	68p multicoloured	2·00	2·25	☐	☐
Set of 5			6·00	6·00	☐	☐
First Day Cover				8·00		☐
Presentation Pack			7·50		☐	
PHQ Cards (*set of* 5)			4·75	15·00	☐	☐
Set of 5 Gutter Pairs			14·00		☐	

1603 Tinkerbell **1604** Wendy, John and Michael Darling in front of Big Ben

1605 Crocodile and Alarm Clock **1606** Captain Hook

1607 Peter Pan

150th Anniversary of Great Ormond Street Children's Hospital. Peter Pan by Sir James Barrie

2002 (20 Aug.) One centre phosphor band (2nd) or two phosphor bands (others). Perf 15 × 14

2304 **1603**	(2nd) multicoloured	75	55	☐	☐	
2305 **1604**	(1st) multicoloured	1·00	80	☐	☐	
2306 **1605**	(E) multicoloured	1·25	1·25	☐	☐	
2307 **1606**	47p multicoloured	1·50	1·50	☐	☐	
2308 **1607**	68p multicoloured	2·00	2·25	☐	☐	
Set of 5		6·00	6·00	☐	☐	
First Day Cover			8·00	☐		
Presentation Pack		7·50		☐		
PHQ Cards (*set of* 5)		4·75	15·00	☐	☐	
Set of 5 Gutter Pairs		14·00		☐		

1608 Millennium Bridge, 2001   **1609** Tower Bridge, 1894

1610 Westminster Bridge, 1864   **1611** 'Blackfriars Bridge, c1800' (William Marlow)

1612 'London Bridge, c1670' (Wenceslaus Hollar)

Bridges of London

2002 (10 Sept.) One centre phosphor band (2nd) or two phosphor bands (others)

(a) Litho. PVA gum. Perf 15 × 14

2309 **1608**	(2nd) multicoloured	75	55	☐	☐	
2310 **1609**	(1st) multicoloured	1·00	80	☐	☐	
2311 **1610**	(E) multicoloured	1·25	1·25	☐	☐	
2312 **1611**	47p multicoloured	1·50	1·50	☐	☐	
2313 **1612**	68p multicoloured	2·00	2·25	☐	☐	
Set of 5		6·50	6·50	☐	☐	
First Day Cover			9·00	☐		
Presentation Pack		55·00		☐		
PHQ Cards (*set of* 5)		4·00	18·00	☐	☐	
Set of 5 Gutter Pairs		15·00		☐		

(b) Photo. Self-adhesive. Die-cut perf 15 × 14

2314 **1609**	(1st) multicoloured	6·00	6·00	☐	☐

No. 2314 was only issued in £1.62 stamp booklets.

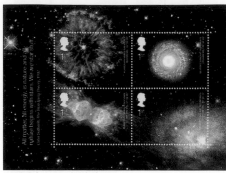

1613 Galaxies and Nebula

Astronomy

2002 (24 Sept.) Sheet 120 × 89 mm. Multicoloured. Two phosphor bands. Perf 14½ × 14

MS2315   1613 (1st) Planetary nebula in Aquila; (1st) Seyfert 2 galaxy in Pegasus; (1st) Planetary nebula in Norma; (1st) Seyfert 2 galaxy in Circinus   5·25   5·25 ☐ ☐

First Day Cover		6·00	☐	
Presentation Pack	18·00		☐	
PHQ Cards (*set of* 5)	4·75	18·00	☐	☐

The five PHQ cards depict the four designs and the complete miniature sheet.

1614 Green Pillar Box, 1857   **1615** Horizontal Aperture Box, 1874

1616 Air Mail Box, 1934   **1617** Double Aperture Box, 1939

1618 Modern Style Box, 1980

150th Anniversary of the First Pillar Box

2002 (8 Oct.) One centre phosphor band (2nd) or two phosphor bands (others). Perf 14 × 14½

2316	**1614**	(2nd) multicoloured	75	55	☐	☐
2317	**1615**	(1st) multicoloured	1·00	80	☐	☐
2318	**1616**	(E) multicoloured	1·75	1·75	☐	☐
2319	**1617**	47p multicoloured	2·00	2·50	☐	☐
2320	**1618**	68p multicoloured	2·50	3·00	☐	☐
Set of 5			7·50	7·50	☐	☐
First Day Cover				8·50	☐	
Presentation Pack			7·50		☐	
PHQ Cards (*set of* 5)			4·75	16·00	☐	☐
Set of 5 Gutter Pairs			16·00		☐	

1619 Blue Spruce Star

1620 Holly

1621 Ivy

1622 Mistletoe

1623 Pine Cone

Christmas

2002 (5 Nov.) Self-adhesive. One centre phosphor band (2nd) or two phosphor bands (others). Die-cut perf 14½ × 14

2321	**1619**	(2nd) multicoloured	75	55	☐	☐
2322	**1620**	(1st) multicoloured	1·00	80	☐	☐
2323	**1621**	(E) multicoloured	1·50	1·50	☐	☐
2324	**1622**	47p multicoloured	2·00	1·75	☐	☐
2325	**1623**	68p multicoloured	3·00	2·75	☐	☐
Set of 5			8·00	7·50	☐	☐
First Day Cover				8·50	☐	
Presentation Pack			7·50		☐	
PHQ Cards (*set of* 5)			4·75	16·00	☐	☐

Collectors Pack 2002

2002 (5 Nov.) Comprises Nos. 2243/57, 2260/4, 2265/88, 2291/2, 2299/313 and **MS**2315/25

CP2325a	Collectors Pack	£110	☐

Post Office Yearbook

2002 (5 Nov.) Comprises Nos. 2243/57, 2260/4, 2265/88, 2291/2, 2299/313 and **MS**2315/25 in hardback book with slip case

YB2325a	Yearbook	£100	☐

50th Anniversary of Wilding Definitives (1st issue)

2002 (5 Dec.) Sheet, 124 × 70 mm, containing designs as T **154/5** and **157/60** (1952–54 issue), but with values in decimal currency as T **1348** or with service indicator as T **1566**, printed on pale cream. One centre phosphor band (2nd) or two phosphor bands (others). W **1565**. Perf 15 × 14 (with one elliptical hole on each vertical side)

MS2326	1p orange-red; 2p ultramarine; 5p red-brown; (2nd) carmine-red; (1st) green; 33p brown; 37p magenta; 47p bistre-brown; 50p green and label showing national emblems	10·00	10·00	☐	☐
First Day Cover			10·00		☐
Presentation Pack		£100		☐	
PHQ Cards (*set of* 5)		3·00	12·00	☐	☐

The PHQ cards depict the (2nd), (1st), 33p, 37p and 47p stamps.

See also No. **MS**2367.

1624 Barn Owl landing

1625 Barn Owl with folded Wings and Legs down

1626 Barn Owl with extended Wings and Legs down

1627 Barn Owl in Flight with Wings lowered

1628 Barn Owl in Flight with Wings raised

1629 Kestrel with Wings folded

1630 Kestrel with Wings fully extended upwards

1631 Kestrel with Wings horizonta l

1632 Kestrel with Wings partly extended downwards

1633 Kestrel with Wings fully extended downwards

T **1624/33** were printed together, *se-tenant*, in blocks of 10 (5 × 2) throughout the sheet.

Birds of Prey

2003 (14 Jan.) Phosphor background. Perf 14½

2327	**1624**	(1st) multicoloured	70	80	☐	☐
		a. Block of 10.				
		Nos. 2327/36	10·00	10·00	☐	☐
2328	**1625**	(1st) multicoloured	70	80	☐	☐
2329	**1626**	(1st) multicoloured	70	80	☐	☐
2330	**1627**	(1st) multicoloured	70	80	☐	☐
2331	**1628**	(1st) multicoloured	70	80	☐	☐
2332	**1629**	(1st) multicoloured	70	80	☐	☐
2333	**1630**	(1st) multicoloured	70	80	☐	☐
2334	**1631**	(1st) multicoloured	70	80	☐	☐
2335	**1632**	(1st) multicoloured	70	80	☐	☐
2336	**1633**	(1st) multicoloured	70	80	☐	☐
Set of 10			10·00	10·00	☐	☐
First Day Cover				11·00		☐
Presentation Pack			12·00		☐	
PHQ Cards (*set of* 10)			9·25	28·00	☐	☐
Gutter Block of 20			24·00		☐	

1634 'Gold star, See me, Playtime'

1635 '1 ♥ U, XXXX, S.W.A.L.K.'

1636 'Angel, Poppet, Little terror'

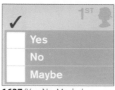

1637 'Yes, No, Maybe'

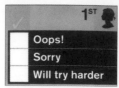

1638 'Oops!, Sorry, Will try harder'

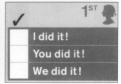

1639 'I did it!, You did it!, We did it!'

T **2337/42** were printed together, *se-tenant*, in blocks of 6 (3 × 2) throughout the sheet.

'Occasions' Greetings Stamps

2003 (4 Feb.) Two phosphor bands. Perf 14½ × 14

2337	**1634**	(1st) lemon and new blue	60	50	☐	☐
		a. Block of 6.				
		Nos. 2337/42	6·50	6·00	☐	☐
2338	**1635**	(1st) red and deep ultramarine	60	50	☐	☐
2339	**1636**	(1st) purple and bright yellow-green	60	50	☐	☐
2340	**1637**	(1st) bright yellow-green and red	60	50	☐	☐
2341	**1638**	(1st) deep ultramarine and lemon	60	50	☐	☐
2342	**1639**	(1st) new blue and purple	60	50	☐	☐
Set of 6			6·50	6·00	☐	☐
First Day Cover				9·00		☐
Presentation Pack			8·00		☐	
PHQ Cards (*set of* 6)			5·25	18·00	☐	☐
Gutter Block of 12			14·00		☐	

Nos. 2337/42 were also available in *se-tenant* sheets of 20 containing four examples of Nos. 2338 and 2340 and three of each of the others. The stamps are accompanied by half stamp-size printed labels or a personal photograph.

1640 Completing the Genome Jigsaw

1641 Ape with Moustache and Scientist

1642 DNA Snakes and Ladders

1643 'Animal Scientists'

1644 Genome Crystal Ball

50th Anniversary of Discovery of DNA

2003 (25 Feb.) One centre phosphor band (2nd) or two phosphor bands (others). Perf 14½

2343	**1640**	(2nd) multicoloured	1·00	55	☐	☐
2344	**1641**	(1st) multicoloured	1·00	80	☐	☐
2345	**1642**	(E) multicoloured	1·25	1·25	☐	☐
2346	**1643**	47p multicoloured	1·50	1·50	☐	☐
2347	**1644**	68p multicoloured	2·00	2·25	☐	☐
Set of 5			6·50	6·00	☐	☐
First Day Cover				10·00		☐
Presentation Pack			8·00		☐	
PHQ Cards (*set of* 5)			4·75	18·00	☐	☐
Set of 5 Gutter Pairs			15·00		☐	

1645 Strawberry   **1646** Potato

1647 Apple   **1648** Red Pepper

1649 Pear   **1650** Orange

1651 Tomato   **1652** Lemon

1653 Brussels Sprout   **1654** Aubergine

T **1645/54** were printed together in sheets of 10 with the surplus self-adhesive paper around each stamp retained. The stamp pane is accompanied by a similar-sized pane of self-adhesive labels showing ears, eyes, mouths, hats etc which are intended for the adornment of fruit and vegetables depicted. This pane is separated from the stamps by a line of roulettes.

Fruit and Vegetables

2003 (25 Mar.) Self-adhesive. Two phosphor bands. Perf 14½ × 14 die-cut (without teeth around protruding tops or bottoms of the designs)

2348	**1645**	(1st) multicoloured	70	50	☐	☐
		a. Sheetlet. Nos. 2348/57				
		and pane of				
		decorative labels	10·00	10·00	☐	☐
2349	**1646**	(1st) multicoloured	70	50	☐	☐
2350	**1647**	(1st) multicoloured	70	50	☐	☐
2351	**1648**	(1st) multicoloured	70	50	☐	☐
2352	**1649**	(1st) multicoloured	70	50	☐	☐
2353	**1650**	(1st) multicoloured	70	50	☐	☐
2354	**1651**	(1st) multicoloured	70	50	☐	☐
2355	**1652**	(1st) multicoloured	70	50	☐	☐
2356	**1653**	(1st) multicoloured	70	50	☐	☐
2357	**1654**	(1st) multicoloured	70	50	☐	☐
Set of 10			10·00	10·00	☐	☐
First Day Cover				12·00		☐
Presentation Pack			60·00		☐	
PHQ Cards (*set of* 10)			12·00	25·00	☐	☐

Nos. 2348/57 were re-issued on 7th March 2006 in sheets of 20 containing two of each of the ten designs, each stamp accompanied by a *se-tenant* speech bubble label. These sheets were printed in lithography instead of photogravure, and have stickers showing eyes, hats, etc in the sheet margin.

1655

Overseas Booklet Stamps

2003 (27 Mar.)–**2004** Self-adhesive. Two phosphor bands. Perf 15 × 14 die-cut with one elliptical hole on each vertical side

2357a		(Worldwide postcard)				
		grey-black, rosine				
		and ultramarine	65	70	☐	☐
2358	**1655**	(Europe) new blue				
		and rosine	80	85	☐	☐
2359		(Worldwide) rosine				
		and new blue	1·60	1·70	☐	☐
First Day Cover (Nos. 2358/9)				5·25		☐
Presentation Pack (Nos. 2358/9)			5·00		☐	
PHQ Card (No. 2358)			45	2·00	☐	☐

Nos. 2358/9 were intended to pay postage on mail up to 40 grams to either Europe (52p) or to foreign destinations outside Europe (£1.12). No. 2357a was intended to pay postcard rate to foreign destinations (43p).

Operationally they were only available in separate booklets of 4, initially sold at £2.08, £4.48 and £1.72, with the surplus self-adhesive paper around each stamp removed. Single examples of the stamps were available from philatelic outlets as sets of two or in presentation packs.

For first day cover and presentation pack for No. 2357a see below Nos. Y1667/1803.

1656 Amy Johnson (pilot) and Biplane

1657 Members of 1953 Everest Team

1658 Freya Stark (traveller and writer) and Desert

1659 Ernest Shackleton (Antarctic explorer) and Wreck of *Endurance*

1660 Francis Chichester (yachtsman) and *Gipsy Moth IV*

1661 Robert Falcon Scott (Antarctic explorer) and Norwegian Expedition at the Pole

Extreme Endeavours (British Explorers)

2003 (29 Apr.) One centre phosphor band (2nd) or two phosphor bands (others).

(a) Photo Questa. PVA gum. Perf 15 × 14½

2360	**1656**	2nd) multicoloured	50	50	☐	☐
2361	**1657**	(1st) multicoloured	75	75	☐	☐
2362	**1658**	(E) multicoloured	1·50	1·50	☐	☐
2363	**1659**	42p multicoloured	1·75	1·75	☐	☐
2364	**1660**	47p multicoloured	2·00	2·00	☐	☐
2365	**1661**	68p multicoloured	2.50	2·50	☐	☐
Set of 6			8·00	8·50	☐	☐
First Day Cover				12·00		☐
Presentation Pack			9·00		☐	
PHQ Cards (*set of* 6)			3·25	12·00	☐	☐
Set of 6 Gutter Pairs			17·00		☐	

(b) Photo De La Rue. Self-adhesive. Die-cut perf 14½

2366	**1657**	(1st) multicoloured	5·00	5·00	☐	☐

The phosphor bands on Nos. 2361/5 are at the centre and right of each stamp.

No. 2366 was only issued in £1.62 stamp booklets in which the surplus self-adhesive paper around each stamp was removed.

50th Anniversary of Wilding Definitives (2nd issue)

2003 (20 May) Sheet, 124 × 70 mm, containing designs as T **155/8** and **160** (1952–54 issue), but with values in decimal currency as T **1348** or with service indicator as T **1566**, printed on pale cream. One centre phosphor band (20p) or two phosphor bands (others). W **1565**. P 15 × 14 (with one elliptical hole on each vertical side).

MS2367	4p deep lilac; 8p ultramarine; 10p reddish purple; 20p bright green; 28p bronze-green; 34p brown-purple; (E) chestnut; 42p Prussian blue; 68p grey-blue and label showing national emblems	10·50	11·25	☐	☐
First Day Cover			13·00		☐
Presentation Pack		18·00		☐	

1662 Guardsmen in Coronation Procession

1663 East End Children reading Coronation Party Poster

1664 Queen Elizabeth II in Coronation Chair with Bishops of Durham and Bath & Wells

1665 Children in Plymouth working on Royal Montage

1666 Queen Elizabeth II in Coronation Robes (photograph by Cecil Beaton)

1667 Children's Race at East End Street Party

1668 Coronation Coach passing through Marble Arch

1669 Children in Fancy Dress

1670 Coronation Coach outside Buckingham Palace

1671 Children eating at London Street Party

T **1662/71** were printed together, *se-tenant*, as blocks of 10 (5 × 2) in sheets of 60 (2 panes of 30).

50th Anniversary of Coronation

2003 (2 June) W **1565**. Two phosphor bands. Perf 14½ × 14

2368	**1662**	(1st) multicoloured	45	50	☐	☐
		a. Block of 10.				
		Nos. 2368/77	9·50	9·50	☐	☐
2369	**1663**	(1st) black and gold	45	50	☐	☐
2370	**1664**	(1st) multicoloured	45	50	☐	☐
2371	**1665**	(1st) black and gold	45	50	☐	☐
2372	**1666**	(1st) multicoloured	45	50	☐	☐
2373	**1667**	(1st) black and gold	45	50	☐	☐
2374	**1668**	(1st) multicoloured	45	50	☐	☐
2375	**1669**	(1st) black and gold	45	50	☐	☐
2376	**1670**	(1st) multicoloured	45	50	☐	☐
2377	**1671**	(1st) black and gold	45	50	☐	☐
Set of 10			9·50	9·50	☐	☐
First Day Cover				12·00	☐	
Presentation Pack			25·00		☐	
PHQ Cards (*set of* 10)			9·25	20·00	☐	☐
Gutter Block of 20			25·00		☐	

No. 2372 does not show the Queen's head in gold as do the other nine designs.

50th Anniversary of Coronation. Booklet Stamps

2003 (2 June) Designs as T **160** (Wilding definitive of 1952) and **163** (Coronation commemorative of 1953), but with values in decimal currency as T **1348**. W **1565**. Two phosphor bands. P 15 × 14 (with one elliptical hole on each vertical side for Nos. 2378/9)

2378	**160**	47p bistre-brown	5·00	2·50	☐	☐
2379		68p grey-blue	5·00	2·50	☐	☐
2380	**163**	£1 deep yellow-green	50·00	45·00	☐	☐
Set of 3			55·00	45·00	☐	☐

Nos. 2378/80 were only available in £7.46 stamp booklets. Stamps as Nos. 2378/9, but on pale cream, were also included in the Wilding miniature sheets, Nos. **MS**2326 or **MS**2367. A £1 design as No. 2380, but on phosphorised paper, was previously included in the "Stamp Show 2000" miniature sheet, No. **MS**2147.

1672 Prince William in September 2001 (Brendan Beirne)

1673 Prince William in September 2000 (Tim Graham)

1674 Prince William in September 2001 (Camera Press)

1675 Prince William in September 2001 (Tim Graham)

21st Birthday of Prince William of Wales

2003 (17 June) Phosphor backgrounds. Perf 14½

2381	**1672**	28p multicoloured	1·00	50	☐	☐
2382	**1673**	(E) dull mauve, grey-black and light green	1·25	1·50	☐	☐
2383	**1674**	47p multicoloured	1·75	2·00	☐	☐
2384	**1675**	68p sage-green, black and bright green	2·50	2·50	☐	☐
Set of 4			8·00	6·00	☐	☐
First Day Cover				10·00		☐
Presentation Pack			25·00		☐	
PHQ Cards (*set of* 4)			7·50	20·00	☐	☐
Set of 4 Gutter Pairs			13·00		☐	

1676 Loch Assynt, Sutherland

1677 Ben More, Isle of Mull

1678 Rothiemurchus, Cairngorms

1679 Dalveen Pass, Lowther Hills

1680 Glenfinnan Viaduct, Lochaber

1681 Papa Little, Shetland Islands

A British Journey: Scotland

2003 (15 July) One centre phosphor band (2nd) or two phosphor bands (others). Perf 14½.

		(a) PVA gum				
2385	**1676**	(2nd) multicoloured	50	35	☐	☐
2386	**1677**	(1st) multicoloured	75	50	☐	☐
2387	**1678**	(E) multicoloured	1·25	1·25	☐	☐

2388 **1679**	42p multicoloured	1·25	1·50	☐ ☐
2389 **1680**	47p multicoloured	1·50	2·00	☐ ☐
2390 **1681**	68p multicoloured	2·00	2·50	☐ ☐
Set of 6		7·00	7·75	☐ ☐
First Day Cover			11·00	☐
Presentation Pack		9·50		☐
PHQ Cards (*set of* 6)		3·00	11·00	☐ ☐
Set of 6 Gutter Pairs		16·00		☐

(b) Self-adhesive. Die-cut perf 14½

2391 1677	(1st) multicoloured	6·00	6·00	☐ ☐

No. 2391 was only issued in £1.68 stamp booklets in which the surplus self-adhesive paper around each stamp was removed.

1682 'The Station'
(Andrew Davidson)

1683 'Black Swan'
(Stanley Chew)

1684 'The Cross Keys'
(George Mackenney)

1685 'The Mayflower'
(Ralph Ellis)

1686 'The Barley Sheaf' (Joy Cooper)

Europa. British Pub Signs

2003 (12 Aug.) Two phosphor bands. Perf 14 × 14½

2392 **1682**	(1st) multicoloured	75	50	☐ ☐
2393 **1683**	(E) multicoloured	2·00	2·00	☐ ☐
2394 **1684**	42p multicoloured	1·50	1·50	☐ ☐
2395 **1685**	47p multicoloured	1·75	2·00	☐ ☐
2396 **1686**	68p multicoloured	2·00	2·25	☐ ☐
Set of 5		7·50	7·75	☐ ☐
First Day Cover			11·00	☐
Presentation Pack		11·00		☐
PHQ Cards (*set of* 5)		3·00	11·00	☐ ☐
Set of 5 Gutter Pairs		17·00		☐

The 1st and E values incorporate the "EUROPA" emblem.

1687 Meccano Constructor
Biplane, c. 1931

1688 Wells-Brimtoy
Clockwork Double-decker
Omnibus, c. 1938

1689 Hornby M1 Clockwork
Locomotive and Tender, c. 1948

1690 Dinky Toys Ford Zephyr,
c. 1956

1691 Mettoy Friction Drive Space Ship Eagle, c. 1960

Classic Transport Toys

2003 (18 Sept.) Two phosphor bands.

(a) Photo Enschedé. PVA gum. Perf 14½ × 14

2397 **1687**	(1st) multicoloured	75	50	☐ ☐
2398 **1688**	(E) multicoloured	1·25	1·25	☐ ☐
2399 **1689**	42p multicoloured	1·50	1·50	☐ ☐
2400 **1690**	47p multicoloured	1·75	1·75	☐ ☐
2401 **1691**	68p multicoloured	2·50	2·50	☐ ☐
Set of 5		7·50	7·50	☐ ☐
First Day Cover			10·00	☐
Presentation Pack		9·00		☐
PHQ Cards (*set of* 6)		3·00	14·00	☐ ☐
Set of 5 Gutter Pairs		16·00		☐
MS2402 115 × 105 mm. Nos. 2397/401		8·00	8·25	☐ ☐
First Day Cover			14·00	☐

(b) Photo DLR. Self-adhesive. Die-cut perf 14½ × 14

2403 **1687**	(1st) multicoloured	6·00	6·00	☐ ☐

The complete miniature sheet is shown on one of the PHQ cards with the others depicting individual stamps.

No. 2403 was only issued in £1.68 stamp booklets in which the surplus self-adhesive paper around each stamp was removed.

1692 Coffin of
Denytenamun,
Egyptian, c. 900BC

1693 Alexander the
Great, Greek, c. 200BC

1694 Sutton Hoo Helmet, Anglo-Saxon, c. AD600

1695 Sculpture of Parvati, South Indian, c. AD1550

1696 Mask of Xiutechuhtli, Mixtec-Aztec, c. AD1500

1697 Hoa Hakananai'a, Easter Island, c. AD1000

250th Anniversary of the British Museum

2003 (7 Oct.) One side phosphor band (2nd), two phosphor bands ((1st), (E), 47p) or phosphor background at left and band at right (42p, 68p). Perf 14 × 14½

2404	**1692**	(2nd) multicoloured	50	35	☐	☐
2405	**1693**	(1st) multicoloured	75	50	☐	☐
2406	**1694**	(E) multicoloured	1·25	1·25	☐	☐
2407	**1695**	42p multicoloured	1·50	1·50	☐	☐
2408	**1696**	47p multicoloured	2·00	2·00	☐	☐
2409	**1697**	68p multicoloured	2·75	2·75	☐	☐
Set of 6			8·00	8·00	☐	
First Day Cover				11·00		☐
Presentation Pack			11·00		☐	
PHQ Cards (*set of* 6)			3·00	14·00	☐	☐
Set of 6 Gutter Pairs			17·00		☐	

1698 Ice Spiral

1699 Icicle Star

1700 Wall of Ice Blocks

1701 Ice Ball

1702 Ice Hole

1703 Snow Pyramids

Christmas. Ice Sculptures by Andy Goldsworthy

2003 (4 Nov.) Self-adhesive. One side phosphor band (2nd), 'all-over' phosphor (1st) or two bands (others). Die-cut perf 14½ × 14

2410	**1698**	(2nd) multicoloured	75	35	☐	☐
2411	**1699**	(1st) multicoloured	1·25	50	☐	☐
2412	**1700**	(E) multicoloured	1·50	1·50	☐	☐
2413	**1701**	53p multicoloured	2·00	2·00	☐	☐
2414	**1702**	68p multicoloured	2·50	2·50	☐	☐
2415	**1703**	£1.12 multicoloured	3·00	3·00	☐	☐
Set of 6			10·00	10·00	☐	☐
First Day Cover				12·50		☐
Presentation Pack			12·00		☐	
PHQ Cards (*set of* 6)			4·00	12·50	☐	☐

The 2nd and 1st class were also issued in separate sheets of 20, each stamp printed in lithography instead of photogravure and accompanied by a half stamp-size *se-tenant* label showing either animals, ice sculptures or a personal photograph.

Collectors Pack 2003

2003 (4 Nov.) Comprises Nos. 2327/57, 2360/5, 2368/77, 2381/90, 2392/401 and 2404/15

CP2415a	Collectors Pack	£110	☐

Post Office Yearbook

2003 (4 Nov.) Comprises Nos. 2327/57, 2360/5, 2368/77, 2381/90, 2392/401 and 2404/15

YB2415a	Yearbook	£100	☐

1704 Rugby Scenes

England's Victory in Rugby World Cup Championship, Australia

2003 (19 Dec.) Sheet 115 × 85 mm. Multicoloured. Two phosphor bands. Perf 14

MS2416	**1704**	(1st) England flags and fans; (1st) England team standing in circle before match; 68p World Cup trophy; 68p Victorious England players after match	14·00	14·00	☐	☐
First Day Cover				14·00		☐
Presentation Pack			35·00		☐	

1705 Dolgoch, Rheilffordd Talyllyn Railway, Gwynedd

1706 CR Class 439, Bo'ness and Kinneil Railway, West Lothian

1707 GCR Class 8K, Leicestershire

1708 GWR Manor Class Bradley Manor, Severn Valley Railway, Worcestershire

1709 SR West Country class Blackmoor Vale, Bluebell Railway, East Sussex

1710 BR Standard class, Keighley & Worth Valley Railway, Yorkshire

Classic Locomotives

2004 (13 Jan.) One side phosphor band (20p) or two phosphor bands (others). Perf 14½

2417 **1705**	20p multicoloured	65	65	☐	☐
2418 **1706**	28p multicoloured	90	90	☐	☐
2419 **1707**	(E) multicoloured	1·20	1·20	☐	☐
2420 **1708**	42p multicoloured	1·50	1·50	☐	☐
2421 **1709**	47p multicoloured	2·00	2·00	☐	☐
2422 **1710**	68p multicoloured	3·00	3·50	☐	☐
Set of 6		8·00	8·50	☐	☐
First Day Cover		12·00			☐
Presentation Pack		35·00		☐	
PHQ Cards (*set of* 6)		8·50	15·00	☐	☐
Set of 6 Gutter Pairs		15·00		☐	☐
MS2423 190 × 67 mm. Nos. 2417/22		35·00	35·00	☐	☐
First Day Cover			35·00		☐

1711 Postman

1712 Face

1713 Duck

1714 Baby

1715 Aircraft

T **1711/15** were printed together, *se-tenant*, as horizontal strips of 5 in sheets of 25 (5 × 5).

'Occasions' Greetings Stamps

2004 (3 Feb.) Two phosphor bands. Perf 14½ × 14

2424 **1711**	(1st) bright mauve and black		50	50	☐	☐
	a. Horiz strip of 5. Nos. 2424/8		6·00	6·00	☐	☐
2425 **1712**	(1st) magenta and black		50	50	☐	☐
2426 **1713**	(1st) lemon and black		50	50	☐	☐
2427 **1714**	(1st) pale turquoise-green and black		50	50	☐	☐
2428 **1715**	(1st) bright new blue and black		50	50	☐	☐
Set of 5			6·00	6·00	☐	☐
First Day Cover				8·00		☐
Presentation Pack			8·00		☐	
PHQ Cards (*set of* 5)			4·75	12·00	☐	☐
Gutter Block of 10			13·00		☐	☐

Nos. 2424/8 were also issued in sheets of 20 containing the five designs *se-tenant* with half stamp-size printed message labels. Similar sheets containing either Nos. 2424 and 2428 or Nos. 2425/7 came with personal photographs on the labels.

1716 Map showing Middle Earth

1717 Forest of Lothlórien in Spring

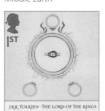

1718 Dust-jacket for *The Fellowship of the Ring*

1719 Rivendell

1720 The Hall at Bag End

1721 Orthanc

1722 Doors of Durin

1723 Barad-dûr

1724 Minas Tirith

1725 Fangorn Forest

T **1716/25** were printed together, *se-tenant*, in blocks of 10 (5 × 2) throughout the sheet.

50th Anniversary of Publication of *The Fellowship of the Ring* and *The Two Towers* by J. R. R. Tolkien

2004 (26 Feb.) Two phosphor bands. Perf 14½

2429	**1716**	(1st) multicoloured	50	50	☐	☐
		a. Block of 10.				
		Nos. 2429/38	10·00	10·00	☐	☐
2430	**1717**	(1st) multicoloured	50	50	☐	☐
2431	**1718**	(1st) multicoloured	50	50	☐	☐
2432	**1719**	(1st) multicoloured	50	50	☐	☐
2433	**1720**	(1st) multicoloured	50	50	☐	☐
2434	**1721**	(1st) multicoloured	50	50	☐	☐
2435	**1722**	(1st) multicoloured	50	50	☐	☐
2436	**1723**	(1st) multicoloured	50	50	☐	☐
2437	**1724**	(1st) multicoloured	50	50	☐	☐
2438	**1725**	(1st) multicoloured	50	50	☐	☐
Set of 10			10·00	10·00	☐	☐
First Day Cover				10·00		☐
Presentation Pack			30·00		☐	
PHQ Cards (*set of 10*)			9·75	18·00	☐	☐
Gutter Block of 20			22·00		☐	

1726 Ely Island, Lower Lough Erne

1727 Giant's Causeway, Antrim Coast

1728 Slemish, Antrim Mountains

1729 Banns Road, Mourne Mountains

1730 Glenelly Valley, Sperrins

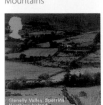
1731 Islandmore, Strangford Lough

A British Journey: Northern Ireland

2004 (16 Mar.) One side phosphor band (2nd) or two phosphor bands (others). Perf 14½

			(a) PVA gum			
2439	**1726**	(2nd) multicoloured	65	65	☐	☐
2440	**1727**	(1st) multicoloured	90	90	☐	☐
2441	**1728**	(E) multicoloured	1·20	1·20	☐	☐
2442	**1729**	42p multicoloured	1·30	1·30	☐	☐
2443	**1730**	47p multicoloured	1·50	1·50	☐	☐
2444	**1731**	68p multicoloured	2·20	2·20	☐	☐
Set of 6			7·75	7·75	☐	☐
First Day Cover				12·50		☐
Presentation Pack			14·00		☐	
PHQ Cards (*set of 6*)			5·75	14·00	☐	☐
Set of 6 Gutter Pairs			16·00		☐	

			(b) Self-adhesive. Die-cut perf 14½			
2445	**1727**	(1st) multicoloured	6·00	6·00	☐	☐

No. 2445 was only issued in £1.68 stamp booklets in which the surplus self-adhesive paper around each stamp was removed.

1732 'Lace 1 (trial proof) 1968' (Sir Terry Frost)

1733 'Coccinelle' (Sonia Delaunay)

Centenary of the Entente Cordiale. Contemporary Paintings

2004 (6 Apr.) Two phosphor bands. Perf 14 × 14½

2446	**1732**	28p grey, black and rosine	1·00	85	☐	☐
2447	**1733**	57p multicoloured	2·25	2·00	☐	☐
Set of 2			3·00	2·75	☐	☐
First Day Cover				4·50		☐

Presentation Pack	35·00		☐	
Presentation Pack (UK and French stamps)	35·00		☐	
PHQ Cards (*set of* 2)	1·90	5·00	☐	☐
Set of 2 Gutter Pairs	7·00		☐	☐
Set of 2 Traffic Light Gutter Blocks of 4	15·00		☐	

Stamps in similar designs were issued by France and these are included in the joint Presentation Pack.

1734 'RMS *Queen Mary 2*, 2004' (Edward D. Walker)

1735 'SS *Canberra* 1961' (David Cobb)

1736 'RMS *Queen Mary* 1936' (Charles Pears)

1737 'RMS *Mauretania*, 1907' (Thomas Henry)

1738 'SS *City of New York*, 1888' (Raphael Monleaon y Torres)

1739 'PS *Great Western*, 1838' (Joseph Walter)

Ocean Liners

2004 (13 Apr.) Two phosphor bands.

(a) PVA gum. Perf 14½ × 14

2448	**1734**	(1st) multicoloured	90	90	☐ ☐
2449	**1735**	(E) multicoloured	1·30	1·30	☐ ☐
2450	**1736**	42p multicoloured	1·30	1·30	☐ ☐
2451	**1737**	47p multicoloured	1·50	1·50	☐ ☐
2452	**1738**	57p multicoloured	1·80	1·80	☐ ☐
2453	**1739**	68p multicoloured	2·20	2·20	☐ ☐
Set of 6			9·00	9·00	☐ ☐
First Day Cover				10·00	☐
Presentation Pack			11·00		☐
PHQ Cards (*set of* 7)			6·75	17·00	☐ ☐
Set of 6 Gutter Pairs			20·00		☐
MS2454 114 × 104 mm. Nos. 2448/53			18·00	18·00	☐ ☐
First Day Cover				18·00	☐

(b) Self-adhesive. Die-cut perf 14½ × 14

2455	**1734**	(1st) multicoloured	6·00	6·00	☐ ☐

Nos. 2448/55 commemorate the introduction to service of the Queen Mary 2.
No. 2455 was only issued in £1.68 stamp booklets in which the surplus self-adhesive paper around each stamp was removed.
The complete miniature sheet is shown on one of the PHQ cards with the others depicting individual stamps.

1740 Dianthus Allwoodii Group

1741 Dahlia 'Garden Princess'

1742 Clematis 'Arabella'

1743 Miltonia 'French Lake'

1744 Lilium 'Lemon Pixie'

1745 Delphinium 'Clifford Sky'

Bicentenary of the Royal Horticultural Society (1st issue)

2004 (25 May) One side phosphor band (2nd) or 'all-over' phosphor (others). Perf 14½

2456	**1740**	(2nd) multicoloured	70	70	☐ ☐
2457	**1741**	(1st) multicoloured	90	90	☐ ☐
2458	**1742**	(E) multicoloured	1·30	1·30	☐ ☐
2459	**1743**	42p multicoloured	2·00	2·00	☐ ☐
2460	**1744**	47p multicoloured	2·50	2·50	☐ ☐
2461	**1745**	68p multicoloured	3·50	3·50	☐ ☐
Set of 6			10·00	10·00	☐ ☐
First Day Cover				12·00	☐
Presentation Pack			11·00		☐
PHQ Cards (*set of* 7)			6·75	17·00	☐ ☐
Set of 6 Gutter Pairs			22·00		☐
MS2462 115 × 105 mm. Nos. 2456/61			14·00	14·00	☐ ☐
First Day Cover				16·00	☐

The complete miniature sheet is shown on one of the PHQ cards with the others depicting individual stamps.
The 1st class stamp was also issued in sheets of 20, printed in lithography instead of photogravure, each stamp accompanied by a *se-tenant* stamp-size label.

Bicentenary of the Royal Horticultural Society (2nd issue). Booklet stamps

2004 (25 May) Designs as Nos. 1955, 1958 and 1962 (1997 Greeting Stamps 19th-century Flower Paintings). Two phosphor bands. Perf 15 × 14 (with one elliptical hole on each vertical side)

2463	**1280**	(1st) multicoloured	8·00	8·00	☐ ☐
2464	**1283**	(1st) multicoloured	4·00	4·00	☐ ☐
2465	**1287**	(1st) multicoloured	8·00	8·00	☐ ☐
Set of 3			18·00	18·00	☐ ☐

On Nos. 2463/5 the phosphor bands appear at the left and the centre of each stamp.
Nos. 2463/5 were only available in £7.23 stamp booklets.

1746 Barmouth Bridge

1747 Hyddgen, Plynlimon

1748 Brecon Beacons

1749 Pen-pych, Rhondda Valley

1750 Rhewl, Dee Valley

1751 Marloes Sands

A British Journey: Wales

2004 (15 June) One centre phosphor band (2nd), 'all-over' phosphor (1st) or two phosphor bands (others).

(a) PVA gum. Perf 14½

2466	**1746**	(2nd) multicoloured	70	70	☐	☐
2467	**1747**	(1st) multicoloured	90	90	☐	☐
2468	**1748**	40p multicoloured	1·75	1·50	☐	☐
2469	**1749**	43p multicoloured	2·00	2·00	☐	☐
2470	**1750**	47p multicoloured	2·50	3·00	☐	☐
2471	**1751**	68p multicoloured	3·50	4·00	☐	☐
Set of 6			10·00	10·00	☐	☐
First Day Cover				11·00		☐
Presentation Pack			11·00		☐	
PHQ Cards (*set of* 6)			5·75	12·00	☐	☐
Set of 6 Gutter Pairs			22·00		☐	

(b) Self-adhesive. Die-cut perf 14½

2472	**1747**	(1st) multicoloured	8·00	8·00	☐	☐

The 1st and 40p values include the 'EUROPA' emblem.
No. 2472 was only issued in £1.68 stamp booklets in which the surplus self-adhesive paper around each stamp was removed.

1752 Sir Rowland Hill Award

1753 William Shipley (Founder of Royal Society of Arts)

1754 'RSA' as Typewriter Keys and Shorthand

1755 Chimney Sweep

1756 'Gill Typeface'

1757 'Zero Waste'

250th Anniversary of the Royal Society of Arts

2004 (10 Aug.) Two phosphor bands. Perf 14

2473	**1752**	(1st) multicoloured	95	95	☐	☐
2474	**1753**	40p multicoloured	1·30	1·30	☐	☐
2475	**1754**	43p multicoloured	1·40	1·40	☐	☐
2476	**1755**	47p multicoloured	1·50	1·50	☐	☐
2477	**1756**	57p silver, vermilion and black	2·20	2·20	☐	☐
2478	**1757**	68p silver, vermilion and black	3·00	3·00	☐	☐
Set of 6			10·00	10·00	☐	☐
First Day Cover				12·00		☐
Presentation Pack			11·00		☐	
PHQ Cards (*set of* 6)			5·75	12·00	☐	☐
Set of 6 Gutter Pairs			22·00		☐	

1758 Pine Marten

1759 Roe Deer

1760 Badger

1761 Yellow-necked Mouse

1762 Wild Cat

1763 Red Squirrel

1764 Stoat

1765 Natterer's Bat

1766 Mole

1767 Fox

T **1758/67** were printed together, *se-tenant*, in blocks of 10 (5 × 2) throughout the sheet.

Woodland Animals

2004 (16 Sept.) Two phosphor bands. P 14½

2479	**1758**	(1st) multicoloured	60	50	☐	☐
		a. Block of 10.				
		Nos. 2479/88	10·00	10·00	☐	☐
2480	**1759**	(1st) multicoloured	60	50	☐	☐
2481	**1760**	(1st) multicoloured	60	50	☐	☐
2482	**1761**	(1st) multicoloured	60	50	☐	☐
2483	**1762**	(1st) multicoloured	60	50	☐	☐
2484	**1763**	(1st) multicoloured	60	50	☐	☐
2485	**1764**	(1st) multicoloured	60	50	☐	☐
2486	**1765**	(1st) multicoloured	60	50	☐	☐
2487	**1766**	(1st) multicoloured	60	50	☐	☐
2488	**1767**	(1st) multicoloured	60	50	☐	☐
Set of 10			10·00	10·00	☐	☐
First Day Cover				12·00		☐
Presentation Pack			12·00		☐	
PHQ Cards (*set of 10*)			9·75	16·00	☐	☐
Gutter Block of 20			22·00		☐	

1768 Pte. McNamara, 5th Dragoon Guards, Heavy Brigade Charge, Battle of Balaklava

1769 Piper Muir, 42nd Regt of Foot, Amphibious Assault on Kerch

1770 Sgt. Maj. Edwards, Scots Fusilier Guards, Gallant Action, Battle of Inkerman

1771 Sgt. Powell, 1st Regt of Foot Guards, Battles of Alma and Inkerman

1772 Sgt. Maj. Poole, Royal Sappers and Miners, Defensive Line, Battle of Inkerman

1773 Sgt. Glasgow, Royal Artillery, Gun Battery besieged Sevastopol

150th Anniversary of the Crimean War

2004 (12 Oct.) One centre phosphor band (2nd) or two phosphor bands (others). Perf 14

2489	**1768**	(2nd) multicoloured	70	70	☐	☐
2490	**1769**	(1st) multicoloured	90	90	☐	☐
2491	**1770**	40p multicoloured	2·00	2·00	☐	☐
2492	**1771**	57p multicoloured	2·50	2·50	☐	☐
2493	**1772**	68p multicoloured	2·75	3·00	☐	☐
2494	**1773**	£1.12 multicoloured	4·50	5·00	☐	☐
Set of 6			12·00	12·00	☐	☐
First Day Cover				13·50		☐
Presentation Pack			12·50		☐	
PHQ Cards (*set of 6*)			5·75	14·00	☐	☐
Set of 6 Gutter Pairs			25·00		☐	
Set of 6 Traffic Light Pairs			30·00		☐	

Nos. 2489/94 show 'Crimean Heroes' photographs taken in 1856.

1774 Father Christmas on Snowy Roof

1775 Celebrating the Sunrise

1776 On Roof in Gale

1777 With Umbrella in Rain

1778 In Fog on Edge of Roof with Torch

1779 Sheltering from Hailstorm behind Chimney

Christmas

2004 (2 Nov.) One centre phosphor band (2nd) or two phosphor bands (others). Perf 14½ ×14.

(a) Self-adhesive.

2495	**1774**	(2nd) multicoloured	70	70	□	□
2496	**1775**	(1st) multicoloured	90	90	□	□
2497	**1776**	40p multicoloured	1·30	1·30	□	□
2498	**1777**	57p multicoloured	1·80	1·80	□	□
2499	**1778**	68p multicoloured	2·20	2·20	□	□
2500	**1779**	£1.12 multicoloured	3·75	3·75	□	□
Set of 6			11·00	12·00	□	□
First Day Cover				13·50		□
Presentation Pack			12·50		□	
PHQ Cards (set of 7)			6·75	15·00	□	□

(b) PVA gum

MS2501 115 × 105 mm.				
As Nos. 2495/500	12·00	12·00	□	□
First Day Cover		13·50		□

The seven PHQ cards depict the six individual stamps and the miniature sheet.

The 2nd and 1st class stamps were also issued in sheets of 20 printed in lithography instead of photogravure containing ten 1st class and ten 2nd class stamps, each stamp accompanied by a se-tenant stamp-size label showing Father Christmas. Separate sheets of either 20 1st or 20 2nd class were available with personal photographs.

Collectors Pack 2004

2004 (2 Nov.) Comprises Nos. 2417/22, 2424/44, 2446/53, 2456/61, 2466/71 and 2473/2500

CP2500a	Collectors Pack	£110	□

Post Office Yearbook

2004 (2 Nov.) Comprises Nos. 2417/22, 2424/44, 2446/53, 2456/61, 2466/71 and 2473/2500

YB2500a	Yearbook	£110	□

1780 British Saddleback Pigs

1781 Khaki Campbell Ducks

1782 Clydesdale Mare and Foal

1783 Dairy Shorthorn Cattle

1784 Border Collie Dog

1785 Light Sussex Chicks

1786 Suffolk Sheep

1787 Bagot Goat

1788 Norfolk Black Turkeys

1789 Embden Geese

T **1780/9** were printed together, se-tenant, in blocks of 10 (5 × 2) throughout the sheet.

Farm Animals

2005 (11 Jan.) Two phosphor bands. Perf 14½

2502	**1780**	(1st) multicoloured	50	60	□	□
		a. Block of 10.				
		Nos. 2502/11	10·00	12·00	□	□
2503	**1781**	(1st) multicoloured	50	60	□	□
2504	**1782**	(1st) multicoloured	50	60	□	□
2505	**1783**	(1st) multicoloured	50	60	□	□
2506	**1784**	(1st) multicoloured	50	60	□	□
2507	**1785**	(1st) multicoloured	50	60	□	□
2508	**1786**	(1st) multicoloured	50	60	□	□
2509	**1787**	(1st) multicoloured	50	60	□	□
2510	**1788**	(1st) multicoloured	50	60	□	□
2511	**1789**	(1st) multicoloured	50	60	□	□
Set of 10			10·00	12·00	□	□
First Day Cover				12·00		□
Presentation Pack			13·00		□	
PHQ Cards (set of 10)			9·75	15·00	□	□
Gutter Block of 20			21·00		□	

Nos. 2502/11 were also issued in sheets of 20, printed in lithography instead of photogravure, containing two of each of the ten designs, arranged in vertical strips of five alternated with printed labels.

1790 Old Harry Rocks,
Studland Bay

1791 Wheal Coates,
St. Agnes

1792 Start Point, Start Bay

1793 Horton Down, Wiltshire

1794 Chiselcombe,
Exmoor

1795 St. James's Stone,
Lundy

A British Journey. South West England

2005 (8 Feb.) One centre phosphor band (2nd) or two phosphor bands (others). Perf 14½

2512	**1790**	(2nd) multicoloured	50	50	☐ ☐
2513	**1791**	(1st) multicoloured	50	75	☐ ☐
2514	**1792**	40p multicoloured	1·50	1·75	☐ ☐
2515	**1793**	43p multicoloured	1·75	2·00	☐ ☐
2516	**1794**	57p multicoloured	2·50	2·50	☐ ☐
2517	**1795**	68p multicoloured	3·50	3·00	☐ ☐
Set of 6			10·00	10·00	☐ ☐
First Day Cover				12·00	☐
Presentation Pack			11·00		☐
PHQ Cards (set of 6)			4·25	10·00	☐ ☐
Set of 6 Gutter Pairs			21·00		☐

1796 'Mr Rochester'

1797 'Come to Me'

1798 'In the Comfort
of her Bonnet

1799 'La Ligne des
Rats'

1800 'Refectory'

1801'Inspection'

**150th Death Anniversary of Charlotte Brontë.
Illustrations of Scenes from** *Jane Eyre* **by Paula
Rego**

2005 (24 Feb.) One centre phosphor band (2nd) or two phosphor bands (others). Perf 14 × 14½

2518	**1796**	(2nd) multicoloured	30	35	☐ ☐
2519	**1797**	(1st) multicoloured	40	45	☐ ☐
2520	**1798**	40p multicoloured	1·00	1·50	☐ ☐
2521	**1799**	57p silver, brownish grey and black	2·50	2·50	☐ ☐
2522	**1800**	68p multicoloured	3·00	3·00	☐ ☐
2523	**1801**	£1.12 silver, brownish grey and black	3·50	3·50	☐ ☐
Set of 6			10·00	11·00	☐ ☐
First Day Cover				12·00	☐
Presentation Pack			11·00		☐
PHQ Cards (set of 6)			11·00	15·00	☐ ☐
Set of 6 Gutter Pairs			21·00		☐
Set of 6 Traffic Light gutter blocks of four			42·00		☐
MS2524 114 × 105 mm. Nos. 2518/23			10·00	10·00	☐ ☐
First Day Cover				12·00	☐

The complete miniature sheet is shown on one of the PHQ cards with the others depicting individual stamps.

1802 Spinning Coin

1803 Rabbit out of Hat Trick

1804 Knotted Scarf Trick

1805 Card Trick

1806 Pyramid under Fez Trick

Centenary of the Magic Circle

2005 (15 Mar.) Two phosphor bands. Perf 14½ × 14

2525	**1802**	(1st) multicoloured	65	45	☐	☐
2526	**1803**	40p multicoloured	1·00	65	☐	☐
2527	**1804**	47p multicoloured	2·50	2·75	☐	☐
2528	**1805**	68p multicoloured	3·00	3·00	☐	☐
2529	**1806**	£1.12 multicoloured	3·50	3·50	☐	☐
Set of 5			10·00	10·00	☐	☐
First Day Cover				11·75		☐
Presentation Pack			12·00		☐	
PHQ Cards (set of 5)			5·00	12·00	☐	☐
Set of 5 Gutter Pairs			21·00		☐	☐

Nos. 2525/9 are each printed with instructions for the illusion or trick on the stamp.

No. 2525 can be rubbed with a coin to reveal the 'head' or 'tail' of a coin. The two versions, which appear identical before rubbing, are printed in alternate rows of the sheet, indicated by the letters H and T in the side margins of the sheet.

No. 2525 was also issued in sheets of 20 with se-tenant labels showing magic tricks, printed in lithography instead of photogravure.

Nos. 2526 and 2528 each show optical illusions.

The spotted scarf on No. 2527 and the fezzes on No. 2529 are printed in thermochromic inks which fade temporarily when exposed to heat, making the pyramid under the centre fez visible.

50th Anniversary of First Castles Definitives

2005 (22 Mar.) Sheet 127 × 73 mm, containing horiz designs as T 166/9 (Castles definitive of 1955-58) but with values in decimal currency, printed on pale cream. 'All-over' phosphor. Perf 11 × 11½

MS2530	**166**	50p brownish-black;				
	169 50p black; **167** £1 dull					
	vermilion; **168** £1 royal blue	10·00	10·00	☐	☐	
First Day Cover				12·00		☐
Presentation Pack			15·00		☐	
PHQ Cards (set of 5)			2·20	12·00	☐	☐

1807 Prince Charles and Mrs Camilla Parker Bowles

Royal Wedding

2005 (9 Apr.) Sheet 85 × 115 mm. Multicoloured. 'All-over' phosphor. Perf 13½ × 14

MS2531	**1807**	30p × 2 Prince Charles and Mrs Camilla Parker Bowles laughing; 68p × 2 Prince Charles and Mrs Camilla Parker Bowles smiling into camera	8·00	8·00	☐	☐
First Day Cover				10·00		☐
Presentation Pack			12·00		☐	

1808 Hadrian's Wall, England

1809 Uluru-Kata Tjuta National Park, Australia

1810 Stonehenge, England

1811 Wet Tropics of Queensland, Australia

1812 Blenheim Palace, England

1813 Greater Blue Mountains Area, Australia

1814 Heart of Neolithic Orkney, Scotland

1815 Purnululu National Park, Australia

Nos. 2532/3, 2534/5, 2536/7 and 2538/9 were each printed together, se-tenant, in horizontal pairs.

World Heritage Sites

2005 (21 Apr.) One side phosphor band (2nd) or two phosphor bands (others). Perf 14½

2532	**1808**	(2nd) multicoloured	30	35	☐	☐
		a. Horiz pair.				
		Nos. 2532/3	1·00	1·00	☐	☐
2533	**1809**	(2nd) multicoloured	30	35	☐	☐
2534	**1810**	(1st) multicoloured	45	45	☐	☐
		a. Horiz pair.				
		Nos. 2534/5	2·00	1·50	☐	☐
2535	**1811**	(1st) multicoloured	45	45	☐	☐

2536	**1812**	47p multicoloured	60	60	☐	☐
		a. Horiz pair.				
		Nos. 2536/7	3·00	3·50	☐	☐
2537	**1813**	47p multicoloured	60	60	☐	☐
2538	**1814**	68p multicoloured	90	90	☐	☐
		a. Horiz pair.				
		Nos. 2538/9	5·00	5·00	☐	☐
2539	**1815**	68p multicoloured	90	90	☐	☐
Set of 8			11·00	11·00	☐	☐
First Day Cover				12·00	☐	☐
Presentation Pack			12·00		☐	
Presentation Pack						
(UK and Australian stamps)			11·00		☐	
PHQ Cards (*set of* 8)			5·00	14·00	☐	☐
Set of 4 Gutter Strips of 4			16·50		☐	

Stamps in these designs were also issued by Australia and these are included in the joint Presentation Pack.

1816 Ensign of the Scots Guards, 2002

1817 Queen taking the salute as Colonel-in-Chief of the Grenadier Guards, 1983

1818 Trumpeter of the Household Calvalry, 2004

1819 Welsh Guardsman, 1990s

1820 Queen riding side-saddle, 1972

1821 Queen and Duke of Edinburgh in Carriage, 2004

Trooping the Colour

2005 (7 June) One phosphor band (2nd), two phosphor bands (others). Perf 14½

2540	**1816**	(2nd) multicoloured	70	80	☐	☐
2541	**1817**	(1st) multicoloured	75	90	☐	☐
2542	**1818**	42p multicoloured	1·00	1·20	☐	☐
2543	**1819**	60p multicoloured	2·00	2·00	☐	☐
2544	**1820**	68p multicoloured	2·50	2·50	☐	☐
2545	**1821**	£1.12 multicoloured	3·50	3·50	☐	☐
Set of 6			10·00	10·00	☐	☐
First Day Cover				12·00	☐	☐
Presentation Pack			15·00		☐	
PHQ Cards (*set of* 6)			5·00	18·00	☐	☐
Set of 6 Gutter Pairs			21·00		☐	
MS2546 115 × 105 mm. Nos. 2540/5			11·00	11·00	☐	☐
First Day Cover				12·00		☐

1822

60th Anniversary of End of the Second World War

2005 (5 July) Sheet 115 × 105 mm containing design as T **1200** (1995 Peace and Freedom) but with service indicator and No. 1664b × 5. Two phosphor bands. Perf 15 × 14 (with one elliptical hole on each vert side) (1664b) or 14½ × 14 (other)

MS2547	**1822**	(1st) gold × 5; (1st)				
		silver, blue and grey-black	6·00	6·00	☐	☐
First Day Cover				8·00		☐

1823 Norton F.1, Road Version of Race Winner (1991)

1824 BSA Rocket 3, Early Three Cylinder 'Superbike' (1969)

1825 Vincent Black Shadow, Fastest Standard Motorcycle (1949)

1826 Triumph Speed Twin, Two Cylinder Innovation (1938)

1827 Brough Superior, Bespoke Luxury Motorcycle (1930)

1828 Royal Enfield, Small Engined Motor Bicycle (1914)

Motorcycles

2005 (19 July) Two phosphor bands. Perf 14 × 14½

2548	**1823**	(1st) multicoloured	75	80	☐	☐
2549	**1824**	40p multicoloured	90	1·00	☐	☐
2550	**1825**	42p multicoloured	1·25	1·00	☐	☐
2551	**1826**	47p multicoloured	1·75	2·00	☐	☐
2552	**1827**	60p multicoloured	2·50	2·50	☐	☐
2553	**1828**	68p multicoloured	3·00	3·00	☐	☐
Set of 6			9·00	9·00	☐	☐
First Day Cover				12·00		☐
Presentation Pack			15·00		☐	
PHQ Cards (*set of* 6)			5·00	14·00	☐	☐
Set of 6 Gutter Pairs			19·00		☐	

1829

London's Successful Bid for Olympic Games, 2012

2005 (5 Aug.) Sheet 115 × 105 mm containing designs as T **1255/9**, but with service indicator. Multicoloured. Two phosphor bands. Perf 14½

MS2554　**1829**　(1st) Athlete celebrating × 2; (1st) Throwing the javelin; (1st) Swimming; (1st) Athlete on starting blocks; (1st) Basketball　　6·00　6·00　☐　☐

First Day Cover　　8·00　　☐
Presentation Pack　12·00　　☐

Stamps from **MS**2554 are all inscribed 'London 2012—Host City' and have imprint date '2005'. The design as Type 1259 omits the Olympic rings.

1830 African Woman eating Rice

1831 Indian Woman drinking Tea

1832 Boy eating Sushi

1833 Woman eating Pasta

1834 Woman eating Chips

1835 Teenage Boy eating Apple

Europa. Gastronomy. Changing Tastes in Britain

2005 (23 Aug.) One side phosphor band (2nd) or two phosphor bands (others). Perf 14½

2555	**1830**	(2nd) multicoloured	60	70	☐	☐
2556	**1831**	(1st) multicoloured	90	1·00	☐	☐
2557	**1832**	42p multicoloured	1·30	1·40	☐	☐
2558	**1833**	47p multicoloured	1·50	1·60	☐	☐
2559	**1834**	60p multicoloured	2·00	1·90	☐	☐
2560	**1835**	68p multicoloured	2·50	2·20	☐	☐
Set of 6			8·00	8·00	☐	☐
First Day Cover				10·00		☐
Presentation Pack			9·00		☐	
PHQ Cards (*set of* 6)			5·00	12·00	☐	☐
Set of 6 Gutter Pairs			17·00		☐	

The 1st and 42p values include the 'EUROPA' emblem.

1836 *Inspector Morse*

1837 *Emmerdale*

1838 *Rising Damp*

1839 *The Avengers*

1840 *The South Bank Show*

1841 *Who Wants to be a Millionaire*

50th Anniversary of Independent Television. Classic ITV Programmes

2005 (15 Sept.) One side phosphor band (2nd) or two phosphor bands (others). Perf 14½ × 14.

2561	**1836**	(2nd) multicoloured	60	70	☐	☐
2562	**1837**	(1st) multicoloured	90	1·00	☐	☐
2563	**1838**	42p multicoloured	1·30	1·40	☐	☐
2564	**1839**	47p multicoloured	1·40	1·50	☐	☐
2565	**1840**	60p multicoloured	2·00	1·90	☐	☐
2566	**1841**	68p multicoloured	2·20	2·20	☐	☐
Set of 6			8·00	8·00	☐	☐
First Day Cover				12·00		☐
Presentation Pack			9·00		☐	

PHQ Cards (set of 6)	5·00	12·00	☐	☐
Set of 6 Gutter Pairs	17·00		☐	

The 1st class stamps were also issued in sheets of 20 with each stamp accompanied by a half stamp-size *se-tenant* label.

1842 Gazania splendens (Charlotte Sowerby)

Nos. 2567/72 were printed together, *se-tenant*, in booklet panes of 6 in which the surplus self-adhesive paper around each stamp was removed.

'Smilers' Booklet stamps (1st series)

2005 (4 Oct.) Designs as Types **992, 1221, 1286, 1517** and 1568/9 but smaller, 20 × 23 mm, and inscribed 1st as T **1842**. Self-adhesive. Two phosphor bands. Die-cut perf 15 × 14½

2567	**1842**	(1st) multicoloured	60	60	☐	☐
		a. Booklet pane.				
		Nos. 2567/72	7·00		☐	
2568	**1569**	(1st) multicoloured	60	60	☐	☐
2569	**1568**	(1st) multicoloured	60	60	☐	☐
2570	**1517**	(1st) multicoloured	60	60	☐	☐
2571	**992**	(1st) multicoloured	60	60	☐	☐
2572	**1221**	(1st) multicoloured	60	60	☐	☐
Set of 6			8·00	8·50	☐	☐
First Day Cover				9·00	☐	

Nos. 2567/72 were re-issued on 4 July 2006 in sheets of 20 with *se-tenant* labels, printed in lithography instead of photogravure.
Nos. 2568/70 were re-issued on 18 January 2008 in sheets of 20 with circular *se-tenant* labels, printed in lithography.
No. 2567 was re-issued on 28 October 2008 in sheets of 10 with circular *se-tenant* 'Flower Fairy' labels, printed in lithography.

1843 Cricket Scenes

England's Ashes Victory

2005 (6 Oct.) Sheet 115 × 90 mm. Multicoloured. Two phosphor bands. Perf 14½ ×14.

MS2573	**1843**	(1st) England team			
		with Ashes trophy; (1st) Kevin			
		Pieterson, Michael Vaughan and			
		Andrew Flintoff on opening day of			
		First Test, Lords; 68p Michael			
		Vaughan, Third Test, Old Trafford;			
		68p Second Test Edgbaston	7·50	7·50	☐	☐
First Day Cover				10·00	☐
Presentation Pack			12·00		☐

1844 *Entrepreante* with dismasted British *Belle Isle*

1845 Nelson wounded on Deck of HMS *Victory*

1846 British Cutter *Entrepreante* attempting to rescue Crew of burning French *Achille*

1847 Cutter and HMS *Pickle* (schooner)

1848 British Fleet attacking in Two Columns

1849 Franco/Spanish Fleet putting to Sea from Cadiz

Nos. 2574/5, 2576/7 and 2578/9 were each printed together, *se-tenant*, in horizontal pairs throughout the sheets, each pair forming a composite design.

Bicentenary of the Battle of Trafalgar (1st issue). Scenes from 'Panorama of the Battle of Trafalgar' by William Heath

2005 (18 Oct.) Two phosphor bands. Perf 15 × 14½

2574	**1844**	(1st) multicoloured	45	45	☐	☐
		a. Horiz pair.				
		Nos. 2574/5	1·75	2·00	☐	☐
2575	**1845**	(1st) multicoloured	45	45	☐	☐
2576	**1846**	42p multicoloured	65	65	☐	☐
		a. Horiz pair.				
		Nos. 2576/7	2·50	2·75	☐	☐
2577	**1847**	42p multicoloured	65	65	☐	☐
2578	**1848**	68p multicoloured	90	90	☐	☐
		a. Horiz pair.				
		Nos. 2578/9	4·00	4·40	☐	☐
2579	**1849**	68p multicoloured	90	90	☐	☐
Set of 6			9·00	10·00	☐	☐
First Day Cover				11·00		☐
Presentation Pack			12·00		☐
PHQ Cards (set of 7)			5·00	12·00	☐	☐
Set of 3 Gutter Strips of 4			11·00		☐

MS2580 190 × 68 mm. Nos. 2574/9　18·00　20·00　☐　☐

First Day Cover　11·00　☐

The phosphor bands are at just left of centre and at right of each stamp

The seven PHQ cards depict the six individual stamps and the miniature sheet.

Bicentenary of the Battle of Trafalgar (2nd issue). Booklet stamp.

2005 (18 Oct.) Design as Type 1516 (White Ensign from 2001 Submarine Centenary). Two phosphor bands. Perf 14½.

2581 **1516**　(1st) multicoloured　6·75　6·75　☐　☐

No. 2581 was only available from two stamp booklets, sold for £7.26 and £7.40.

1850 Black Madonna and Child from Haiti

1851 'Madonna and Child' (Marianne Stokes)

1852 'The Virgin Mary with the Infant Christ'

1853 Choctaw Virgin Mother and Child (Fr. John Giuliani)

1854 'Madonna and the Infant Jesus' (from India)

1855 'Come let us adore Him' (Dianne Tchumut)

Christmas. Madonna and Child Paintings

2005 (1 Nov.) One side phosphor band (2nd) or two phosphor bands (others). Perf 14½ × 14

	(a) Self-adhesive				
2582 **1850**	(2nd) multicoloured	60	70	☐	☐
2583 **1851**	(1st) multicoloured	90	1·00	☐	☐
2584 **1852**	42p multicoloured	1·30	1·40	☐	☐
2585 **1853**	60p multicoloured	1·80	1·90	☐	☐
2586 **1854**	68p multicoloured	2·00	2·20	☐	☐
2587 **1855**	£1.12 multicoloured	3·40	3·60	☐	☐
Set of 6		10·00	11·00	☐	☐
First Day Cover			11·00		☐
Presentation Pack		11·00		☐	
PHQ Cards (set of 7)		4·00	12·00	☐	☐

	(b) PVA gum				
MS2588 115 × 102 mm.					
As Nos. 2582/7		10·50	11·00	☐	☐
First Day Cover			11·00		☐

The seven PHQ cards depict the six individual stamps and the miniature sheet.

Collectors Pack

2005 (1 Nov.) Comprises Nos. 2502/23, 2525/9, **MS**2531/45, 2548/53, 2555/66, 2574/9 and 2582/7

CP2587a　Collectors Pack　£110　☐

Post Office Yearbook

2005 (1 Nov.) Comprises Nos. 2502/23, 2525/9, **MS**2531/45, 2548/53, 2555/66, 2574/9 and 2582/7

YB2587a　Yearbook　95·00　☐

Miniature Sheet Collection

2005 (21 Nov.) Comprises Nos. **MS**2524, **MS**2530/1, **MS**2546/7, **MS**2554, **MS**2573, **MS**2580 and **MS**2588 **MS**2588a Miniature Sheet Collection　75·00　☐

1856 The Tale of Mr. Jeremy Fisher (Beatrix Potter)

1857 Kipper (Mick Inkpen)

1858 The Enormous Crocodile (Roald Dahl)

1859 More About Paddington (Michael Bond)

1860 Comic Adventures of Boots (Satoshi Kitamura)

1861 Alice's Adventures in Wonderland (Lewis Carroll)

1862 The Very Hungry Caterpillar (Eric Carle)

1863 Maisy's ABC (Lucy Cousins)

Nos. 2589/90, 2591/2, 2593/4 and 2595/6 were printed together, se-tenant, as horizontal pairs in sheets of 60 (2 panes 6 × 5).

Animal Tales

2006 (10 Jan.) One side phosphor band (2nd) or two phosphor bands (others). Perf 14½

2589	**1856**	(2nd) multicoloured	30	35	☐	☐
		a. Horiz pair.				
		Nos. 2589/90	70	70	☐	☐
2590	**1857**	(2nd) multicoloured	30	35	☐	☐
2591	**1858**	(1st) multicoloured	45	50	☐	☐
		a. Horiz pair.				
		Nos. 2591/2	1·50	1·50	☐	☐
2592	**1859**	(1st) multicoloured	45	50	☐	☐
2593	**1860**	42p multicoloured	65	70	☐	☐
		a. Horiz pair.				
		Nos. 2593/4	3·75	3·75	☐	☐
2594	**1861**	42p multicoloured	65	70	☐	☐
2595	**1862**	68p multicoloured	1·00	1·10	☐	☐
		a. Horiz pair.				
		Nos. 2595/6	4·75	4·75	☐	☐
2596	**1863**	68p multicoloured	1·00	1·10	☐	☐
Set of 8			8·50	8·50	☐	☐
First Day Cover				8·00	☐	
Presentation Pack			12·00		☐	
PHQ Cards (*set of* 8)			4·50	12·00	☐	☐
Set of 4 Gutter Blocks of 4			13·00		☐	
Set of 4 Traffic Light Gutter Blocks of 8		28·00			☐	

No. 2595 contains two die-cut holes.

A design as No. 2592 but self-adhesive was also issued in sheets of 20 with each stamp accompanied by a *se-tenant* label.

1864 Carding Mill Valley, Shropshire

1865 Beachy Head, Sussex

1866 St. Paul's Cathedral, London

1867 Brancaster, Norfolk

1868 Derwent Edge, Peak District

1869 Robin Hood's Bay, Yorkshire

1870 Buttermere, Lake District

1871 Chipping Campden, Cotswolds

1872 St. Boniface Down, Isle of Wight

1873 Chamberlain Square, Birmingham

Nos. 2597/606 were printed together, *se-tenant*, as blocks of ten (5 × 2) in sheets of 60 (2 panes of 30).

A British Journey: England

2006 (7 Feb.) Two phosphor bands. Perf 14½

2597	**1864**	(1st) multicoloured	45	50	☐	☐
		a. Block of 10.				
		Nos. 2597/606	9·00	9·00	☐	☐
2598	**1865**	(1st) multicoloured	45	50	☐	☐
2599	**1866**	(1st) multicoloured	45	50	☐	☐
2600	**1867**	(1st) multicoloured	45	50	☐	☐
2601	**1868**	(1st) multicoloured	45	50	☐	☐
2602	**1869**	(1st) multicoloured	45	50	☐	☐
2603	**1870**	(1st) multicoloured	45	50	☐	☐
2604	**1871**	(1st) multicoloured	45	50	☐	☐
2605	**1872**	(1st) multicoloured	45	50	☐	☐
2606	**1873**	(1st) multicoloured	45	50	☐	☐
Set of 10			9·00	9·00	☐	☐
First Day Cover				10·00		☐
Presentation Pack			12·00		☐	☐
PHQ Cards (*set of* 10)			5·75	9·50	☐	☐
Gutter Block of 20			18·00		☐	

1874 Royal Albert Bridge

1875 Box Tunnel

1876 Paddington Station

1877 PSS Great Eastern (paddle steamer)

1878 Clifton Suspension Bridge Design

1879 Maidenhead Bridge

Birth Bicentenary of Isambard Kingdom Brunel (engineer) (1st issue)

2006 (23 Feb.) Phosphor-coated paper (42p) or two phosphor bands (others). Perf 14 × 13½

2607	**1874**	(1st) multicoloured	45	50	☐	☐
2608	**1875**	40p multicoloured	75	75	☐	☐
2609	**1876**	42p multicoloured	1·00	1·00	☐	☐
2610	**1877**	47p multicoloured	1·00	1·00	☐	☐
2611	**1878**	60p multicoloured	1·50	1·75	☐	☐
2612	**1879**	68p multicoloured	2·00	2·25	☐	☐
Set of 6			6·50	6·75	☐	☐
First Day Cover				7·00		☐
Presentation Pack			12·00		☐	
PHQ Cards (*set of 7*)			4·00	14·00	☐	
Set of 6 Gutter Pairs			14·00		☐	
MS2613 190 × 65 mm. Nos. 2607/12			6·50	6·50	☐	☐
First Day Cover				7·00	☐	☐

The phosphor bands on Nos. 2607/8 and 2610/12 are at just left of centre and at right of each stamp.

The complete miniature sheet is shown on one of the PHQ cards with the others depicting individual stamps.

Birth Bicentenary of Isambard Kingdom Brunel (engineer) (2nd issue). Booklet stamp

2006 (23 Feb.) Design as Type **1739** (PS Great Western from 2004 Ocean Liners). Two phosphor bands. Perf 14½ × 14

2614	**1739**	68p multicoloured	10·00	10·50	☐	☐

No. 2614 was only available in £7.40 stamp booklets.

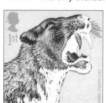
1880 Sabre-tooth Cat

1881 Giant Deer

1882 Woolly Rhino

1883 Woolly Mammoth

1884 Cave Bear

Ice Age Animals

2006 (21 Mar.) Two phosphor bands. Perf 14½

2615	**1880**	(1st) black and silver	45	50	☐	☐
2616	**1881**	42p black and silver	75	80	☐	☐
2617	**1882**	47p black and silver	2·00	2·00	☐	☐
2618	**1883**	68p black and silver	2·25	2·25	☐	☐
2619	**1884**	£1.12 black and silver	3·00	3·00	☐	☐
Set of 5			7·50	7·50	☐	☐
First Day Cover				8·50		☐
Presentation Pack			12·00		☐	
PHQ Cards (*set of 5*)			2·75	12·00	☐	☐
Set of 5 Gutter Pairs			16·00		☐	

1885 On *Britannia*, 1972

1886 At Royal Windsor Horse Show, 1985

1887 At Heathrow Airport, 2001

1888 As Young Princess Elizabeth with Duchess of York, 1931

1889 At State Banquet, Ottawa, 1951

1890 Queen Elizabeth II in 1960

1891 As Princess Elizabeth, 1940

1892 With Duke of Edinburgh, 1951

Nos. 2620/1, 2622/3, 2624/5 and 2626/7 were each printed together, *se-tenant*, as horizontal pairs in sheets of 60 (2 panes 6 × 5).

80th Birthday of Queen Elizabeth II

2006 (18 Apr.) One side phosphor band (No. 2620), one centre phosphor band (No. 2621) or two phosphor bands (others). Perf 14½

2620	**1885**	(2nd) black, turquoise green and grey	35	40	☐	☐
		a. Horiz pair. Nos. 2620/1	95	95	☐	☐
2621	**1886**	(2nd) black, turquoise-green and grey	35	40	☐	☐
2622	**1887**	(1st) black, turquoise-green and grey	45	45	☐	☐
		a. Horiz pair. Nos. 2622/3	1·75	1·75	☐	☐
2623	**1888**	(1st) black, turquoise-green and grey	45	45	☐	☐
2624	**1889**	44p black, turquoise-green and grey	65	65	☐	☐
		a. Horiz pair. Nos. 2624/5	2·75	2·75	☐	☐
2625	**1890**	44p black, turquoise-green and grey	65	65	☐	☐
2626	**1891**	72p black, turquoise-green and grey	1·10	1·10	☐	☐
		a. Horiz pair. Nos. 2626/7	4·50	4·50	☐	☐
2627	**1892**	72p black, turquoise-green and grey	1·10	1·10	☐	☐
Set of 8			9·50	9·50	☐	☐
First Day Cover				10·00		☐
Presentation Pack			12·00		☐	
PHQ Cards (*set of* 8)			4·50	15·00	☐	☐
Set of 4 Gutter Strips of 4			19·00		☐	

1893 England (1966)

1894 Italy (1934, 1938, 1982)

1895 Argentina (1978, 1986)

1896 Germany (1954, 1974, 1990)

1897 France (1998)

1898 Brazil (1958, 1962, 1970, 1994, 2002)

World Cup Football Championship, Germany. World Cup Winners

2006 (6 June) Two phosphor bands. Perf 14½

2628	**1893**	(1st) multicoloured	45	50	☐	☐
2629	**1894**	42p multicoloured	65	70	☐	☐
2630	**1895**	44p multicoloured	1·25	1·25	☐	☐
2631	**1896**	50p multicoloured	1·75	1·75	☐	☐
2632	**1897**	64p multicoloured	2·25	2·25	☐	☐
2633	**1898**	72p multicoloured	3·00	3·00	☐	☐
Set of 6			8·00	8·00	☐	☐
First Day Cover				9·00		☐
Presentation Pack			12·00		☐	
PHQ Cards (*set of* 6)			4·00	12·00	☐	☐
Set of 6 Gutter Pairs			17·00		☐	

The 1st class stamp was also issued in sheets of 20 with each stamp accompanied by a *se-tenant* label showing scenes from the 1966 World Cup final.

1899 30 St. Mary Axe, London

1900 Maggie's Centre, Dundee

1901 Selfridges, Birmingham

1902 Downland Gridshell, Chichester

1903 An Turas, Isle of Tiree

1904 The Deep, Hull

Modern Architecture

2006 (20 June). Two phosphor bands. Perf 14½

2634	**1899**	(1st) multicoloured	45	50	☐	☐
2635	**1900**	42p multicoloured	65	70	☐	☐
2636	**1901**	44p multicoloured	1·00	1·00	☐	☐
2637	**1902**	50p multicoloured	2·00	2·00	☐	☐
2638	**1903**	64p multicoloured	3·00	3·00	☐	☐
2639	**1904**	72p multicoloured	3·50	3·50	☐	☐
Set of 6			8·00	8·00	☐	☐
First Day Cover				9·00		☐
Presentation Pack			12·00		☐	
PHQ Cards (*set of* 6)			4·00	10·00	☐	☐
Set of 6 Gutter Pairs			17·00		☐	

1905 'Sir Winston Churchill' (Walter Sickert)

1906 'Sir Joshua Reynolds' (self-portrait)

1907 'T. S. Eliot' (Patrick Heron)

1908 'Emmeline Pankhurst' (Georgina Agnes Brackenbury)

1909 Virginia Woolf (photo by George Charles Beresford)

1910 Bust of Sir Walter Scott (Sir Francis Leggatt Chantry)

1911 'Mary Seacole' (Albert Charles Challen)

1912 'William Shakespeare' (attrib to John Taylor)

1913 'Dame Cicely Saunders' (Catherine Goodman)

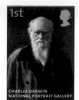

1914 'Charles Darwin' (John Collier)

Nos. 2640/9 were printed together, *se-tenant*, as blocks of ten (5 × 2) in sheets of 60 (2 panes of 30).

150th Anniversary of National Portrait Gallery, London

2006 (18 July) Two phosphor bands. Perf 14½

2640	**1905**	(1st) multicoloured	45	50	☐	☐
		a. Block of 10.				
		Nos. 2640/9	9·00		☐	☐
2641	**1906**	(1st) multicoloured	45	50	☐	☐
2642	**1907**	(1st) multicoloured	45	50	☐	☐
2643	**1908**	(1st) multicoloured	45	50	☐	☐
2644	**1909**	(1st) multicoloured	45	50	☐	☐
2645	**1910**	(1st) multicoloured	45	50	☐	☐
2646	**1911**	(1st) multicoloured	45	50	☐	☐
2647	**1912**	(1st) multicoloured	45	50	☐	☐
2648	**1913**	(1st) multicoloured	45	50	☐	☐
2649	**1914**	(1st) multicoloured	45	50	☐	☐
Set of 10			9·00	9·00	☐	☐
First Day Cover				10·00		☐
Presentation Pack			12·00		☐	
PHQ Cards (*set of* 10)			6·75	15·00	☐	☐
Gutter Block of 20			19·00		☐	
Traffic Light Gutter Block of 20			25·00		☐	

1915

1916

'Pricing in Proportion'

2006 (1 Aug–12 Sept.) Perf 15 × 14 (with one elliptical hole on each vertical side).

(a) PVA gum. Photo De La Rue (No. 2651 also from Enschedé prestige booklet).

		(i) As T **1915**				
2650	(2nd)	bright blue (1 centre band)	50	40	☐	☐
2651	(1st)	gold (2 bands)	75	50	☐	☐

		(ii) As T **1916**.				
2652	(2nd Large)	bright blue (2 bands)	1·00	60	☐	☐
2653	(1st Large)	gold (2 bands)	1·50	70	☐	☐

(b) Self-adhesive. Photo Walsall.

		(i) As T **1915**				
2654	(2nd)	bright blue (1 centre band)				
		(12 Sept)	50	40	☐	☐
2655	(1st)	gold (2 bands) (12 Sept)	75	50	☐	☐

(ii) As T **1916**.

2656	(2nd Large) bright blue (2 bands)			
	(15 Aug)	55	60	☐ ☐
2657	(1st Large) gold (2 bands) (15 Aug)	65	70	☐ ☐
First Day Cover (Nos. Y1676b/c, 2650/3)			6·00	☐
Presentation Pack				
(Nos. Y1676b/c, 2650/3)		4·75		☐

No. 2654 was issued in booklets of twelve sold at £2.76.

No. 2655 was available in booklets of six or twelve, sold at £1.92 or £3.84.

Nos. 2656/7 were issued in separate booklets of four, sold at £1.48 or £1.76.

All these booklets had the surplus self-adhesive paper around each stamp removed.

1917

70th Anniversary of the Year of Three Kings

2006 (31 Aug.) Sheet 127 × 72 mm containing No. Y1728. Multicoloured. Two phosphor bands. Perf 15 × 14 (with one elliptical hole on each vertical side).

MS2658	**1917**	£3 deep mauve	10·00	10·00	☐ ☐
First Day Cover				11·00	☐

1918 Corporal Agansing Rai

1919 Boy Seaman Jack Cornwell

1920 Midshipman Charles Lucas

1921 Captain Noel Chavasse

1922 Captain Albert Ball

1923 Captain Charles Upham

Nos. 2659/60, 2661/2 and 2663/4 were each printed together, *se-tenant*, as horizontal pairs in sheets of 60 (2 panes 6 × 5).

150th Anniversary of the Victoria Cross (1st issue)

2006 (21 Sept.) One side phosphor band. Perf 14½ × 14

2659	**1918**	(1st) multicoloured	45	50	☐ ☐
	a. Horiz pair.				
		Nos. 2659/60	1·00	1·00	☐ ☐
2660	**1919**	(1st) multicoloured	45	50	☐ ☐
2661	**1920**	64p multicoloured	1·25	1·25	☐ ☐
	a. Horiz pair.				
		Nos. 2661/2	3·50	3·50	☐ ☐
2662	**1921**	64p multicoloured	1·25	1·25	☐ ☐
2663	**1922**	72p multicoloured	2·00	2·25	☐ ☐
	a. Horiz pair.				
		Nos. 2663/4	6·00	6·00	☐ ☐
2664	**1923**	72p multicoloured	2·00	2·25	☐ ☐
Set of 6			9·50	9·50	☐ ☐
First Day Cover				10·00	☐
Presentation Pack			12·00		☐
Set of 3 Gutter Strips of 4			19·00		☐
MS2665 190 × 67 mm. No. 2666 and					
as Nos. 2659/64 but 'all-over'					
phosphor			10·00	10·00	☐ ☐
First Day Cover				10·50	☐
PHQ Cards (set of 7)			4·50	15·00	☐ ☐

The seven PHQ cards depict the six individual stamps and the miniature sheet.

150th Anniversary of the Victoria Cross (2nd issue). Booklet stamp

2006 (21 Sept.) Design as No. 1517 (1990 Gallantry Awards). 'All-over' phosphor. Perf 14

2666	**959**	20p multicoloured	6·50	7·00	☐ ☐

No. 2666 was only issued in No. **MS**2665 and in £7.44 stamp booklets.

1924 Sitar Player and Dancer

1925 Reggae Bass Guitarist and African Drummer

1926 Fiddler and Harpist

1927 Sax Player and Blues Guitarist

1928 Maraca Player and Salsa Dancers

Europa. Integration. Sounds of Britain

2006 (3 Oct.) 'All-over' phosphor. Perf 14½

2667	**1924**	(1st) multicoloured	45	50
2668	**1925**	42p multicoloured	1·00	1·00
2669	**1926**	50p multicoloured	1·25	1·25
2670	**1927**	72p multicoloured	1·75	1·75
2671	**1928**	£1.19 multicoloured	2·50	3·00
Set of 5			9·00	9·00
First Day Cover				11·00
Presentation Pack			12·00	
PHQ Cards (set of 5)			3·75	9·50
Set of 5 Gutter Pairs			19·00	

The 1st class and 50p values include the 'EUROPA' emblem.

1929 'New Baby' (Alison Carmichael)

1930 'Best Wishes' (Alan Kitching)

1931 'THANK YOU' (Alan Kitching)

1932 Balloons (Ivan Chermayeff)

1933 Firework (Kam Tang)

1934 Champagne, Flowers and Butterflies (Olaf Hajek)

Nos. 2672/7 were printed together, *se-tenant*, in booklet panes of 6 in which the surplus self-adhesive paper around each stamp was removed.

'Smilers' Booklet stamps (2nd series). Occasions

2006 (17 Oct.) Self-adhesive. Two phosphor bands. Die-cut perf 15 × 14½

2672	**1929**	(1st) chrome-yellow	1·25	1·20
		a. Booklet pane. Nos. 2672/7	7·50	
2673	**1930**	(1st) turquoise-blue	1·25	1·20
2674	**1931**	(1st) scarlet-vermilion, rosine and yellow	1·25	1·20
2675	**1932**	(1st) multicoloured	1·25	1·20
2676	**1933**	(1st) multicoloured	1·25	1·20
2677	**1934**	(1st) multicoloured	1·25	1·20
Set of 6			7·50	7·00
First Day Cover				8·00
Presentation Pack			18·00	
PHQ Cards			2·75	7·50

Nos. 2672/7 were issued in £1.92 stamp booklets.

They were also issued in sheets of 20, containing four of Nos. 2672 and 2677, and three of the other designs, and *se-tenant* labels. Separate sheets of each design were available with personal photographs on the labels.

Stamps as No. 2672 but perforated with one eliptical hole on each vertical side were issued on 28 October 2008 in sheets of 10 or 20 with circular *se-tenant* Peter Rabbit labels.

These generic sheets were all printed in lithography instead of photogravure.

1935 Snowman

1936 Father Christmas

1937 Snowman

1938 Father Christmas

1939 Reindeer

1940 Christmas Tree

2006 (7 Nov.) One centre phosphor band (2nd) or two phosphor bands (others). Perf 15 × 14.

(a) Self-adhesive

2678	**1935**	(2nd) multicoloured	35	40	☐	☐
2679	**1936**	(1st) multicoloured	50	50	☐	☐
2680	**1937**	(2nd Large) multicoloured	65	65	☐	☐
2681	**1938**	(1st Large) multicoloured	75	75	☐	☐
2682	**1939**	72p multicoloured	3·25	3·25	☐	☐
2683	**1940**	£1.19 multicoloured	4·50	4·50	☐	☐
Set of 6			9·00	9·00	☐	☐
First Day Cover				9·50		☐
Presentation Pack			12·00		☐	
PHQ Cards (*set of* 7)			3·00	18·00	☐	☐

(b) PVA gum

MS2684 115 × 102 mm.

As Nos. 2678/83	8·00	9·00	☐	☐
First Day Cover	10·00			☐

The seven PHQ cards depict the six individual stamps and the miniature sheet.

The 2nd and 1st class stamps were also issued in sheets of 20 printed in lithography instead of photogravure containing ten 1st class and ten 2nd class stamps, each stamp accompanied by a *se-tenant* label. Separate sheets of 20 1st or 20 2nd class were available with personal photographs.

1941

'Lest We Forget' (1st issue). 90th Anniversary of the Battle of the Somme

2006 (9 Nov.) Sheet 124 × 71 mm containing new stamp and designs as Nos. EN13, W105, S116 and NI101. Two phosphor bands. Perf 14½ (1st) or 15 × 14 (72p).

MS2685   **1941**   (1st) Poppies on
        barbed wire stems; 72p ×4 As Nos.

EN13, W105, S116 and NI101	9·00	9·00	☐ ☐
First Day Cover		9·50	☐
Presentation Pack	12·00		☐

No. **MS**2685 (including the Northern Ireland stamp) is printed in gravure.

The 1st class stamp was also issued in sheets of 20 with *se-tenant* labels showing war memorials, printed in lithography instead of photogravure.

Collectors Pack

2006 (9 Nov.) Comprises Nos. 2589/612, 2615/49, 2659/64, 2667/71, 2678/83 and **MS**2685

CP2685a	Collectors Pack	£120	☐

Post Office Yearbook

2006 (9 Nov.) Comprises Nos. 2589/612, 2615/49, 2659/64, 2667/71, 2678/83 and **MS**2685

YB2685a	Yearbook	£100	☐

Miniature Sheet Collection

2006 (30 Nov.) Comprises Nos. **MS**2613, **MS**2658, **MS**2665, **MS**2684/5 and **MS**S133

MS2685a	Miniature Sheet Collection	45·00	☐

1942 'with the beatles'

1943 'Sgt Pepper's Lonely Hearts Club Band

1944 'Help!'

1945 'Abbey Road'

1946 'Revolver'

1947 'Let It Be'

1948 Beatles Memorabilia

The Beatles. Album Covers

2007 (9 Jan.) Two phosphor bands.

(a) Photo Walsall. Self-adhesive. Die-cut irregular perf 13½ × 14½

2686	**1942**	(1st) multicoloured	70	75	☐	☐
2687	**1943**	(1st) multicoloured	70	75	☐	☐
2688	**1944**	64p multicoloured	1·75	1·75	☐	☐
2689	**1945**	64p multicoloured	1·75	1·75	☐	☐
2690	**1946**	72p multicoloured	2·00	2·00	☐	☐
2691	**1947**	72p multicoloured	2·00	2·00	☐	☐
Set of 6			8·50	8·50	☐	☐
First Day Cover				9·00		☐
Presentation Pack			15·00		☐	
PHQ Cards (*set of* 11)			5·00	18·00	☐	☐

(b) Litho Walsall. PVA gum. Two phosphor bands. P 14

MS2692 115 × 89 mm. **1948** (1st) Guitar;

(1st) Yellow Submarine lunch-box
and key-rings; (1st) Record 'Love
Me Do'; (1st) Beatles badges   5·00   5·00   ☐   ☐

First Day Cover   6·00   ☐

Nos. 2686/91 are all die-cut in the shape of a pile of records.
Nos. 2686/7, 2688/9 and 2690/1 were each printed together in
sheets of 60 (2 panes of 30), with the two designs alternating
horizontally and the surplus backing paper around each
stamp removed.

Nos. 2686/92 commemorate the 50th anniversary of the first
meeting of Paul McCartney and John Lennon.

'Smilers' Booklet stamp (3rd series)

2007 (16 Jan.) – **2008** As No. 2569. Self-adhesive. Two
phosphor bands. Perf 15 × 14 (with one elliptical hole on each
vertical side)

2693   (1st)multicoloured   10·00   10·00   ☐   ☐

a. Booklet pane. No. 2655 × 5
and No. 2693   30·00   ☐

b. Booklet pane. No. 2693 × 2
with two attached labels
and No. 1668 × 4   20·00   ☐

No. 2693 was only issued in stamp booklets in which the
surplus backing paper around each stamp was removed.
Nos. 2694/8 are left vacant.

1949 Moon Jellyfish   **1950** Common Starfish

1951 Beadlet Anemone   **1952** Bass

1953 Thornback Ray   **1954** Lesser Octopus

1955 Common Mussels   **1956** Grey Seal

1957 Shore Crab   **1958** Common Sun Star

Nos. 2699/708 were printed together, *se-tenant*, as blocks of
ten (5 × 2) in sheets of 60 (2 panes of 30).

Sea Life

2007 (1 Feb.) Two phosphor bands. P 14½

2699	**1949**	(1st) multicoloured	75	80	☐ ☐
		a. Block of 10.			
		Nos. 2699/708	9·00	9·00	☐ ☐
2700	**1950**	(1st) multicoloured	75	80	☐ ☐
2701	**1951**	(1st) multicoloured	75	80	☐ ☐
2702	**1952**	(1st) multicoloured	75	80	☐ ☐
2703	**1953**	(1st) multicoloured	75	80	☐ ☐
2704	**1954**	(1st) multicoloured	75	80	☐ ☐
2705	**1955**	(1st) multicoloured	75	80	☐ ☐
2706	**1956**	(1st) multicoloured	75	80	☐ ☐
2707	**1957**	(1st) multicoloured	75	80	☐ ☐
2708	**1958**	(1st) multicoloured	75	80	☐ ☐
Set of 10			9·00	9·00	
First Day Cover				9·50	
Presentation Pack			12·00		☐
PHQ Cards (*set of* 10)			4·50	12·50	☐ ☐
Gutter Block of 20			19·00		☐

1959 Saturn Nebula
C55   **1960** Eskimo Nebula
C39

1961 Cat's Eye Nebula
C6   **1962** Helix Nebula
C63

1963 Flaming Star
Nebula C31   **1964** The Spindle C53

50th Anniversary of 'The Sky at Night' (TV programme). Nebulae

2007 (13 Feb.) Self-adhesive. Two phosphor bands. Die-cut
perf 14½ × 14

2709	**1959**	(1st) multicoloured	75	75	☐ ☐
2710	**1960**	(1st) multicoloured	75	75	☐ ☐

2711 **1961**	50p multicoloured	1·20	1·20	☐	☐
2712 **1962**	50p multicoloured	1·20	1·20	☐	☐
2713 **1963**	72p multicoloured	1·70	1·70	☐	☐
2714 **1964**	72p multicoloured	1·70	1·70	☐	☐
Set of 6		9·00	9·00	☐	☐
First Day Cover			10·00		☐
Presentation Pack		11·00		☐	
PHQ Cards (*set of* 6)		2·75	12·00	☐	☐

Nos. 2709/10, 2711/12 and 2713/14 were each printed together in sheets of 60 (2 panes of 30), with the two designs alternating horizontally and the surplus backing paper around each stamp removed.

1965 Iron Bridge (Thomas Telford)

1966 Steam Locomotive and Railway Tracks

1967 Map of British Isles and Australia (telephone)

1968 Camera and Television (John Logie Baird)

1969 Globe as Web (email and internet)

1970 Couple with Suitcases on Moon (space travel)

World of Invention (1st series)

2007 (1 Mar.) Self-adhesive. Two phosphor bands. Die-cut perf 14½ × 14

2715 **1965**	(1st) multicoloured	50	50	☐	☐
2716 **1966**	(1st) multicoloured	50	50	☐	☐
2717 **1967**	64p multicoloured	1·75	1·75	☐	☐
2718 **1968**	64p multicoloured	1·75	1·75	☐	☐
2719 **1969**	72p multicoloured	3·00	3·00	☐	☐
2720 **1970**	72p multicoloured	3·00	3·00	☐	☐
Set of 6		10·00	10·00	☐	☐
First Day Cover			11·00		☐
Presentation Pack		11·00		☐	
PHQ Cards (*set of* 7)		4·50	22·00	☐	☐
Set of 3 Gutter Strips of 4		20·00			☐

The seven PHQ Cards depict the six individual stamps and **MS**2727.

Nos. 2715/16, 2717/18 and 2719/20 were each printed together in sheets of 60 (2 panes of 30), with the two designs alternating horizontally and the surplus backing paper around each stamp removed.

World of Invention (2nd series)

2007 (1 Mar.) Two phosphor bands. Perf 14½ × 14

2721 **1965**	(1st) multicoloured	50	50	☐	☐
2722 **1966**	(1st) multicoloured	50	50	☐	☐
2723 **1967**	64p multicoloured	2·50	2·50	☐	☐
2724 **1968**	64p multicoloured	2·50	2·50	☐	☐
2725 **1969**	72p multicoloured	4·50	4·50	☐	☐
2726 **1970**	72p multicoloured	4·50	4·50	☐	☐
Set of 6		14·00	14·00	☐	☐
MS2727 115 × 104 mm. Nos. 2721/6		14·00	14·00	☐	☐
First Day Cover			14·00		☐

Nos. 2721/6 were only issued in £7.49 stamp booklets, No. DX38 and in **MS**2727.

1971 William Wilberforce and Anti-Slavery Poster

1972 Olaudah Equiano and Map of Slave Trade Routes

1973 Granville Sharp and Slave Ship

1974 Thomas Clarkson and Diagram of Slave Ship

1975 Hannah More and Title Page of *The Sorrows of Yamba*

1976 Ignatius Sancho and Trade/Business Card

Nos. 2728/9, 2730/1 and 2732/3 were each printed together, *se-tenant*, in horizontal pairs throughout the sheets.

Bicentenary of the Abolition of the Slave Trade

2007 (22 Mar.) Two phosphor bands. Perf 14½

2728 **1971**	(1st) multicoloured	75	75	☐	☐
	a. Horiz pair.				
	Nos. 2728/9	1·50	1·50	☐	☐
2729 **1972**	(1st) multicoloured	75	75	☐	☐
2730 **1973**	50p multicoloured	1·20	1·20	☐	☐
	a. Horiz pair.				
	Nos. 2730/1	2·50	2·50	☐	☐
2731 **1974**	50p multicoloured	1·20	1·20	☐	☐
2732 **1975**	72p multicoloured	1·70	1·70	☐	☐
	a. Horiz pair.				
	Nos. 2732/3	3·25	3·25	☐	☐
2733 **1976**	72p multicoloured	1·70	1·70	☐	☐

Set of 6	7·00	7·00	☐	☐
First Day Cover		7·50		☐
Presentation Pack	10·00		☐	
PHQ Cards (*set of 6*)	4·50	14·00	☐	☐
Set of 3 Gutter Strips of 4	14·00		☐	
Set of 3 Traffic Light Gutter Strips of 4	16·00		☐	

1977 Ice Cream Cone

1978 Sandcastle

1979 Carousel Horse

1980 Beach Huts

1981 Deckchairs

1982 Beach Donkeys

'Beside the Seaside'

2007 (15 May) Two phosphor bands. Perf 14½

2734	**1977**	(1st) multicoloured	75	75	☐	☐
2735	**1978**	46p multicoloured	1·00	1·00	☐	☐
2736	**1979**	48p multicoloured	1·20	1·20	☐	☐
2737	**1980**	54p multicoloured	1·75	1·75	☐	☐
2738	**1981**	69p multicoloured	2·00	2·00	☐	☐
2739	**1982**	78p multicoloured	2·25	2·25	☐	☐
Set of 6			8·50	8·50	☐	☐
First Day Cover				9·00		☐
Presentation Pack			11·00		☐	
PHQ Cards (*set of 6*)			3·00	10·00	☐	☐
Set of 6 Gutter Pairs			14·50		☐	

1983

New Wembley Stadium, London

2007 (17 May) Sheet 113 × 103 mm containing design as Type 1593 but with 'WORLD CUP 2002' inscription omitted, and Nos. EN6 and EN15, each × 2. One centre band (2nd) or two phosphor bands (others). Perf 14½ × 14 (1st) or 15 × 14 (with one elliptical hole on each vertical side) (2nd, 78p)

MS2740 **1983** (1st) As Type 1593; (2nd) No. EN6 × 2; 78p No. EN15 × 2 and one central stamp-size label	6·00 6·50	☐	☐
First Day Cover	7·00		☐

The design as Type 1593 omits the 'WORLD CUP 2002' inscription at the left of the stamp.

1984 Arnold Machin

1985 1967 4d. Machin

1986

40th Anniversary of the First Machin Definitives

2007 (5 June) Sheet 127 × 73 mm containing new stamps and Nos. Y1725 and Y1725b. Two phosphor bands (£1). Perf 14½ (1st) or 15 × 14 (with one elliptical hole on each vertical side) (£1)

2741	**1984**	(1st) multicoloured	1·50 1·50	☐	☐
2742	**1985**	(1st) multicoloured	1·50 1·50	☐	☐
MS2743 **1986** Nos. 2741/2, Y1725 and Y1725b			7·00 7·00	☐	☐
First Day Cover (**MS**2743)			8·00		☐
Presentation Pack (**MS**2743)			9·50	☐	
PHQ Cards (*Set of 3*) (Nos. 2741/ **MS**2743)			1·40 18·00	☐	☐

Nos. 2741/2 were only issued in £7.66 stamp booklets (No. DX39) and in **MS**2743.

Stamps as Type **1984** but with phosphor frames were issued in sheets of 20 with *se-tenant* labels showing the 1967–9 Machin definitives.

1987 Stirling Moss in Vanwall 2.5L, 1957

1988 Graham Hill in BRM P57, 1962

1989 Jim Clark in Lotus 25 Climax, 1963

1990 Jackie Stewart in Tyrrell 006/2, 1973

1991 James Hunt in McLaren M23, 1976

1992 Nigel Mansell in Williams FW11, 1986

50th Anniversary of the British Grand Prix, Silverstone. Racing Cars

2007 (3 July) Two phosphor bands. Perf 14½

2744	**1987**	(1st) multicoloured	75	75	☐	☐
2745	**1988**	(1st) multicoloured	75	75	☐	☐
2746	**1989**	54p multicoloured	2·00	2·00	☐	☐
2747	**1990**	54p multicoloured	2·00	2·00	☐	☐
2748	**1991**	78p multicoloured	2·50	2·50	☐	☐
2749	**1992**	78p multicoloured	2·50	2·50	☐	☐
Set of 6			9·50	9·50	☐	☐
First Day Cover				10·00		☐
Presentation Pack			10·00		☐	
PHQ Cards (set of 6)			3·00	12·00	☐	☐
Set of 6 Gutter Pairs			19·00		☐	

1993 Harry Potter and the Philosopher's Stone

1994 Harry Potter and the Chamber of Secrets

1995 Harry Potter and the prisoner of Azkaban

1996 Harry Potter and the Goblet of Fire

1997 Harry Potter and the Order of the Phoenix

1998 Harry Potter and the Half-Blood Prince

1999 Harry Potter and the Deathly Hallows

Nos. 2750/6 were printed together, se-tenant, as horizontal strips of seven stamps in sheets of 56 (2 panes 7 × 4).

2000 Crests of Hogwarts School and its Four Houses

Publication of Final Book in the Harry Potter Series

2007 (17 July).

(a) Book Covers. 'All-over' phosphor. Perf 14½

2750	**1993**	(1st) multicoloured	75	75	☐	☐
		a. Horiz strip of 7.				
		Nos. 2750/6	6·00	6·00	☐	☐
2751	**1994**	(1st) multicoloured	75	75	☐	☐
2752	**1995**	(1st) multicoloured	75	75	☐	☐
2753	**1996**	(1st) multicoloured	75	75	☐	☐
2754	**1997**	(1st) multicoloured	75	75	☐	☐
2755	**1998**	(1st) multicoloured	75	75	☐	☐
2756	**1999**	(1st) multicoloured	75	75	☐	☐
Set of 7			6·00	6·00	☐	☐
First Day Cover				7·00		☐
Presentation Pack (Nos. 2750/**MS**2757)			16·00		☐	
PHQ Cards (set of 13)			7·50	27·00	☐	☐
Gutter Block of 14			12·00		☐	
Traffic Light Gutter Block of 14			15·00		☐	☐

(b) Crests of Hogwarts School and its Four Houses.
Multicoloured. Two phosphor bands. Perf 15 × 14
MS2757 123 × 70 mm. 2000 (1st)
Gryffindor; (1st) Hufflepuff; (1st)
Hogwarts; (1st) Ravenclaw;

(1st) Slytherin		5·00	5·00	☐	☐
First Day Cover			6·00		☐

The complete miniature sheet is shown on one of the thirteen PHQ cards with the others depicting the individual stamps including those from **MS**2757.

Stamps as those within **MS**2757 but self-adhesive were issued in sheets of 20 containing the five designs *se-tenant* with labels depicting either magic spells or personal photographs. The magic spells labels are printed in thermochromic ink which fades temporarily when exposed to heat, revealing the meaning of the spells.

2001 Scout and Camp Fire   **2002** Scouts Rock climbing

2003 Scout planting Tree   **2004** Adult Volunteer teaching Scout Archery

2005 Scouts learning gliding   **2006** Scouts from Many Nations

Centenary of Scouting and 21st World Scout Jamboree, Chelmsford, Essex

2007 (26 July) Two phosphor bands. Perf 14½ ×14

2758	**2001**	(1st) multicoloured	75	75	☐ ☐
2759	**2002**	46p multicoloured	1·00	1·00	☐ ☐
2760	**2003**	48p multicoloured	1·10	1·10	☐ ☐
2761	**2004**	54p multicoloured	1·20	1·20	☐ ☐
2762	**2005**	69p multicoloured	1·50	1·50	☐ ☐
2763	**2006**	78p multicoloured	1·70	1·70	☐ ☐
Set of 6			8·00	8·00	☐
First Day Cover				9·00	☐
Presentation Pack			10·00		☐
PHQ Cards (*set of* 6)			3·00	12·00	☐ ☐
Set of 6 Gutter Pairs			16·00		☐

2007 White-tailed Eagle   **2008** Bearded Tit

2009 Red Kite   **2010** Cirl Bunting

2011 Marsh Harrier   **2012** Avocet

2013 Bittern   **2014** Dartford Warbler

2015 Corncrake   **2016** Peregrine Falcon

Nos. 2764/73 were printed together, *se-tenant*, in blocks of ten (5 × 2) in sheets of 60 (2 panes of 30).

'Action for Species' (1st series). Birds

2007 (4 Sept.) Two phosphor bands. Perf 14½

2764	**2007**	(1st) multicoloured	75	75	☐ ☐
		a. Block of 10.			
		Nos. 2764/73	9·50	9·50	☐ ☐
2765	**2008**	(1st) multicoloured	75	75	☐ ☐
2766	**2009**	(1st) multicoloured	75	75	☐ ☐
2767	**2010**	(1st) multicoloured	75	75	☐ ☐
2768	**2011**	(1st) multicoloured	75	75	☐ ☐
2769	**2012**	(1st) multicoloured	75	75	☐ ☐
2770	**2013**	(1st) multicoloured	75	75	☐ ☐
2771	**2014**	(1st) multicoloured	75	75	☐ ☐
2772	**2015**	(1st) multicoloured	75	75	☐ ☐
2773	**2016**	(1st) multicoloured	75	75	☐ ☐
Set of 10			9·50	9·50	☐ ☐
First Day Cover				10·00	☐
Presentation Pack			12·00		☐
PHQ Cards (*set of* 10)			6·00	15·00	☐ ☐
Gutter Block of 20			19·00		☐

2017 NCO, Royal Military Police, 1999   **2018** Tank Commander, 5th Royal Tank Regiment, 1944

2019 Observer, Royal Field Artillery, 1917

2020 Rifleman, 95th Rifles, 1813

2021 Grenadier, Royal Regiment of Foot of Ireland, 1704

2022 Trooper, Earl of Oxford's Horse, 1661

Nos. 2774/6 and 2777/9 were each printed together, *se-tenant*, in horizontal strips of three stamps in sheets of 60 (2 panes 6 × 5).

Military Uniforms (1st series). British Army Uniforms

2007 (20 Sept.) Two phosphor bands. Perf 14½

2774	**2017**	(1st) multicoloured	80	80	☐	☐
		a. Horiz strip of 3.				
		Nos. 2774/6	3·00	3·00	☐	☐
2775	**2018**	(1st) multicoloured	80	80	☐	☐
2776	**2019**	(1st) multicoloured	80	80	☐	☐
2777	**2020**	78p multicoloured	1·70	1·70	☐	☐
		a. Horiz strip of 3.				
		Nos. 2777/9	7·00	7·00	☐	☐
2778	**2021**	78p multicoloured	1·70	1·70	☐	☐
2779	**2022**	78p multicoloured	1·70	1·70	☐	☐
Set of 6			9·50	9·50	☐	☐
First Day Cover				9·00		☐
Presentation Pack			11·00		☐	
PHQ Cards (*set of* 6)			3·00	12·00	☐	☐
Set of 2 Gutter Strips of 6			20·00		☐	
Set of 2 Traffic Light Gutter Strips of 6			24·00		☐	

2023 Leaving St. Paul's Cathedral after Thanksgiving Service, 2006

2024 Inspecting King's Troop Royal Horse Artillery, Regents Park, 1997

2025 At Garter Ceremony, Windsor, 1980

2026 At Royal Ascot, 1969

2027 At Premiere of The Guns of Navarone, 1961

2028 At Clydebank, 1947

Nos. 2780/1, 2782/3 and 2784/5 were each printed together, *se-tenant*, in horizontal pairs throughout the sheets.

2029 Photographs of the Royal Family

Diamond Wedding of Queen Elizabeth II and Duke of Edinburgh

2007 (16 Oct.)

(a) PVA gum. Litho Cartor. 'All-over' phosphor. Perf 14½ × 14

2780	**2023**	(1st) blackish-brown and black	75	75	☐	☐
		a. Horiz pair. Nos. 2780/1	1·50	1·50	☐	☐
2781	**2024**	(1st) blackish-brown and black	75	75	☐	☐
2782	**2025**	54p blackish-brown and black	1·20	1·20	☐	☐
		a. Horiz pair. Nos. 2782/3	3·75	3·75	☐	☐
2783	**2026**	54p blackish-brown and black	1·20	1·20	☐	☐
2784	**2027**	78p blackish-brown and black	1·90	1·90	☐	☐
		a. Horiz pair. Nos. 2784/5	5·50	5·50	☐	☐
2785	**2028**	78p blackish-brown and black	1·90	1·90	☐	☐
Set of 6			9·50	9·50	☐	☐
First Day Cover				10·00		☐
Presentation Pack (Nos. 2780/**MS**2786)			16·00		☐	
PHQ Cards (*set of* 11)			6·00	27·00	☐	☐
Set of 3 Gutter Strips of 4			19·00		☐	

(b) Self-adhesive. Photo Walsall. Two phosphor bands. Perf 14½

MS2786 115 × 89 mm. (1st) Royal family, Balmoral, 1972; (1st) Queen and Prince Philip, Buckingham Palace, 2007; 69p. Royal family, Windsor Castle, 1965; 78p. Princess Elizabeth, Prince Philip, Prince Charles and Princess Anne, Clarence House, 1951	6·00 6·00 ☐ ☐

First Day Cover   8·50   ☐

The complete miniature sheet is shown on one of the eleven PHQ cards with the others depicting individual stamps including those from **MS**2786.

2030 'Madonna and Child' (William Dyce), c 1827

2031 'The Madonna of Humility' (Lippo di Dalmasio), c 1390–1400

Christmas (1st issue). Paintings of the Madonna and Child

2007 (6 Nov.) One centre band (2nd) or two phosphor bands (1st). Self-adhesive. Die-cut perf 15 × 14 (with one elliptical hole on each vertical side)

2787	**2030**	(2nd) multicoloured	50	50	☐	☐
2788	**2031**	(1st) multicoloured	75	75	☐	☐
First Day Cover				4·00	☐	

2032 Angel playing Trumpet ('PEACE')

2033 Angel playing Lute ('GOODWILL')

2034 Angel playing Trumpet ('PEACE')

2035 Angel playing Lute ('GOODWILL')

2036 Angel playing Flute ('JOY')

2037 Angel playing Tambourine ('GLORY')

Christmas (2nd issue). Angels

2007 (6 Nov.) One centre band (2nd) or two phosphor bands (others). Perf 15 × 14.

		(a) Self-adhesive				
2789	**2032**	(2nd) multicoloured	55	55	☐	☐
2790	**2033**	(1st) multicoloured	75	75	☐	☐
2791	**2034**	(2nd Large) multicoloured	90	90	☐	☐
2792	**2035**	(1st Large) multicoloured	2·00	2·00	☐	☐
2793	**2036**	78p multicoloured	3·00	3·00	☐	☐
2794	**2037**	£1.24 multicoloured	4·50	4·50	☐	☐
Set of 6			9·50	9·50	☐	
First Day Cover				10·00	☐	
Presentation Pack (Nos. 2787/94)			12·00		☐	
PHQ Cards (set of 9)			6·00	18·00	☐	☐

(b) PVA gum

MS2795 115 × 102 mm.					
As Nos. 2789/94		10·00	10·00	☐	☐
First Day Cover			11·00		☐

The phosphor bands on Nos. 2791/2 are at the centre and right of each stamp.

The PHQ cards depict Nos. 2787/94 and **MS**2795.

The 2nd class, 1st class and 78p stamps were also issued in sheets of 20 printed in lithography instead of photogravure containing eight 1st class, eight 2nd class and four 78p stamps, each stamp accompanied by a *se-tenant* label. Separate sheets of 20 1st, 20 2nd or 10 78p were available with personal photographs.

2038

'Lest We Forget' (2nd issue). 90th Anniv of the Battle of Passchendaele

2007 (8 Nov.) Sheet 124 × 70 mm containing new stamp and designs as Nos. EN15, NI105, S118 and W107. Two phosphor bands. Perf 14½ (1st) or 15 × 14 (with one elliptical hole on each vertical side) (78p)

MS2796	**2038**	(1st) Soldiers in poppy flower; 78p. × 4 As Nos. EN15, NI103, S118 and W107		10·00	10·00	☐ ☐
First Day Cover				11·00		☐
Presentation Pack			11·00			☐

No. **MS**2796 (including the England, Scotland and Wales stamps) is printed in lithography.

The 1st class stamp was also issued in sheets of 20 with *se-tenant* labels showing soldiers and their letters home.

Collectors Pack

2007 (8 Nov.) Comprises Nos. 2686/92, 2699/720, 2728/39, **MS**2743/94 and **MS**2796

CP2796a	Collectors Pack	£110	☐

Post Office Yearbook

2007 (8 Nov.) Comprises Nos. 2686/92, 2699/720, 2728/39, **MS**2743/94 and **MS**2796

YB2796a	Yearbook	£130	☐

Miniature Sheet Collection

2007 (8 Nov.) Comprises Nos. **MS**2692, **MS**2727, **MS**2740, **MS**2743, **MS**2757, **MS**2786 and **MS**2795/6

MS2796a	Miniature Sheet Collection	60·00 ☐

2039 *Casino Royale*

2040 *Dr. No*

2041 *Goldfinger*

2042 *Diamonds are Forever*

2043 *For Your Eyes Only*

2044 *From Russia with Love*

Birth Centenary of Ian Fleming (author of James Bond books) (1st issue). Book Covers

2008 (8 Jan.) Two phosphor bands. Perf 15 × 14½

2797	**2039**	(1st) multicoloured	75	75	☐	☐
2798	**2040**	(1st) multicoloured	75	75	☐	☐
2799	**2041**	54p multicoloured	1·50	1·50	☐	☐
2800	**2042**	54p multicoloured	1·50	1·50	☐	☐
2801	**2043**	78p multicoloured	2·50	2·50	☐	☐
2802	**2044**	78p multicoloured	2·50	2·50	☐	☐
Set of 6			8·50	8·50	☐	
First Day Cover				9·00		☐
Presentation Pack			11·00			☐
PHQ Cards (*set of* 7)			4·75	20·00	☐	☐
Set of 6 Gutter Pairs			17·00		☐	
MS2803 189 × 68 mm. Nos. 2797/802			8·50	8·50	☐	☐
First Day Cover				9·00		☐

The seven PHQ cards depict the individual stamps and **MS**2803.

Birth Centenary of Ian Fleming (author of James Bond books) (2nd issue). Booklet stamps

2008 (8 Jan.) Design as Type **1517** but printed in lithography. Two phosphor bands. Perf 14½

2805	**1517**	(1st) multicoloured	85	85	☐	☐

No. 2805 was only issued in £7·40 stamp booklets.

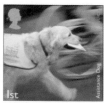

2045 Assistance Dog carrying Letter (Labrador 'Rowan')

2046 Mountain Rescue Dog (Cross-bred 'Merrick')

2047 Police Dog (German Shepherd 'Max')

2048 Customs Dog (Springer Spaniel 'Max')

2049 Sheepdog (Border Collie 'Bob')

2050 Guide Dog (Labrador 'Warwick')

Working Dogs

2008 (5 Feb.) Two phosphor bands. Perf 14½

2806	**2045**	(1st) multicoloured	80	80	☐	☐
2807	**2046**	46p multicoloured	1·00	1·00	☐	☐
2808	**2047**	48p multicoloured	1·50	1·50	☐	☐
2809	**2048**	54p multicoloured	1·75	1·75	☐	☐
2810	**2049**	69p multicoloured	2·00	2·00	☐	☐
2811	**2050**	78p multicoloured	2·50	2·50	☐	☐
Set of 6			8·50	8·50	☐	☐
First Day Cover				9·00		☐
Presentation Pack			11·00		☐	
PHQ Cards (*set of* 6)			4·00	14·00	☐	☐
Set of 6 Gutter Pairs			17·00		☐	

The 1st value includes the 'EUROPA' emblem.

2051 Henry IV (1399-1413)

2052 Henry V (1413–1422)

2053 Henry VI (1422-1461 & 1470-1471)

2054 Edward IV (1461–1470 & 1471–1473)

2055 Edward V
(1483)

2056 Richard III
(1483–1485)

2057 The Age of Lancaster and York

Kings and Queens (1st issue). Houses of Lancaster and York

2008 (28 Feb.) Two phosphor bands. Perf 14½

2812	**2051**	(1st) multicoloured	80	80	☐	☐
2813	**2052**	(1st) multicoloured	80	80	☐	☐
2814	**2053**	54p multicoloured	1·50	1·50	☐	☐
2815	**2054**	54p multicoloured	1·50	1·50	☐	☐
2816	**2055**	69p multicoloured	2·50	2·50	☐	☐
2817	**2056**	69p multicoloured	2·50	2·50	☐	☐
Set of 6			8·50	8·50	☐	
First Day Cover				9·00		☐
Presentation Pack			16·00		☐	
PHQ Cards (*set of* 11)			7·25	26·00	☐	☐
Set of 6 Gutter Pairs			17·00		☐	
Set of 6 Traffic Light Gutter Blocks of 4			26·00		☐	

MS2818 123 × 70 mm. **2057** (1st) Owain
   Glyn Dwr ('Parliament'), **1404**; (1st)
   Henry V's triumph at Battle of Agincourt,
   1415; 78p. Yorkish victory at Battle of
   Tewkesbury, **1471**; 78p. William
   Caxton, first English printer, **1477**   6·50   6·50   ☐ ☐

First Day Cover   8·00   ☐

The complete miniature sheet is shown on one of the eleven PHQ cards with the others depicting individual stamps including those from **MS**2818.

'Smilers' Booklet stamps (4th series)

2008 (28 Feb.) Designs as Nos. 2567/8, 2570 and 2675/7. Self-adhesive. Two phosphor bands. Die-cut perf 15 × 14½ (with one elliptical hole on each vertical side).

2819	**1569**	(1st) multicoloured	1·25	1·25	☐	☐
		a. Booklet pane. Nos.				
		2819/24	6·00		☐	
2820	**1842**	(1st) multicoloured	1·25	1·25	☐	☐
2821	**1517**	(1st) multicoloured	1·25	1·25	☐	☐
2822	**1932**	(1st) multicoloured	1·25	1·25	☐	☐
2823	**1933**	(1st) multicoloured	1·25	1·25	☐	☐
2824	**1934**	(1st) multicoloured	1·25	1·25	☐	☐
Set of 6			6·00	6·00	☐	☐

Nos. 2819/24 were issued in £2.04 booklets in which the surplus backing paper around each stamp was removed.

Nos. 2820 and 2822 were reissued on 28 October 2008 in separate sheets of 10 or 20 with circular *se-tenant* labels showing the Almond Blossom fairy (2820), Mr. Men or Noddy (2822).
Nos. 2819, 2820 and 2822 were issued again on 30 April 2009 in separate sheets of 10 or 20 with circular *se-tenant* labels showing Jeremy Fisher (2820), Wild Cherry fairy (2820), Little Miss Sunshine or Big Ears (2822).
All these sheets were printed in lithography instead of photogravure.

2058 Lifeboat, Barra

2059 Lifeboat approaching Dinghy, Appledore

2060 Helicopter Winchman, Portland

2061 Inshore lifeboat, St. Ives

2062 Rescue Helicopter, Lee-on-Solent

2063 Launch of Lifeboat, Dinbych-y-Pysgod, Tenby

Rescue at Sea

2008 (13 Mar.) 'All-over' phosphor. Perf 14½ × 14

2825	**2058**	(1st) multicoloured	80	80	☐	☐
2826	**2059**	46p multicoloured	1·00	1·00	☐	☐
2827	**2060**	48p multicoloured	1·50	1·50	☐	☐
2828	**2061**	54p multicoloured	1·75	1·75	☐	☐
2829	**2062**	69p multicoloured	2·00	2·00	☐	☐
2830	**2063**	78p multicoloured	2·50	2·50	☐	☐
Set of 6			8·50	8·50	☐	☐
First Day Cover				9·00		☐
Presentation Pack			11·00		☐	
PHQ Cards (*set of* 6)			4·00	14·00	☐	☐
Set of 6 Gutter Pairs			17·00		☐	

*Nos. 2825/30 have interrupted perforations along the top and bottom edges of the stamps, the gaps in the perforations forming the three dots and three dashes that spell out 'SOS' in morse code.

2064 *Lysandra bellargus* (Adonis Blue)

2065 *Coenagrion mercuriale* (southern damselfly)

2066 *Formica rufibarbis*
(red-barbed ant)

2067 *Pareulype berberata*
(barberry carpet moth)

2068 *Lucanus cervus*
(stag beetle)

2069 *Cryptocephalus coryli*
(hazel pot beetle)

2070 *Gryllus campestris*
(field cricket)

2071 *Hesperia comma*
(silver-spotted skipper)

2072 *Pseudepipona herrichii*
(Purbeck mason wasp)

2073 *Gnorimus nobilis*
(noble chafer)

Nos. 2831/40 were printed together, *se-tenant*, in blocks of ten (5 × 2) in sheets of 60 (2 panes of 30).

'Action for Species' (2nd series). Insects

2008 (15 Apr.) Phosphor background. Perf 14½

2831	**2064**	(1st) multicoloured	80	80	☐	☐
		a. Block of 10.				
		Nos. 2831/40	8·00	8·00	☐	☐
2832	**2065**	(1st) multicoloured	80	80	☐	☐
2833	**2066**	(1st) multicoloured	80	80	☐	☐
2834	**2067**	(1st) multicoloured	80	80	☐	☐
2835	**2068**	(1st) multicoloured	80	80	☐	☐
2836	**2069**	(1st) multicoloured	80	80	☐	☐
2837	**2070**	(1st) multicoloured	80	80	☐	☐
2838	**2071**	(1st) multicoloured	80	80	☐	☐
2839	**2072**	(1st) multicoloured	80	80	☐	☐
2840	**2073**	(1st) multicoloured	80	80	☐	☐
Set of 10			8·00	8·00	☐	☐
First Day Cover				8·75		☐
Presentation Pack			9·25		☐	
PHQ Cards (*set of* 10)			6·75	16·00	☐	☐
Gutter Block of 20			16·00		☐	

2074 Lichfield
Cathedral

2075 Belfast
Cathedral

2076 Gloucester
Cathedral

2077 St. David's
Cathedral

2078 Westminster
Cathedral

2079 St. Magnus
Cathedral, Kirkwall,
Orkney

2080 St. Paul's Cathedral

Cathedrals

2008 (13 May). 'All-over' phosphor. Perf 14½

2841	**2074**	(1st) multicoloured	85	85	☐	☐
2842	**2075**	48p multicoloured	1·10	1·10	☐	☐
2843	**2076**	50p multicoloured	1·50	1·50	☐	☐
2844	**2077**	56p multicoloured	1·75	1·75	☐	☐
2845	**2078**	72p multicoloured	2·50	2·50	☐	☐
2846	**2079**	81p multicoloured	3·50	3·50	☐	☐
Set of 6			9·00	9·00	☐	☐
First Day Cover				9·50		☐
Presentation Pack			17·00		☐	
PHQ Cards (*set of* 11)			7·25	24·00	☐	☐
Set of 6 Gutter Pairs			18·00		☐	
Set of 6 Traffic Light Gutter Pairs			20·00		☐	

MS2847 115 × 89 mm. (1st) multicoloured;
(1st) multicoloured; 81p. multicoloured;
81p. multicoloured. Perf 14½ × 14   6·00 ☐ ☐
First Day Cover   7·50   ☐
No. **MS**2847 commemorates the 300th anniversary of St.
Paul's Cathedral.
The complete miniature sheet is shown on one of the eleven
PHQ cards with the others depicting individual stamps
including those from **MS**2847.

'Beside the Seaside' (2nd series)

2008 (13 May). As Type 1977 but self-adhesive. Two phosphor
bands. Die-cut perf 14½
2848 **1977**   (1st) multicoloured   2·00   2·00 ☐ ☐
No. 2848 was only issued in £2.16 booklets.

2081 *Carry on Sergeant*

2082 *Dracula*

2083 *Carry on Cleo*

2084 *The Curse of Frankenstein*

2085 *Carry on Screaming*

2086 *The Mummy*

Posters for Carry On and Hammer Horror Films

2008 (10 June). Two phosphor bands. Perf 14
2849 **2081**   (1st) multicoloured   85   85   ☐ ☐
2850 **2082**   48p multicoloured   1·10   1·10 ☐ ☐
2851 **2083**   50p multicoloured   1·50   1·50 ☐ ☐
2852 **2084**   56p multicoloured   1·75   1·75 ☐ ☐
2853 **2085**   72p multicoloured   2·00   2·00 ☐ ☐
2854 **2086**   81p multicoloured   2·50   2·50 ☐ ☐
Set of 6   8·50   8·50 ☐ ☐
First Day Cover   9·00   ☐
Presentation Pack   11·00   ☐
PHQ Cards (*set of* 6)   4·00 14·00 ☐ ☐
Set of 6 Gutter Pairs   17·00   ☐
Nos. 2849/54 commemorate the 50th anniversary of Dracula
and the first Carry On film (Carry on Sergeant).

2087 Red Arrows, Dartmouth
Regatta Airshow, 2006

2088 RAF Falcons Parachute
Team, Biggin Hill, 2006

2089 Spectator watching Red
Arrows, Farnborough

2090 Prototype Avro Vulcan
Bombers and Avro 707s,
Farnborough, 1953

2091 Parachutist Robert
Wyndham on Wing of Avro
504, 1933

2092 Air Race rounding the
Beacon, Hendon, c. 1912

Air Displays

2008 (17 July). Two phosphor bands. Perf 14½ × 14
2855 **2087**   (1st) multicoloured   85   85   ☐ ☐
2856 **2088**   48p multicoloured   1·10   1·10 ☐ ☐
2857 **2089**   50p multicoloured   1·50   1·50 ☐ ☐
2858 **2090**   56p multicoloured   1·75   1·75 ☐ ☐
2859 **2091**   72p multicoloured   2·00   2·00 ☐ ☐
2860 **2092**   81p multicoloured   2·50   2·50 ☐ ☐
Set of 6   8·50   8·50 ☐ ☐
First Day Cover   9·00   ☐
Presentation Pack   11·00   ☐
PHQ Cards (*set of* 6)   4·00 14·00 ☐ ☐
Set of 6 Gutter Pairs   17·00   ☐
The 1st class stamp was also issued in sheets of 20 with
se-tenant labels, printed in lithography instead of
photogravure.

2093 Landmarks of Beijing and London

Handover of Olympic Flag from Beijing to London

2008 (22 Aug.) Sheet 115 × 76 mm. Phosphorised paper. Perf
14½
MS2861   **2093**   (1st) National Stadium,
Beijing; (1st) London Eye; (1st) Tower
of London; (1st) Corner Tower of the
Forbidden City, Beijing   3·25   3·25 ☐ ☐
First Day Cover   4·00   ☐
Presentation Pack   4·25   ☐
PHQ Cards (*set of* 5)   3·00 10·00 ☐ ☐
The Olympic rings overprinted on **MS**2861 are in silk-screen
varnish.
The five PHQ cards show the four individual stamps and the
complete miniature sheet.

2094 Drum Major, RAF Central Band, 2007

2095 Helicopter Rescue Winchman, 1984

2100 Millicent Garrett Fawcett (suffragist)

2101 Elizabeth Garrett Anderson (physician–women's health)

2096 Hawker Hunter Pilot, 1951

2097 Lancaster Air Gunner, 1944

2102 Marie Stopes (family planning pioneer)

2103 Eleanor Rathbone (family allowance campaigner)

2098 WAAF Plotter, 1940

2099 Pilot, 1918

2104 Claudia Jones (civil rights activist)

2105 Barbara Castle (politician–Equal Pay Act)

Nos. 2862/4 and 2865/7 were each printed together, *se-tenant*, in horizontal strips of three stamps in sheets of 60 (2 panes 6 × 5).

Military Uniforms (2nd series). RAF Uniforms

2008 (18 Sept.) Two phosphor bands. Perf 14

2862	**2094**	(1st) multicoloured	80	80	☐	☐
		a. Horiz strip of 3.				
		Nos. 2862/4	4·00	4·00	☐	☐
2863	**2095**	(1st) multicoloured	80	80	☐	☐
2864	**2096**	(1st) multicoloured	80	80	☐	☐
2865	**2097**	81p multicoloured	1·70	1·70	☐	☐
		a. Horiz strip of 3.				
		Nos. 2865/7	6·50	6·50	☐	☐
2866	**2098**	81p multicoloured	1·70	1·70	☐	☐
2867	**2099**	81p multicoloured	1·70	1·70	☐	☐
Set of 6			9·00	9·00	☐	☐
First Day Cover				9·00	☐	
Presentation Pack			11·00		☐	
PHQ Cards (set of 6)			2·75	14·00	☐	☐
Set of 2 Gutter Strips of 6			18·00		☐	
Set of 2 Traffic Light Gutter Blocks of 12		26.00			☐	

'Pilot to Plane'. RAF Uniforms. Booklet stamps

2008 (18 Sept.) Designs as Types 1307 (Spitfire from 1997 British Aircraft Designers) and 2087 (Red Arrows from 2008 Air Displays) but printed in lithography. Two phosphor bands. Perf 14

2868	**1307**	20p multicoloured	4·00	4·50	☐	☐
2869	**2087**	(1st) multicoloured	4·00	4·50	☐	☐

Nos. 2868/9 were only available from £7.15 stamp booklets.

Women of Distinction

2008 (14 Oct.) 'All-over' phosphor. Perf 14 × 14½

2870	**2100**	(1st) multicoloured	85	85	☐	☐
2871	**2101**	48p multicoloured	1·10	1·10	☐	☐
2872	**2102**	50p multicoloured	1·50	1·50	☐	☐
2873	**2103**	56p multicoloured	1·75	1·75	☐	☐
2874	**2104**	72p multicoloured	2·00	2·00	☐	☐
2875	**2105**	81p multicoloured	2·50	2·50	☐	☐
Set of 6			9·00	9·00	☐	☐
First Day Cover				10·00		☐
Presentation Pack			11·00			☐
PHQ Cards (set of 6)			4·00	14·00	☐	☐
Set of 6 Gutter Pairs			18·00		☐	

2106 Ugly Sisters from *Cinderella*

2107 Genie from *Aladdin*

2108 Ugly Sisters from *Cinderella*

2109 Captain Hook from *Peter Pan*

2110 Genie from
Aladdin

2111 Wicked
Queen from
Snow White

Christmas

2008 (4 Nov.) One centre band (2nd) or two phosphor bands (others). Perf 15 × 14.

	(a) Self-adhesive				
2876	**2106**	(2nd) multicoloured	55	55	☐ ☐
2877	**2107**	(1st) multicoloured	85	85	☐ ☐
2878	**2108**	(2nd Large) multicoloured	90	90	☐ ☐
2879	**2109**	50p multicoloured	1·10	1·10	☐ ☐
2880	**2110**	(1st Large) multicoloured	1·10	1·10	☐ ☐
2881	**2111**	81p multicoloured	1·80	1·80	☐ ☐
Set of 6			6·50	6·50	☐ ☐
First Day Cover				7·00	☐
Presentation Pack			10·00		☐
PHQ Cards (*set of 7*)			4·00	12·00	☐ ☐
	(b) PVA gum				
MS2882 114 × 102 mm. As					
Nos. 2876/81			6·50	6·50	☐ ☐
First Day Cover				7·00	☐

The phosphor bands on Nos. 2878/9 are at the centre and right of each stamp.
The seven PHQ cards depict the six stamps and **MS**2882. The 2nd class, 1st class and 81p stamps were also issued in sheets of 20 printed in lithography instead of photogravure containing eight 1st class, eight 2nd class and four 81p stamps, each stamp accompanied by a *se-tenant* label. Separate sheets of 20 1st, 20 2nd, 10 1st or 10 81p were available with personal photographs.

2112 Poppies on Barbed Wire Stems

2113 Soldiers in Poppy Flower

2114 Soldier's Face in Poppy Flower

Nos. 2883/5 were printed together, *se-tenant*, in horizontal strips of three stamps in sheets of 30.

2115

'Lest We Forget' (3rd issue). 90th Anniversary of the Armistice

2008 (6 Nov.) Phosphor background (No. 2885) or two phosphor bands (others). Perf 14½ (1st) or 15 × 14 (with one elliptical hole on each vertical side) (81p)

2883	**2112**	(1st) multicoloured	75	75	☐ ☐
		a. Horiz strip of 3. Nos.			
		2883/5	2·75	2·75	☐ ☐
2884	**2113**	(1st) multicoloured	75	75	☐ ☐
2885	**2114**	(1st) multicoloured	75	75	☐ ☐
Set of 3			2·75	2·75	☐ ☐
Presentation Pack			11·00		☐
PHQ Cards (*set of 6*)			4·75	14·00	☐ ☐
Gutter Strip of 3			5·50		☐
MS2886 124 × 70 mm. S115 No. 2885					
and as Nos. EN18, NI107,					
S120 and W109			7·75	7·75	☐ ☐
First Day Cover				9·50	☐

No. **MS**2886 (including the Northern Ireland, Scotland and Wales stamps) is printed in lithography.
The six PHQ cards depict Nos. **MS**2685, **MS**2796 and 2883/**MS**2886.
The 1st class stamp was also issued in sheets of 20 with *se-tenant* labels.

Collectors Pack

2008 (6 Nov.) Comprises Nos. 2797/802, 2806/**MS**2818, 2825/**MS**2847, 2849/67, 2870/81, **MS**2886 and **MS**NI110
CP2886a   Collectors Pack   £120   ☐

Post Office Yearbook

2008 (6 Nov.) Comprises Nos. 2797/802, 2806/**MS**2818, 2825/**MS**2847, 2849/67, 2870/81, **MS**2886 and **MS**NI110
YB2886a   Yearbook   £125   ☐

Miniature Sheet Collection

2008 (6 Nov.) Comprises Nos. **MS**2803, **MS**2818, **MS**2847, **MS**2882, **MS**2886 and **MS**NI110/11
MS2886a   Miniature Sheet Collection 67·00   ☐

2116 Supermarine Spitfire
(R. J. Mitchell)

2117 Mini Skirt
(Mary Quant)

2118 Mini
(Sir Alec Issigonis)

2119 Anglepoise Lamp
(George Carwardine)

2120 Concorde
(Aérospatiale-BAC)

2121 K2 Telephone Kiosk
(Sir Giles Gilbert Scott)

2122 Polypropylene Chair
(Robin Day)

2123 Penguin Books
(Edward Young)

2124 London
Underground Map

2125 Routemaster Bus
(design team led by AAM
Durrant)

T **2116/25** were printed together, *se-tenant*, in blocks of ten
(2×5) throughout the sheet.

British Design Classics (1st series)

2009 (13 Jan.) Printed in lithography. Phosphor background.
Perf 14½

2887 **2116**	(1st) multicoloured	90	90	☐	☐	
	a. Block of 10. Nos.					
	2887/96	8·75	8·75	☐	☐	
2888 **2117**	(1st) multicoloured	90	90	☐	☐	
2889 **2118**	(1st) multicoloured	90	90	☐	☐	
2890 **2119**	(1st) multicoloured	90	90	☐	☐	
2891 **2120**	(1st) multicoloured	90	90	☐	☐	
2892 **2121**	(1st) multicoloured	90	90	☐	☐	
2893 **2122**	(1st) multicoloured	90	90	☐	☐	
2894 **2123**	(1st) multicoloured	90	90	☐	☐	
2895 **2124**	(1st) multicoloured	90	90	☐	☐	
2896 **2125**	(1st) multicoloured	90	90	☐	☐	
Set of 10		8·75	8·75	☐	☐	
First Day Cover			9·00	☐		
Presentation Pack		9·25		☐		
PHQ Cards (*set of* 10)		4·00	12·00	☐	☐	

Gutter Block of 20	17·00	☐

No. 2889 was also issued in sheets of 20 with *se-tenant* labels,
perforated 14×14½.
No. 2891 was also issued in sheets of 20 with *se-tenant* labels,
perforated 14×14½, issued on 2 March 2009.

British Design Classics (2nd series). Booklet stamp

2009 (13 Jan.) Design as Type **1589** (Concorde from 2002
Passenger Jet Aviation) but printed in lithography. Two
phosphor bands. Perf 14½

2897 **1589**	(1st) multicoloured	1·60	1·60	☐	☐	

No. 2897 was only available from £7.68 booklets.

2126 Charles Darwin

2127 Marine Iguana

2128 Finches

2129 Atoll

2130 Bee Orchid

2131 Orang-utan

2132 Fauna and Map of the Galapagos Islands

**Birth Bicentenary of Charles Darwin (naturalist
and evolutionary theorist) (1st issue)**

2009 (12 Feb.)

(a) Self-adhesive. Printed in photogravure. 'All-over'
phosphor. Perf 14

2898 **2126**	(1st) multicoloured	85	85	☐	☐	
2899 **2127**	48p multicoloured	1·10	1·10	☐	☐	
2900 **2128**	50p multicoloured	1·10	1·10	☐	☐	
2901 **2129**	56p multicoloured	1·25	1·25	☐	☐	
2902 **2130**	72p multicoloured	1·60	1·60	☐	☐	

2903 **2131**	81p multicoloured	1·90	1·90	☐	☐
Set of 6		7·75	7·75	☐	☐
First Day Cover			10·00		☐
Presentation Pack		14·00		☐	
PHQ Cards (*set of* 11)		4·50	12·00	☐	☐

(b) Ordinary gum. Printed in lithography. Two phosphor bands. Perf 14

MS2904 115×89 mm. (1st) Flightless cormorant; (1st) Giant tortoise and cactus finch; 81p Marine iguana; 81p Floreana mockingbird

	5·25	5·25	☐ ☐
First Day Cover		7·00	☐

Nos. 2898/903 have 'jigsaw' perforations on the two vertical sides.

Birth Bicentenary of Charles Darwin (naturalist) (2nd issue). Booklet stamps

2009 (12 Feb.) Printed in photogravure. 'All-over' phosphor. Perf 14

2905 **2126**	(1st) multicoloured	85	85	☐	☐
2906 **2127**	48p multicoloured	1·10	1·10	☐	☐
2907 **2128**	50p multicoloured	1·25	1·25	☐	☐
2908 **2129**	56p multicoloured	1·25	1·25	☐	☐
2909 **2130**	72p multicoloured	1·75	1·75	☐	☐
2910 **2131**	81p multicoloured	1·90	1·90	☐	☐
Set of 6		8·00	8·00	☐	☐

Nos. 2905/10 were only issued in £7.75 booklets. They have 'jigsaw' perforations on both vertical sides.

2009 (17 Feb.–31 Mar.) Self-adhesive. Designs as T **367**, T **913/14**, or T **1916**. One centre band (2nd) or two bands (others). U-shaped slits. Iridescent overprint. Die-cut perf 14½×14 (with one elliptical hole on each verticalside)

(a) Sheet stamps. Photo De La Rue

U2911	(2nd) bright blue	60	60	☐	☐
U2912	(1st) gold	80	80	☐	☐
U2913	(2nd Large) bright blue	90	90	☐	☐
U2914	50p grey	1·10	1·10	☐	☐
U2915	(1st Large) gold	1·10	1·10	☐	☐
U2916	£1 magenta	2·25	2·25	☐	☐
U2917	£1.50 brown-red	3·25	3·25	☐	☐
U2918	£2 deep blue-green	4·25	4·25	☐	☐
U2919	£3 deep mauve	6·25	6·25	☐	☐
U2920	£5 azure	10·50	10·50	☐	☐
Set of 10		30·00	30·00	☐	☐
First Day Cover (Nos. U2911/16)			9·00		☐
First Day Cover (Nos. U2917/20)			30·00		☐
Presentation Pack (Nos. U2911/16)		8·00		☐	
Presentation Pack (Nos. U2917/20)		30·00		☐	

(b) Booklet stamps. Photo Walsall

U2931	(2nd) bright blue (31 Mar)	60	60	☐	☐
U2932	(1st) gold (31 Mar)	80	80	☐	☐
U2933	(2nd Large) bright blue (31 Mar)	95	95	☐	☐
U2934	(1st Large) gold (31 Mar)	1·25	1·25	☐	☐

Nos. U2911/20 and U2931/4 each have four U-shaped die-cut slits to discourage the removal of used stamps for re-use. The booklet stamps, Nos. U2931/4, can be distinguised from sheet stamps by having the four U-shaped slits broken at top and foot.

Nos. U2911/20 and U2931/4 all have an iridescent overprint with the words 'ROYAL MAIL' repeated throughout.

Nos. U2913 and U2933 were inscr '2nd Large' and initially sold for 42p.

Nos. U2914 and U2934 were inscr '1st Large' and initially sold for 52p.

British Design Classics (3rd series). Booklet stamps

2009 (10 Mar.)**–09** (17 Sept.) Designs as Nos. 2888/9, 2891/2 and 2896. Printed in photogravure. Self-adhesive. Phosphor background. Die-cut perf 14½

2911 **2121**	(1st) multicoloured	85	85	☐	☐
2912 **2125**	(1st) multicoloured	85	85	☐	☐
2913 **2118**	(1st) multicoloured (21 Apr)	85	85	☐	☐
2914 **2120**	(1st) multicoloured (18 Aug)	85	85	☐	☐
2915 **2117**	(1st) multicoloured (17 Sept)	85	85	☐	☐
Set of 5		4·25	4·25	☐	☐

Nos. 2911/15 were only issued in booklets.

 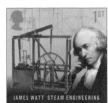

2133 Matthew Boulton and Factory (manufacturing)

2134 James Watt and Boulton & Watt Condensing Engine (steam engineering)

2135 Richard Arkwright and Spinning Machine (textiles)

2136 Josiah Wedgwood and Black Basalt Teapot and Vase (ceramics)

2137 George Stephenson and Locomotion (railways)

2138 Henry Maudslay and Table Engine (machine making)

2139 James Brindley and Bridgewater Canal Aqueduct (canal engineering)

2140 John McAdam (road building)

Nos. 2916/17, 2918/19, 2920/1 and 2922/3 were each printed together, *se-tenant*, in horizontal pairs throughout the sheets.

Pioneers of the Industrial Revolution

2009 (10 Mar.) 'All-over' phosphor. Perf 14×14½

2916	**2133**	(1st) multicoloured	85	85	☐	☐
		a. Horiz pair.				
		Nos. 2916/17	1·60	1·60	☐	☐
2917	**2134**	(1st) multicoloured	85	85	☐	☐
2918	**2135**	50p multicoloured	1·00	1·00	☐	☐
		a. Horiz pair.				
		Nos. 2918/19	2·00	2·00	☐	☐
2919	**2136**	50p multicoloured	1·00	1·00	☐	☐
2920	**2137**	56p multicoloured	1·25	1·25	☐	☐
		a. Horiz pair.				
		Nos. 2920/1	2·50	2·50	☐	☐
2921	**2138**	56p multicoloured	1·25	1·25	☐	☐
2922	**2139**	72p multicoloured	1·75	1·75	☐	☐
		a. Booklet pane.				
		Nos. 2922/3	3·50	3·50	☐	☐
2923	**2140**	72p multicoloured	1·75	1·75	☐	☐
Set of 8			9·50	9·50	☐	☐
First Day Cover				11·50		☐
Presentation Pack			10·50		☐	
PHQ Cards (set of 8)			4·75	13·50	☐	☐
Set of 4 Gutter Strips of 4			18·00		☐	

2141 Henry VII (1485–1509)

2142 Henry VIII (1509–47)

2143 Edward VI (1547–53)

2144 Lady Jane Grey (1553)

2145 Mary I (1553–8)

2146 Elizabeth I (1558–1603)

2147 The Age of the Tudors

Kings and Queens (2nd issue). The House of Tudor

2009 (21 Apr.) Two phosphor bands. Perf 14

2924	**2141**	(1st) multicoloured	85	85	☐	☐
2925	**2142**	(1st) multicoloured	85	85	☐	☐
2926	**2143**	62p multicoloured	1·40	1·40	☐	☐
2927	**2144**	62p multicoloured	1·40	1·40	☐	☐
2928	**2145**	81p multicoloured	1·75	1·75	☐	☐
2929	**2146**	81p multicoloured	1·75	1·75	☐	☐
Set of 6			8·00	8·00	☐	☐
First Day Cover				10·00		☐
Presentation Pack			15·00		☐	
PHQ Cards (set of 11)			6·50	13·00	☐	☐
Set of 6 Gutter Pairs			16·00		☐	
Set of 6 Traffic Light Gutter Blocks of 4			32·00		☐	

MS2930 123×70 mm. **2147** (1st) Mary Rose (galleon), **1510**; (1st) Field of Cloth of Gold Royal Conference, **1520**; 90p Royal Exchange (centre of commerce), **1565**; 90p Francis Drake (circumnavigation), **1580**   5·75   5·75   ☐ ☐

First Day Cover   7·50   ☐

The complete miniature sheet is shown on one of the eleven PHQ cards with the others depicting individual stamps including those from **MS**2930.

2148 *Allium sphaerocephalon* (round-headed leek)

2149 *Luronium natans* (floating water-plantain)

2150 *Cypripedium calceolus* (lady's slipper orchid)

2151 *Polygala amarella* (dwarf milkwort)

2152 *Saxifraga hirculus* (marsh saxifrage)

2153 *Stachys germanica* (downy woundwort)

2154 *Euphorbia serrulata* (upright spurge)

2155 *Pyrus cordata* (Plymouth pear)

2156 *Polygonum maritimum* (Sea knotgrass)

2157 *Dianthus armeria* (Deptford pink)

T **2148/57** were printed together, *se-tenant*, in blocks of ten (5×2) throughout the sheet.

2158 Royal Botanic Gardens, Kew

'Action for Species' (3rd series). Plants and 250th Anniversary of Royal Botanic Gardens, Kew (MS2941)

2009 (19 May)

		(a) Phosphor background. Perf 14½				
2931	**2148**	(1st) multicoloured	85	85	☐	☐
		a. Block of 10.				
		Nos. 2931/40	8·50	8·50	☐	☐
2932	**2149**	(1st) multicoloured	85	85	☐	☐
2933	**2150**	(1st) multicoloured	85	85	☐	☐
2934	**2151**	(1st) multicoloured	85	85	☐	☐
2935	**2152**	(1st) multicoloured	85	85	☐	☐
2936	**2153**	(1st) multicoloured	85	85	☐	☐
2937	**2154**	(1st) multicoloured	85	85	☐	☐
2938	**2155**	(1st) multicoloured	85	85	☐	☐
2939	**2156**	(1st) multicoloured	85	85	☐	☐
2940	**2157**	(1st) multicoloured	85	85	☐	☐
Set of 10			8·50	8·50	☐	☐
First Day Cover				11·00		☐
Presentation Pack			15·00		☐	
PHQ Cards (*set of* 15)			8·75	15·00	☐	☐
Gutter Block of 10			16·00		☐	

		(b) Two phosphor bands. Perf 14×14½				
MS2941 115×89 mm. **2158** (1st) Palm House, Kew Gardens; (1st) Millennium Seed Bank, Wakehurst Place; 90p Pagoda, Kew Gardens; 90p Sackler Crossing, Kew Gardens			5·75	5·75	☐	☐
First Day Cover				7·50		☐

The complete miniature sheet is shown on one of the fifteen PHQ cards with the others depicting individual stamps including those from **MS**2941.

50th Anniversary of NAFAS (National Association of Flower Arrangement Societies). Booklet stamps

2009 (21 May) Designs as Nos. 1958 and 1962 (1997 Greeting Stamps 19th-century FlowerPaintings) but printed in photogravure. Self-adhesive. Two phosphor bands. Die-cut perf 14 (with one elliptical hole on each vert side)

2942	**1287**	(1st) multicoloured	85	85	☐	☐
2943	**1283**	(1st) multicoloured	85	85	☐	☐

Nos. 2942/3 were only issued in stamp booklets.

2159 Dragon

2160 Unicorn

2161 Giant

2162 Pixie

2163 Mermaid

2164 Fairy

Mythical Creatures

2009 (16 June) 'All-over' phosphor. Perf 14½

2944	**2159**	(1st) multicoloured	85	85	☐	☐
2945	**2160**	(1st) multicoloured	85	85	☐	☐
2946	**2161**	62p multicoloured	1·40	1·40	☐	☐
2947	**2162**	62p multicoloured	1·40	1·40	☐	☐
2948	**2163**	90p multicoloured	2·00	2·00	☐	☐
2949	**2164**	90p multicoloured	2·00	2·00	☐	☐
Set of 6			8·25	8·25	☐	☐
First Day Cover				11·00		☐
Presentation Pack			9·50		☐	
PHQ Cards (*set of* 6)			2·50	12·00	☐	☐
Set of 6 Gutter Pairs			16·00		☐	

2165 George V Type B Wall Letter Box, 1933–6

2166 Edward VII Ludlow Letter Box, 1901–10

2167 Victorian Lamp Letter Box, 1896

2168 Elizabeth II Type A Wall Letter Box, 1962–3

2169 Post Boxes

Post Boxes (1st series)

2009 (18 Aug.) 'All-over' phosphor. Perf 14

2950	**2165**	(1st) multicoloured	85	85	☐	☐
2951	**2166**	56p multicoloured	1·25	1·25	☐	☐
2952	**2167**	81p multicoloured	1·75	1·75	☐	☐
2953	**2168**	90p multicoloured	2·00	2·00	☐	☐
Set of 4			5·75	5·75	☐	☐
MS2954	**2169**	145×74 mm. 2169				
	Nos. 2950/3		5·75	5·75	☐	☐
First Day Cover			8·25			☐
Presentation Pack			7·00		☐	
PHQ Cards (set of 5)			2·50	9·00	☐	☐

Nos. 2950/3 were only issued in £8.18 stamp booklets and in **MS**2954.

Type **2165** was also issued in sheets of 20 with *se-tenant* labels showing post boxes.

'Treasures of the Archive' (1st series). Booklet stamps

2009 (18 Aug.) Designs as Type **929** (1990 150th anniv of the Penny Black) and **1446** (with with redrawn 1st face value). Printed in lithography. Two phosphor bands. Perf 14½ × 14 (with one elliptical hole on each vert side)

2955	**929**	20p brownish-black and grey-brown	45	45	☐	☐
2956		(1st) brownish-black and grey-brown	90	90	☐	☐

Nos. 2955/6 were only available from £8.18 stamp booklets.

'Treasures of the Archive' (2nd series). Booklet stamps

2009 (18 Aug.) Design as Type **919** (1989 Lord Mayor's Show) but printed in lithography. 'All-over' phosphor. Perf 14

2957	**919**	20p multicoloured	45	45	☐	☐

No. 2957 was only available from £8.18 stamp booklets.

2170 Firefighting

2171 Chemical Fire

2172 Emergency Rescue

2173 Flood Rescue

2174 Search and Rescue

2175 Fire Safety

Fire and Rescue Service

2009 (1 Sept.) 'All-over' phosphor. Perf 14×14½

2958	**2170**	(1st) multicoloured	85	85	☐	☐
2959	**2171**	54p multicoloured	1·10	1·10	☐	☐
2960	**2172**	56p multicoloured	1·25	1·25	☐	☐
2961	**2173**	62p multicoloured	1·40	1·40	☐	☐
2962	**2174**	81p multicoloured	1·75	1·75	☐	☐
2963	**2175**	90p multicoloured	2·00	2·00	☐	☐
Set of 6			8·25	8·25	☐	
First Day Cover				11·00		☐
Presentation Pack			9·50		☐	
PHQ Cards (set of 6)			3·50	12·00	☐	☐
Set of 6 Gutter Pairs			16·00		☐	

2176 Flight Deck Officer, 2009

2177 Captain, 1941

2178 Second Officer WRNS, 1918

2179 Able Seaman, 1880

2180 Royal Marine, 1805

2181 Admiral, 1795

2186 Mary Wollstonecraft 1759–97 (pioneering feminist)

2187 Sir Arthur Conan Doyle 1859–1930 (writer and creator of Sherlock Holmes)

Nos. 2964/6 and 2967/9 were each printed together, *se-tenant*, in horizontal strips of three throughout the sheets.

Military Uniforms (3rd series). Royal Navy Uniforms

2009 (17 Sept.) Phosphor background. Perf 14

2964	**2176**	(1st) multicoloured	85	85	☐	☐
		a. Horiz strip of 3.				
		Nos. 2964/6	2·50	2·50	☐	☐
2965	**2177**	(1st) multicoloured	85	85	☐	☐
2966	**2178**	(1st) multicoloured	85	85	☐	☐
2967	**2179**	90p multicoloured	2·00	2·00	☐	☐
		a. Horiz strip of 3.				
		Nos. 2967/9	6·00	6·00	☐	☐
2968	**2180**	90p multicoloured	2·00	2·00	☐	☐
2969	**2181**	90p multicoloured	2·00	2·00	☐	☐
Set of 6			8·50	8·50	☐	
First Day Cover				11·00		☐
Presentation Pack			9·50		☐	
PHQ Cards (*set of* 6)			3·50	12·00	☐	☐
Set of 2 Gutter Strips of 6			16·00		☐	

Royal Navy Uniforms. Booklet stamp

2009 (17 Sept.) Design as Type **1518** (Jolly Roger flag from 2001 Submarine Centenary) but printed in lithography. Two phosphor bands. Perf 14½

2970	**1518**	(1st) multicoloured	90	90	☐	☐

No. 2970 was only issued in £7.93 stamp booklets.

2188 Donald Campbell 1921–67 (water speed record broken 1959)

2189 Judy Fryd 1909–2000 (campaigner and founder of MENCAP)

2190 Samuel Johnson 1709–84 (lexicographer, critic and poet)

2191 Sir Martin Ryle 1918–84 (radio survey of the Universe 1959)

Nos. 2971/5 and 2976/80 were each printed together, *se-tenant*, in horizontal strips of five stamps throughout the sheets.

2182 Fred Perry 1909–95 (lawn tennis champion)

2183 Henry Purcell 1659–95 (composer and musician)

2184 Sir Matt Busby 1909–94 (footballer and football manager)

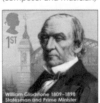

2185 William Gladstone 1809–98 (statesman and Prime Minister)

Eminent Britons

2009 (8 Oct.) Phosphor background. Perf 14½

2971	**2182**	(1st) multicoloured	85	85	☐	☐
		a. Horiz strip of 5.				
		Nos. 2971/5	4·25	4·25	☐	☐
2972	**2183**	(1st) multicoloured	85	85	☐	☐
2973	**2184**	(1st) multicoloured	85	85	☐	☐
2974	**2185**	(1st) multicoloured	85	85	☐	☐
2975	**2186**	(1st) multicoloured	85	85	☐	☐
2976	**2187**	(1st) multicoloured	85	85	☐	☐
		a. Horiz strip of 5.				
		Nos. 2976/80	4·25	4·25	☐	☐
2977	**2188**	(1st) multicoloured	85	85	☐	☐
2978	**2189**	(1st) multicoloured	85	85	☐	☐
2979	**2190**	(1st) multicoloured	85	85	☐	☐
2980	**2191**	(1st) multicoloured	85	85	☐	☐
Set of 10			8·50	8·50	☐	
First Day Cover				11·00		☐
Presentation Pack			9·50		☐	
PHQ Cards (*set of* 10)			5·75	13·00	☐	☐
Set of 2 Gutter Strips of 10			16·00		☐	

2192 Canoe Slalom

2193 Paralympic Games Archery

2194 Athletics: Track

2195 Diving

2196 Paralympic Games Boccia

2197 Judo

2198 Paralympic Games Dressage

2199 Badminton

2200 Weightlifting

2201 Basketball

Nos. 2981/5 and 2986/90 were each printed together, *se-tenant*, in horizontal strips of five stamps throughout the sheets.

Olympic and Paralympic Games, London (2012) (1st issue)

2009 (22 Oct.) 'All-over' phosphor. Perf 14½

2981	**2192**	(1st) multicoloured	85	85	☐	☐
		a. Horiz strip of 5.				
		Nos. 2981/5	4·25	4·25	☐	☐
2982	**2193**	(1st) multicoloured	85	85	☐	☐
2983	**2194**	(1st) multicoloured	85	85	☐	☐
2984	**2195**	(1st) multicoloured	85	85	☐	☐
2985	**2196**	(1st) multicoloured	85	85	☐	☐
2986	**2197**	(1st) multicoloured	85	85	☐	☐

		a. Horiz strip of 5.				
		Nos. 2986/90	4·25	4·25	☐	☐
2987	**2198**	(1st) multicoloured	85	85	☐	☐
2988	**2199**	(1st) multicoloured	85	85	☐	☐
2989	**2200**	(1st) multicoloured	85	85	☐	☐
2990	**2201**	(1st) multicoloured	85	85	☐	☐
Set of 10			8·50	8·50	☐	☐
First Day Cover				11·00		☐
Presentation Pack			9·50		☐	
PHQ Cards (set of 10)			5·75	12·00	☐	☐
Set of 2 Gutter Strips of 10			16·00		☐	

2202 Angel playing Lute (William Morris), Church of St. James, Staveley, Kendal, Cumbria

2203 Madonna and Child (Henry Holiday), Church of Ormesby St. Michael, Great Yarmouth, Norfolk

2204 Angel playing Lute (William Morris), Church of St. James, Staveley, Kendal, Cumbria

2205 Madonna and Child (Henry Holiday), Church of Ormesby St. Michael, Ormesby, Great Yarmouth, Norfolk

2206 Joseph (Henry Holiday), Parish Church of St. Michael, Minehead, Somerset

2207 Wise Man (Sir Edward Burne-Jones), Church of St. Mary the Virgin, Rye, East Sussex

2208 Shepherd (Henry Holiday), St. Mary's Church, Upavon, Wiltshire

Christmas

2009 (3 Nov.) One centre band (2nd) or two phosphor bands (others). Perf 14½×14 (with one elliptical hole on- each vert side)

(a) Self-adhesive						
2991	**2202**	(2nd) multicoloured	60	60	☐	☐
2992	**2203**	(1st) multicoloured	85	85	☐	☐
2993	**2204**	(2nd Large) multicoloured	95	95	☐	☐
2994	**2205**	56p multicoloured	1·25	1·25	☐	☐
2995	**2206**	(1st Large) multicoloured	1·25	1·25	☐	☐
2996	**2207**	90p multicoloured	2·00	2·00	☐	☐
2997	**2208**	£1.35 multicoloured	2·75	2·75	☐	☐

Set of 7	9·50	9·50	☐	☐
First Day Cover		11·50		☐
Presentation Pack	10·50		☐	
PHQ Cards (*set of* 7)	4·75	13·00	☐	☐

(b) Ordinary gum				
MS2998 115×102 mm. As Nos. 2991/7	9·50	9·50	☐	☐
First Day Cover		11·50		☐

The 2nd class, 1st class, 50p and 81p stamps were also issued in sheets of 20 containing eight 2nd class, eight 1st class, two 50p and two 81p stamps, each stamp accompanied by a *se-tenant* label. Separate sheets of 20 2nd, 20 1st, ten 1st, ten 56p and ten 90p were available with personal photographs.

Collectors Pack

2009 (3 Nov.) Comprises Nos. 2887/96, 2898/**MS**2904, 2916/**MS**2941, 2944/9, **MS**2954, 2958/69, 2971/97, **MS**S137 and **MS**W125.

CP2998a	Collectors Pack	£120	☐

Post Office Yearbook

2009 (3 Nov.) Comprises Nos. 2887/96, 2898/**MS**2904, 2916/**MS**2941, 2944/9, **MS**2954, 2958/69, 2971/97, **MS**S137 and **MS**W125.

YB2998a	Yearbook	£130	☐

Miniature Sheet Collection

2009 (3 Nov.) Comprises Nos. **MS**2904, **MS**2930, **MS**2941, **MS**2954, **MS**2998, **MS**S137 and **MS**W125.

MS2998a	Miniature Sheet Collection	42·00	☐

REGIONAL ISSUES

PERFORATION AND WATERMARK. All the following Regional stamps are perforated 15 × 14, unless otherwise stated. For listing of First Day Covers see pages 173/5.

1 England

EN **1** Three Lions

EN **2** Crowned Lion with Shield of St. George

EN **3** Oak Tree

EN **4** Tudor Rose

2001 (23 Apr.)–**02** Printed in photogravure by De La Rue or Questa (Nos. EN1/2), De La Rue (others). One centre phosphor band (2nd) or two phosphor bands (others). Perf 15 × 14 (with one elliptical hole on each vertical side)

EN1	EN **1**	(2nd)	slate-green and silver	1·00	1·00	☐ ☐
EN2	EN **2**	(1st)	lake-brown and silver	1·00	1·00	☐ ☐
EN3	EN **3**	(E)	olive-green and silver	1·75	1·75	☐ ☐
EN4	EN **4**	65p	deep reddish lilac and silver	3·00	3·00	☐ ☐
EN5		68p	deep reddish lilac and silver	3·00	3·00	☐ ☐

Presentation Pack (P.O. Pack No. 54) (Nos. EN1/4)	7·50		☐
PHQ Cards (set of 4) (Nos. EN1/4)	2·00	10·00	☐ ☐

Nos. EN1/3 were initially sold at 19p, 27p and 36p, the latter representing the basic European airmail rate.

Combined Presentation Packs for England, Northern Ireland, Scotland and Wales

Presentation Pack (P.O. Pack No. 59) (contains 68p from England, Northern Ireland, Scotland and Wales (Nos. EN5, NI93, S99, W88))   **9·00**   ☐

Presentation Pack (P.O. Pack No. 68) (contains 40p from England, Northern Ireland, Scotland and Wales (Nos. EN9, NI97, S112, W101))   **8·00**   ☐

Presentation Pack (P.O. Pack No. 70) (contains 42p from England, Northern Ireland, Scotland and Wales (Nos. EN10, NI98, S113, W102))   **8·00**   ☐

Presentation Pack (P.O. Pack No. 73) (contains 44p and 72p from England, Northern Ireland, Scotland and Wales (Nos. EN15, EN14, NI99, NI101, S114, S118, W103 and W107))   **9·00**   ☐

Presentation Pack (P.O. Pack No. 76) (contains 48p and 78p from England, Northern Ireland, Scotland and Wales (Nos. EN12, EN16, NI104, NI106, S115, S119, W104 and W108))   **12·50**   ☐

Presentation Pack (P.O. Pack No. 79) (contains 50p and 81p from England, Northern Ireland, Scotland and Wales (Nos. EN13, EN17, NI105, NI107, S116, S120, W105 and W109))   **11·50**   ☐

Presentation Pack (P.O. Pack No. 81) (contains 2nd, 1st, 50p and 81p from England, Northern Ireland, Scotland and Wales (Nos. EN6/7, EN13, EN17, NI102/3, NI105, NI107, S109/10, S116, S120, W98/9, W105 and W109))   **16·00**   ☐

Presentation Packs (P.O. Pack No. 85) (contains 56p and 90p from England, Northern Ireland, Scotland and Wales (Nos. EN17a, NI105a, NI 107a, S116a, S120a, W105a and W109a   **13·50**   ☐

2003 (14 Oct.)–**09**. As Nos. EN1/3 and EN5 but with white borders. One centre phosphor band (2nd) or two phosphor bands (others). Perf 15 × 14 (with one elliptical hole on each vertical side)

(a) Printed in photogravure by Walsall or De La Rue (2nd), 40p, 42p) or De La Rue (others)

EN6	EN **1**	(2nd)	slate-green and silver	75	60	☐ ☐
EN7	EN **2**	(1st)	lake-brown and silver	80	75	☐ ☐
EN8	EN **3**	(E)	olive-green and silver	2·00	2·00	☐ ☐
EN9		40p	olive-green and silver	1·50	1·50	☐ ☐
EN10		42p	olive-green and silver	1·25	1·25	☐ ☐
EN11		44p	olive-green and silver	1·50	1·50	☐ ☐
EN12		48p	olive-green and silver	1·25	1·25	☐ ☐
EN13		50p	olive-green and silver	90	85	☐ ☐
EN 13a		56p	olive-green and silver	1·25	1·25	☐ ☐
EN14	EN **4**	68p	deep reddish lilac and silver	2·50	2·50	☐ ☐
EN15		72p	deep reddish lilac and silver	2·50	2·50	☐ ☐
EN16		78p	deep reddish lilac and silver	2·50	2·50	☐ ☐
EN17		81p	deep reddish lilac and silver	2·00	2·00	☐ ☐
EN 17a		90p	deep reddish lilac and silver	2·00	2·00	☐ ☐

(b) Printed in lithography by Enschedé

EN18	EN **2**	(1st)	lake-brown and silver	7·00	7·00	☐ ☐

Presentation Pack (P.O. Pack No. 63) (Nos. EN6/8, EN13)	6·00		☐
PHQ Cards (set of 4) (Nos. EN6/8, EN13)	2·00	6·00	☐ ☐

Nos. EN6/8 were initially sold at 20p, 28p and 38p, the latter representing the basic European airmail rate.

Stamps as No. EN18 but self-adhesive were issued on 23 April 2007 in sheets of 20 with *se-tenant* labels. These sheets were printed in lithography by Cartor and perforated 15 × 14 without the elliptical holes. The labels show either English scenes or personal photographs.

No. EN18 was only issued in £7.66 stamp booklets.

Stamps as Nos. EN18, NI95, S131 and W120 but self-adhesive were issued on 29 September 2008 in sheets of 20 containing five of each design with *se-tenant* labels. These sheets were printed in lithograhy by Cartor and perforated 15 × 14 with one elliptical hole on each vertical side.

EN **5**

Celebrating England

2007 (23 Apr.) Sheet 123 × 70 mm. Printed in photogravure by De La Rue. Two phosphor bands. Perf 15 × 14 (with one elliptical hole on each vertical side) (1st) or 15 × 14½ (78p)

MSEN19 (1st) No. EN7; (1st) St. George's
flag; 78p St. George; 78p Houses of

Parliament, London	7·50	7·50
First Day Cover	5·50	
Presentation Pack	8·00	
PHQ Cards (set of 5)	2·20	10·00

The five PHQ cards show the four individual stamps and the complete miniature sheet.

Stamps as the 1st class St. George's flag stamp within **MS**EN19 but self-adhesive were issued on 23 April 2009 on sheets of 20 with *se-tenant* labels showing English castles. These sheets were printed in Lithography by Cartor.

2 Northern Ireland

N 1   **N 2**   **N 3**   **N 4**

1958–67 Wmk 179

NI1	N **1**	3d lilac	15	10	
		p. One centre phosphor band	15	15	
NI2		4d blue	15	15	
		p. Two phosphor bands	15	15	
NI3	N **2**	6d purple	30	30	
NI4		9d bronze-green (2 phosphor bands)	30	70	
NI5	N **3**	1s 3d green	30	70	
NI6		1s 6d blue (2 phosphor bands)	30	70	

1968–69 One centre phosphor band (Nos. NI8/9) or two phosphor bands (others). No wmk

NI7	N **1**	4d blue	15	15	
NI8		4d sepia	15	15	
NI9		4d vermilion	20	20	
NI10		5d blue	20	20	
NI11	N **3**	1s 6d blue	2·25	2·50	
Presentation Pack (comprises Nos. NI1p, NI4/6, NI8/10)			3·50		

Decimal Currency

1971–91 Type N **4**. No wmk

(a) Printed in photogravure with phosphor bands

NI12	2½p magenta (1 centre band)	70	60	
NI13	3p ultramarine (2 bands)	30	30	
NI14	3p ultramarine (1 centre band)	20	15	
NI15	3½p olive-grey (2 bands)	20	25	
NI16	3½p olive-grey (1 centre band)	20	25	
NI17	4½p grey-blue (2 bands)	30	25	
NI18	5p violet (2 bands)	1·00	1·00	
NI19	5½p violet (2 bands)	20	20	
NI20	5½p violet (1 centre band)	20	25	
NI21	6½p blue (1 centre band)	20	20	
NI22	7p brown (1 centre band)	35	25	
NI23	7½p chestnut (2 bands)	1·75	1·75	

NI24	8p rosine (2 bands)	35	35
NI25	8½p yellow-green (2 bands)	35	40
NI26	9p violet (2 bands)	40	40
NI27	10p orange-brown (2 bands)	40	50
NI28	10p orange-brown (1 centre band)	50	50
NI29	10½p blue (2 bands)	40	50
NI30	11p scarlet (2 bands)	50	50

(b) Printed in photogravure on phosphorised paper

NI31	12p yellowish green	50	50
NI32	13½p purple-brown	60	70
NI33	15p ultramarine	60	70

(c) Printed in lithography. Perf 14 (11½p, 12½p, 14p (No. NI38), 15½p, 16p, 18p, (No. NI45), 19½p, 20½p, 22p (No. NI53), 26p (No. NI60), 28p (No. NI62)) or 15 × 14 (others)

NI34	11½p drab (1 side band)	85	85
NI35	12p bright emerald (1 side band)	90	90
NI36	12½p light emerald (1 side band)	60	60
	a. Perf 15 × 14	5·25	5·25
NI37	13p pale chestnut (1 side band)	80	50
NI38	14p grey-blue (phosphorised paper)	75	75
NI39	14p deep blue (1 centre band)	75	60
NI40	15p bright blue (1 centre band)	90	60
NI41	15½p pale violet (phosphorised paper)	80	80
NI42	16p drab (phosphorised paper)	1·00	1·00
	a. Perf 15 × 14	8·25	8·50
NI43	17p grey-blue (phosphorised paper)	90	95
NI44	17p deep blue (1 centre band)	1·00	80
NI45	18p deep violet (phosphorised paper)	1·00	1·00
NI46	18p olive-grey (phosphorised paper)	1·00	90
NI47	18p bright green (1 centre band)	1·00	95
	a. Perf 14	5·00	5·00
NI48	18p bright green (1 side band)	2·25	2·25
NI49	19p bright orange-red (phosphorised paper)	1·00	1·00
NI50	19½p olive-grey (phosphorised paper)	1·50	1·75
NI51	20p brownish black (phosphorised paper)	1·00	80
NI52	20½p ultramarine (phosphorised paper)	4·50	4·25
NI53	22p blue (phosphorised paper)	1·10	1·10
NI54	22p yellow-green (phosphorised paper)	1·10	1·10
NI55	22p bright orange-red (phosphorised paper)	1·25	90
NI56	23p bright green (phosphorised paper)	1·25	1·10
NI57	24p Indian red (phosphorised paper)	1·25	1·25

NI58	24p	chestnut		
		(phosphorised paper)	1·10	90
NI59	24p	chestnut (2 bands)	2·25	2·50
NI60	26p	rosine (phosphorised		
		paper)	1·25	1·25
	a.	Perf 15 × 14	3·00	3·25
NI61	26p	drab		
		(phosphorised paper)	1·75	1·75
NI62	28p	deep violet-blue		
		(phosphorised paper)	1·50	1·50
	a.	Perf 15 × 14	1·25	1·25
NI63	28p	deep bluish grey		
		(phosphorised paper)	1·50	1·50
NI64	31p	bright purple		
		(phosphorised paper)	1·75	2·00
NI65	32p	greenish blue		
		(phosphorised paper)	1·75	1·75
NI66	34p	deep bluish grey		
		(phosphorised paper)	1·75	1·75
NI67	37p	rosine (phosphorised		
		paper)	2·00	2·50
NI68	39p	bright mauve		
		(phosphorised paper)	2·00	2·25

Nos. NI48 and NI59 were only issued in stamp booklets.

Presentation Pack (P.O. Pack No. 29) (contains
2½p (NI12), 3p (NI13), 5p (NI18), 7½p (NI23)) **3·50**

Presentation Pack (P.O. Pack No. 61) (contains 3p
(NI14), 3½p (NI15), 5½p (NI19), 8p (NI24) later
with 4½p (NI17) added) **2·25**

Presentation Pack (P.O. Pack No. 84) (contains
6½p (NI21), 8½p (NI25), 10p (NI27),
11p (NI30)) **2·00**

Presentation Pack (P.O. Pack No. 129d) (contains
7p (NI22), 9p (NI26), 10½p (NI29), 11½p (NI34),
12p (NI31), 13½p (NI32), 14p (NI38), 15p (NI33),
18p (NI45), 22p (NI53)) **9·00**

Presentation Pack (P.O. Pack No. 4) (contains 10p
(NI28), 12½p (NI36), 16p (NI42), 20½p (NI52),
26p (NI60), 28p (NI62)) **18·00**

Presentation Pack (P.O. Pack No. 8) (contains 10p
(NI28), 13p (NI37), 16p (NI42a), 17p (NI43), 22p
(NI54), 26p (NI60), 28p (NI62), 31p (NI64)) **18·00**

Presentation Pack (P.O. Pack No. 12) (contains
12p (NI35), 13p (NI37), 17p (NI43), 18p (NI46),
22p (NI54), 26p (NI60a), 28p (NI62a),
31p (NI64)) **20·00**

**Combined Presentation Packs for Northern Ireland,
Scotland and Wales**

Presentation Pack (P.O. Pack No. 17) (contains
14p, 19p, 23p, 32p from Northern Ireland,
Scotland and Wales (Nos. NI39, NI49, NI56, NI65,
S54, S62, S67, S77, W40, W50, W57, W66)) **17·00**

Presentation Pack (P.O. Pack No. 20) (contains
15p, 20p, 24p, 34p from Northern Ireland,
Scotland and Wales (Nos. NI40, NI5I, NI57, NI66,
S56, S64, S69, S78, W41, W52, W58, W67)) **16·00**

Presentation Pack (P.O. Pack No. 23) (contains
17p, 22p, 26p, 37p from Northern Ireland,
Scotland and Wales (Nos. NI44, NI55, NI6I, NI67,
S58, S66, S73, S79, W45, W56, W62, W68)) **16·00**

Presentation Pack (P.O. Pack No. 26) (contains
18p, 24p, 28p, 39p from Northern Ireland,
Scotland and Wales (Nos. NI47, NI58, NI63, NI68,
S60, S70, S75, S80, W48, W59, W64, W69)) **16·00**

1993 (7 Dec.)–**2000** (a) Printed in lithography by Questa. Perf 15 × 14 (with one elliptical hole on each vertical side)

NI69	N **4**	19p	bistre (1 centre band)	90	80
NI70		19p	bistre (1 side band)	1·25	1·75
NI71		20p	bright green		
			(1 centre band)	1·50	1·50
NI72		25p	red (2 bands)	75	75
NI73		26p	red-brown (2 bands)	1·75	1·75
NI74		30p	deep olive-grey		
			(2 bands)	1·25	1·25
NI75		37p	bright mauve		
			(2 bands)	2·75	3·00
NI76		41p	grey-brown		
			(2 bands)	1·50	1·75
NI77		63p	light emerald		
			(2 bands)	5·00	5·00

(b) Printed in photogravure by Walsall (19p, 20p, 26p (No. NI81b), 38p, 40p, 63p, 64p, 65p), Harrison or Walsall (26p (No. NI81), 37p). Perf 14 (No. NI80) or 15 × 14 (others) (both with one elliptical hole on each vertical side)

NI78	N **4**	19p	bistre (1 centre band)	3·00	3·00
NI79		20p	bright green		
			(1 centre band)	90	80
NI80		20p	bright green		
			(1 side band)	3·00	3·00
NI81		26p	chestnut (2 bands)	1·25	1·00
		b.	Perf 14	3·00	3·00
NI82		37p	bright mauve (2 bands)	2·25	2·25
NI83		38p	ultramarine (2 bands)	8·00	8·00
NI84		40p	deep azure (2 bands)	2·50	2·50
NI85		63p	light emerald (2 bands)	5·00	5·00
NI86		64p	turquoise-green		
			(2 bands)	9·00	9·00
NI87		65p	greenish blue (2 bands)	2·75	3·00

Nos. NI70, NI80 and NI81b were only issued in stamp booklets.
No. NI70 exists with the phosphor band at the left or right of the stamp.

Presentation Pack (P.O. Pack No. 47) (contains
19p, 26p, 38p, 64p (Nos. NI78, NI81,
NI83 NI86)) **17·00**

Presentation Pack (P.O. Pack No. 52) (contains 1st,
40p, 65p) (Nos. NI84, NI87, NI88b) **15·00**

Combined Presentation Packs for Northern Ireland,

Scotland and Wales

Presentation Pack (P.O. Pack No. 31) (contains
19p, 25p, 30p, 41p from Northern Ireland,
Scotland and Wales (Nos. NI69, NI72, NI74, NI76,
S81, S84, S86, S88, W70, W73, W75, W77)) **16·00**

Presentation Pack (P.O. Pack No. 36) (contains
20p, 26p, 37p, 63p from Northern Ireland,
Scotland and Wales (Nos. NI71, NI73, NI75, NI77,
S83, S85, S87, S89, W72, W74 W76, W78)) **26·00**

Presentation Pack (P.O. Pack No. 42) (contains
20p (1 centre band), 26p, 37p, 63p from
Northern Ireland, Scotland and Wales (Nos.
NI79, NI81/2, NI85, S90/3, W79/82)) **26·00**

N **5**

2000 (15 Feb.–25 Apr.) Type N **4** redrawn with '1st' face value as Type N **5**. Two phosphor bands. Perf 14 (with one elliptical hole on each vertical side)

NI88	N **5**	(1st) bright orange-red	3·00	3·00	☐	☐
		b. Perf 15 × 14 (25 Apr.)	10·00	10·00	☐	☐

No. NI88 was only issued in stamp booklets. No. NI88b was issued in sheets on 25 April.

N **6** Basalt Columns, Giant's Causeway

N **7** Aerial View of Patchwork Fields

N **8** Linen Pattern

N **9** Vase Pattern from Belleck

2001 (6 Mar.)–02 Printed in lithography by De La Rue (68p), De La Rue or Walsall (E), Walsall or Enschedé (2nd) or Walsall (others). One centre phosphor band (2nd) or two phosphor bands (others). Perf 15 × 14 (with one elliptical hole on each vertical side)

NI89	N **6**	(2nd) black, new blue, bright magenta and greenish yellow	75	75	☐	☐
NI90	N **7**	(1st) black, new blue and greenish yellow	1·20	1·20	☐	☐
NI91	N **8**	(E) black, new blue and pale orange	1·50	1·50	☐	☐
NI92	N **9**	65p black, bright magenta and greenish yellow	3·00	3·00	☐	☐
NI93		68p black, bright magenta and greenish yellow	3·25	3·25	☐	☐
Presentation Pack (P.O. Pack No. 53) (Nos. NI89/92)			7·00		☐	
PHQ Cards (set of 4) (Nos. NI89/92)			2·00	10·00	☐	☐

Nos. NI89, NI90 and NI91 were initially sold at 19p, 27p and 36p, the latter representing the basic European airmail rate. For combined presentation packs for all four Regions, see under England.

2003 (14 Oct.)–**09**. As Nos. NI89/91 and NI93 but with white borders. One centre phosphor band (2nd) or two phosphor bands (others). Perf 15 × 14 (with one elliptical hole on each vertical side)

(a) Printed in lithography by Walsall (NI98) or De La Rue (others)

NI94	N **6**	(2nd) black, new blue, bright magenta and greenish yellow	1·00	1·00	☐	☐
NI95	N **7**	(1st) black, new blue and greenish yellow	1·00	1·00	☐	☐
NI96	N **8**	(E) black and new blue	2·50	2·50	☐	☐
NI97		40p black and new blue	1·75	1·75	☐	☐
NI98		42p black, new blue and orange-yellow	1·75	1·75	☐	☐
		a. Black, new blue and greenish yellow	1·50	1·50	☐	☐
NI99		44p black, new blue and greenish yellow	1·00	1·00	☐	☐
NI100	N **9**	68p black, bright magenta and greenish yellow	2·75	2·75	☐	☐
NI101		72p black, greyish black, bright magenta and greenish yellow	2·50	2·50	☐	☐

(b) Printed in photogravure by De La Rue

NI102	N **6**	(2nd) bright magenta, greenish yellow, new blue and black	70	60	☐	☐
NI103	N **7**	(1st) greenish yellow, new blue and black	80	75	☐	☐
NI104	N **8**	48p olive-grey and black	1·20	1·20	☐	☐
NI105		50p olive-grey and black	1·20	1·20	☐	☐
NI105a		56p olive-grey and black	1·25	1·25	☐	☐
NI106		78p bright magenta, greenish yellow and black	2·00	2·00	☐	☐
NI107		81p bright magenta, greenish yellow and black	2·00	2·00	☐	☐
NI107a		81p bright magenta, greenish yellow and black	2·00	2·00	☐	☐
Presentation Pack (P.O. Pack No. 66) (Nos. NI94/6, NI101)			7·00		☐	
PHQ Cards (set of 4) (Nos. NI94/6, NI101)			2·00	10·00	☐	☐

Nos. NI94/6 were initially sold at 20p, 28p and 38p, the latter representing the basic European airmail rate.

No. NI98 (Walsall printing) appears bluish grey and No. NI98a (De La Rue printing) appears olive-grey.

Stamps as NI95 but self-adhesive were issued on 11 March 2008 in sheets of 20 with *se-tenant* labels. These sheets were printed in lithography by Cartor and perforated 15 × 14 without the ellipitcal holes. The labels show either Northern Ireland scenes or personal photographs.

Stamps as No. NI95 but self-adhesive were issued again on 17 March 2009 in sheets of 20 with *se-tenant* labels showing Northern Island castles. These sheets were printed in lithography by Cartor.

Stamps as Nos. EN18, NI95, S131 and W120 but self-adhesive were issued on 29 September 2008 in sheets of 20 containing five of each design with *se-tenant* labels.

N **10**

Celebrating Northern Ireland

2008 (11 Mar.) Sheet 123 × 70 mm. Printed in lithography by De La Rue. Two phosphor bands. Perf 15 × 14½ (with one elliptical hole on each vertical side) (1st) or 15 × 14½ (78p)

MSNI110	(1st) Carrickfergus Castle; (1st) Giant's Causeway; 78p. St. Patrick; 78p. Queen's Bridge and 'Angel of Thanksgiving' sculpture, Belfast	5·00	5·00	☐	☐
First Day Cover			5·75		☐
Presentation Pack		6·25		☐	
PHQ Cards (set of 5)		3·25	10·00	☐	☐

The five PHQ cards depict the complete miniature sheet and the four stamps within it.

N **11**

50th Anniv of the Country Definitives (1st issue)

2008 (29 Sept.) Sheet 124 × 70 mm, containing designs as Nos. NI1, NI3, NI5, S1, S3, S5, W1, W3 and W5 (regional definitives of 1958) but inscribed 1st and printed in photogravure by De La Rue on pale cream. Two phosphor bands. Perf 15 × 14 (with one elliptical hole on each vertical side)

MSNI111 N **11** (1st) As No. W1; (1st) As
  No. S1; (1st) As No. W5; (1st) As No. S5;
  (1st) As No. NI1; (1st) As No. W3; (1st)
  As No. S3; (1st) As No. NI3; (1st) As No.
  NI5   8·25   8·25 ☐ ☐

50th Anniv of the Country Definitives (2nd issue)

2008 (29 Sept.) As Nos. NI1, NI3 and NI5 (definitives of 1958) but inscribed 1st and printed in lithography by De La Rue. Two phosphor bands. Perf 15 × 14½ (with one elliptical hole on each vertical side)

NI112	N **1**	(1st)	deep lilac	1·25	1·25	☐ ☐
NI113	N **3**	(1st)	green	1·25	1·25	☐ ☐
NI114	N **2**	(1st)	deep claret	1·25	1·25	☐ ☐

Nos. NI112/14 come from £9.72 stamp booklets.

3 Scotland

S **1**    S **2**    S **3**    S **4**

1958–67 Wmk 179

S1	S **1**	3d lilac		15	15	☐ ☐
		p. Two phosphor bands	13·00	2·75		☐ ☐
		pa. One side band	20	25		☐ ☐
		pd. One centre phosphor band		15	15	☐ ☐
S2		4d blue		15	15	☐ ☐
		p. Two phosphor bands		15	15	☐ ☐
S3	S **2**	6d purple		20	15	☐ ☐
		p. Two phosphor bands		20	20	☐ ☐
S4		9d bronze-green (2 phosphor bands)		35	40	☐ ☐
S5	S **3** 1s 3d green		40	40	☐ ☐
		p. Two phosphor bands		40	40	☐ ☐
S6		1s 6d blue (2 phosphor bands)	45	50		☐ ☐

No. S1pa exists with the phosphor band at the left or right of the stamp.

1967–70 One centre phosphor band (Nos. S7, S9/10) or two phosphor bands (others). No wmk

S7	S **1**	3d lilac	10	15	☐ ☐

S8		4d blue	10	15	☐ ☐
S9		4d sepia	10	10	☐ ☐
S10		4d vermilion	10	10	☐ ☐
S11		5d blue	20	10	☐ ☐
S12	S **2**	9d bronze-green	6·00	6·00	☐ ☐
S13	S **3** 1s 6d blue	1·75	1·50	☐ ☐

Presentation Pack (containing Nos. S3,
        S5p, S7, S9/13)   8·00   ☐

Decimal Currency

1971–93 Type S **4**. No wmk

(a) Printed in photogravure by Harrison and Sons with phosphor bands. Perf 15 × 14

S14	2½p magenta (1 centre band)	25	20	☐ ☐
S15	3p ultramarine (2 bands)	35	15	☐ ☐
S16	3p ultramarine (1 centre band)	15	15	☐ ☐
S17	3½p olive-grey (2 bands)	20	25	☐ ☐
S18	3½p olive-grey (1 centre band)	20	25	☐ ☐
S19	4½p grey-blue (2 bands)	30	25	☐ ☐
S20	5p violet (2 bands)	1·00	1·25	☐ ☐
S21	5½p violet (2 bands)	20	20	☐ ☐
S22	5½p violet (1 centre band)	20	25	☐ ☐
S23	6½p blue (1 centre band)	20	20	☐ ☐
S24	7p brown (1 centre band)	30	30	☐ ☐
S25	7½p chestnut (2 bands)	1·25	1·25	☐ ☐
S26	8p rosine (2 bands)	45	40	☐ ☐
S27	8½p yellow-green (2 bands)	40	40	☐ ☐
S28	9p violet (2 bands)	40	40	☐ ☐
S29	10p orange-brown (2 bands)	45	50	☐ ☐
S30	10p orange-brown (1 centre band)	40	50	☐ ☐
S31	10½p blue (2 bands)	45	50	☐ ☐
S32	11p scarlet (2 bands)	50	50	☐ ☐

(b) Printed in photogravure by Harrison and Sons on phosphorised paper. Perf 15 × 14

S33	12p yellowish green	50	50	☐ ☐
S34	13½p purple-brown	70	80	☐ ☐
S35	15p ultramarine	60	70	☐ ☐

(c) Printed in lithography by John Waddington. One side phosphor band (11½p, 12p, 12½p, 13p) or phosphorised paper (others). Perf 14

S36	11½p drab	80	80	☐ ☐
S37	12p bright emerald	2·00	2·00	☐ ☐
S38	12½p light emerald	60	70	☐ ☐
S39	13p pale chestnut	85	75	☐ ☐
S40	14p grey-blue	75	75	☐ ☐
S41	15½p pale violet	80	80	☐ ☐
S42	16p drab	80	85	☐ ☐
S43	17p grey-blue	1·50	1·50	☐ ☐
S44	18p deep violet	80	80	☐ ☐
S45	19½p olive-grey	1·75	1·75	☐ ☐
S46	20½p ultramarine	3·50	3·50	☐ ☐
S47	22p blue	1·00	1·00	☐ ☐
S48	22p yellow-green	4·25	4·25	☐ ☐
S49	26p rosine	1·25	1·25	☐ ☐
S50	28p deep violet-blue	1·25	1·25	☐ ☐
S51	31p bright purple	2·50	2·50	☐ ☐

(d) Printed in lithography by Questa. Perf 15 × 14

S52	12p bright emerald (1 side band)	2·00	2·25	☐ ☐
S53	13p pale chestnut (1 side band)	70	75	☐ ☐
S54	14p deep blue (1 centre band)	60	70	☐ ☐

S55	14p	deep blue (1 side band)	80	90	☐	☐
S56	15p	bright blue (1 centre band)	70	70	☐	☐
S57	17p	grey-blue (phosphorised paper)	4·00	4·00	☐	☐
S58	17p	deep blue (1 centre band)	1·00	1·10	☐	☐
S59	18p	olive-grey (phosphorised paper)	1·10	85	☐	☐
S60	18p	bright green (1 centre band)	1·25	90	☐	☐
		a. Perf 14	1·00	1·00	☐	☐
S61	18p	bright green (1 side band)	2·75	3·00	☐	☐
S62	19p	bright orange-red (phosphorised paper)	70	70	☐	☐
S63	19p	bright orange-red (2 bands)	2·25	2·00	☐	☐
S64	20p	brownish black (phosphorised paper)	95	95	☐	☐
S65	22p	yellow-green (phosphorised paper)	1·25	1·50	☐	☐
S66	22p	bright orange-red (phosphorised paper)	1·25	90	☐	☐
S67	23p	bright green (phosphorised paper)	1·25	1·10	☐	☐
S68	23p	bright green (2 bands)	14·00	14·00	☐	☐
S69	24p	Indian red (phosphorised paper)	1·25	1·25	☐	☐
S70	24p	chestnut (phosphorised paper)	1·40	1·25	☐	☐
		a. Perf 14	6·00	6·00	☐	☐
S71	24p	chestnut (2 bands)	2·75	3·00	☐	☐
S72	26p	rosine (phosphorised paper)	3·75	4·00	☐	☐
S73	26p	drab (phosphorised paper)	1·25	1·25	☐	☐
S74	28p	deep violet-blue (phosphorised paper)	1·25	1·25	☐	☐
S75	28p	deep bluish grey (phosphorised paper)	1·25	1·50	☐	☐
		a. Perf 14	8·00	8·00	☐	☐
S76	31p	bright purple (phosphorised paper)	2·25	2·25	☐	☐
S77	32p	greenish blue (phosphorised paper)	1·75	2·00	☐	☐
S78	34p	deep bluish grey (phosphorised paper)	1·75	1·75	☐	☐
S79	37p	rosine (phosphorised paper)	2·00	2·25	☐	☐
S80	39p	bright mauve (phosphorised paper)	2·00	2·25	☐	☐
		a. Perf 14	7·00	7·00	☐	☐

Nos. S55, S61, S63, S68 and S71 were only issued in stamp booklets.

Presentation Pack (P.O. Pack No. 27) (contains 2½p (S14), 3p (S15), 5p (S20), 7½p (S25)) **3·50** ☐

Presentation Pack (P.O. Pack No. 62) (contains 3p (S16), 3½p (S17), 5½p (S21), 8p (S26), later with 4½p (S19) added) **2·50** ☐

Presentation Pack (P.O. Pack No. 85) (contains 6½p (S23), 8½p (S27), 10p (S29), 11p (S32)) **2·00** ☐

Presentation Pack (P.O. Pack No. 129b) (contains 7p (S24), 9p (S28), 10½p (S31), 11½p (S36), 12p (S33), 13½p (S34), 14p (S40), 15p (S35), 18p (S44), 22p (S47)) **9·00** ☐

Presentation Pack (P.O. Pack No. 2) (contains 10p (S30), 12½p (S38), 16p (S42), 20½p (S46), 26p (S49), 28p (S50)) **18·00** ☐

Presentation Pack (P.O. Pack No. 6) (contains 10p (S30), 13p (S39), 16p (S42), 17p (S43), 22p (S48), 26p (S49), 28p (S50), 31p (S51)) **17·00** ☐

Presentation Pack (P.O. Pack No. 10) (contains 12p (S52), 13p (S53), 17p (S57), 18p (S59), 22p (S65), 26p (S72), 28p (S74), 31p (S76)) **20·00** ☐

For combined packs containing values from all three Regions see under Northern Ireland.

1993 (7 Dec.)–**98** (a) Printed in lithography by Questa. Perf 15 × 14 (with one elliptical hole on each vertical side)

S81	S **4**	19p bistre (1 centre band)	80	70	☐	☐
S82		19p bistre (1 side band)	3·00	3·25	☐	☐
S83		20p bright green (1 centre band)	1·50	1·50	☐	☐
S84		25p red (2 bands)	1·10	1·00	☐	☐
S85		26p red-brown (2 bands)	1·75	2·00	☐	☐
S86		30p deep olive-grey (2 bands)	1·25	1·25	☐	☐
S87		37p bright mauve (2 bands)	2·75	3·00	☐	☐
S88		41p grey-brown (2 bands)	1·75	2·00	☐	☐
S89		63p light emerald (2 bands)	4·00	4·25	☐	☐

(b) Printed in photogravure by Walsall (20p, 26p (No. S91a), 63p), Harrison or Walsall (26p (No. S91), 37p).

Perf 14 (No. S90a) or 15 × 14 (others) (both with one elliptical hole on each vertical side)

S90	S **4**	20p bright green (1 centre band)	1·00	90	☐	☐
S90a		20p bright green (1 side band)	3·50	3·50	☐	☐
S91		26p chestnut (2 bands)	1·20	1·20	☐	☐
		a. Perf 14	3·50	3·50	☐	☐
S92		37p bright mauve (2 bands)	1·50	1·50	☐	☐
S93		63p light emerald (2 bands)	4·00	4·00	☐	☐

Nos. S82, S90a and S91a were only issued in stamp booklets. For combined presentation packs for all three Regions, see under Northern Ireland.

S 5 Scottish Flag   **S** 6 Scottish Lion   **S** 7 Thistle   **S** 8 Tartan

1999 (8 June)–**2002** Printed in photogravure by De La Rue (68p), De La Rue, Questa or Walsall (2nd, 1st) or Walsall (others). One centre phosphor band (2nd) or two phosphor bands (others). Perf 15 × 14 (with one elliptical hole on each vertical side)

S94	S **5**	(2nd) new blue, blue and silver	75	75	☐	☐
S95	S **6**	(1st) greenish yellow, deep rose-red, rose-red and silver	1·00	1·00	☐	☐
S96	S **7**	(E) bright lilac, deep lilac and silver	2·00	2·00	☐	☐

S97	S **8**	64p	greenish yellow, bright magenta, new blue, grey-black and silver	9·00	9·00	☐ ☐
S98		65p	greenish yellow, bright magenta, new blue, grey-black and silver	3·00	3·25	☐ ☐
S99		68p	greenish yellow, bright magenta, new blue, grey-black and silver	3·25	3·25	☐ ☐

Presentation Pack (P.O. Pack No. 45) (contains 2nd, 1st, E, 64p) (Nos. S94/7)) 14·00 ☐

Presentation Pack (P.O. Pack No. 50) (contains 65p) (No. S98)) 11·00 ☐

Presentation Pack (P.O. Pack No. 55) (contains 2nd, 1st, E, 65p) (Nos. S94/6, S98) 15·00 ☐

PHQ Cards (Nos. S94/7) 8·00 14·00 ☐ ☐

Nos. S94, S95 and S96 were initially sold at 19p, 26p and 30p, the latter representing the basic European airmail rate.

For combined presentation packs for all four Regions, see under England.

S 9

2000 (15 Feb.) Type S **4** redrawn with '1st' face value as Type S **9**. Two phosphor bands. Perf 14 (with one elliptical hole on each vertical side)

| S108 | S **9** | (1st) | bright orange-red | 3·00 | 3·25 | ☐ ☐ |

No. S108 was only issued in stamp booklets.

2003 (14 Oct.)–**08**. As Nos. S94/6 and S99 but with white borders. One centre phosphor band (2nd) or two phosphor bands (others). Perf 15 × 14 (with one elliptical hole on each vertical side)

(a) Printed in photogravure by Walsall or De La Rue (42p) or De La Rue (others)

S109	S **5**	(2nd)	new blue, blue and silver	60	60	☐ ☐
S110	S **6**	(1st)	rose-red, greenish yellow, deep rose-red and silver	85	85	☐ ☐
S111	S **7**	(E)	bright lilac, deep lilac and silver	2·50	2·50	☐ ☐
S112		40p	bright lilac, deep lilac and silver	1·75	1·75	☐ ☐
S113		42p	bright lilac, deep lilac and silver	1·75	1·75	☐ ☐
S114		44p	bright lilac, deep lilac and silver	1·50	1·50	☐ ☐
S115		48p	bright lilac, deep lilac and silver	90	90	☐ ☐
S116		50p	bright lilac, deep lilac and silver	80	75	☐ ☐
S116a		56p	bright lilac, deep lilac and silver	1·25	1·25	☐ ☐
S117	S **8**	68p	bright magenta, greenish yellow, new blue, grey-black and silver	2·00	2·00	☐ ☐
S118		72p	bright magenta, greenish yellow, new blue, grey-black and silver	1·75	1·75	☐ ☐
S119		78p	bright magenta, greenish yellow, new blue, grey-black and silver	1·50	1·50	☐ ☐
S120		81p	bright magenta, greenish yellow, new blue, grey-black and silver	1·40	1·30	☐ ☐
S120a		90p	bright magenta, greenish yellow, new blue, grey-black and silver	2·00	2·00	☐ ☐

(b) Printed in lithography by Enschedé

| S131 | S **6** | (1st) | rose-red, greenish yellow, deep rose-red and silver | 7·50 | 7·50 | ☐ ☐ |

Presentation Pack (P.O. Pack No. 64) (Nos. S109/11, S116) 6·00 ☐

PHQ Cards (set of 4) (Nos. S109/11, S116) 2·00 10·00 ☐ ☐

Nos. S109/11 were initially sold at 20p, 28p and 38p, the latter representing the basic European airmail rate.

No. S119 was only issued in £7.66 stamp booklets. Stamps as No. S131 but self-adhesive were issued on 30 November 2007 in sheets of 20 with se-tenant labels. These sheets were printed by Cartor in lithography, and perforated

15 × 14 without the elliptical holes. The labels show either Scottish scenes or personal photographs.

Stamps as Nos. EN18, NI95, S131 and W120 but self-adhesive were issued on 29 September 2008 in sheets of 20 containing five of each design with se-tenant labels.

Opening of New Scottish Parliament Building

2004 (5 Oct.) Sheet 123 × 70 mm. Printed in photogravure by De La Rue. One centre phosphor band (2nd) or two phosphor bands (others). Perf 15 × 14 (with one elliptical hole on each vertical side)

| **MS**S132 | Nos. S109, S110 × 2 and S112 × 2 | 6·00 | 6·00 | ☐ ☐ |
| | First Day Cover | | 8·00 | ☐ |

CELEBRATING SCOTLAND

S 10

Celebrating Scotland

2006 (30 Nov.) Sheet 124 × 71 mm. Printed in photogravure by De La Rue. Two phosphor bands. Perf 15 × 14 (with one elliptical hole on each vertical side) (1st) or 14 × 14 (72p)

MSS133	(1st) As No. S110; (1st) Scottish Flag; 72p St. Andrew; 72p Edinburgh Castle	4·00	4·00	☐ ☐
	First Day Cover		6·50	☐
	Presentation Pack	4·50		☐
	PHQ Cards (set of 5)	2·25	5·50	☐ ☐

50th Anniv of the Country Definitives

2008 (29 Sept.) As Nos. S1, S3 and S5 (definitives of 1958) but inscribed 1st and printed in lithography by De La Rue. Two phosphor bands. Perf 15 × 14½ (with one elliptical hole on each vertical side)

S134	S **1**	(1st)	deep lilac	1·25	1·25	☐ ☐
S135	S **3**	(1st)	green	1·25	1·25	☐ ☐
S136	S **2**	(1st)	deep claret	1·25	1·25	☐ ☐

Nos. S134/6 come from £9.72 stamp booklets.

S 112 50th Birth Anniv of Robert Burns (Scottish poet)

2009 (22 Jan.). Sheet 145×74 mm. Printed in photogravure by Enschedé. One centre band (2nd) or two phosphor bands (others). Perf 14½ (size 34×34 mm) or 15×14 (with one elliptical hole on each vert side) (others).

MSS137 (2nd) No. S109; (1st) 'A Man's a
Man for a' that' and Burns ploughing
(detail) (James Sargent Storer) (34×34
mm); (1st) No. S110; (1st) Portrait of
Burns (Alexander Nasmyth) (34×34

mm); 50p No. S116; 81p No. S120	6·00	6·00	☐ ☐
First Day Cover		6·50	☐
Presentation Pack	7·25		☐
PHQ Cards (set of 3)	1·75	7·00	☐ ☐

The three PHQ cards show the two 34×34 mm Robert Burns stamps and the complete miniature sheet.

4 Wales

W **1**   W **2**   W **3**

1958–67 Wmk 179

W1	W **1**	3d	lilac	15	15	☐ ☐
		p.	One centre phosphorband	20	15	☐ ☐
W2		4d	blue	20	15	☐ ☐
		p.	Two phosphor bands	20	15	☐ ☐
W3	W **2**	6d	purple	35	30	☐ ☐
W4		9d	bronze-green (2 phosphor bands)	40	35	☐ ☐
W5	W **3**	1s 3d	green	40	40	☐ ☐
W6		1s 6d	blue (2 phosphor bands)	40	40	☐ ☐

1967–69 One centre phosphor band (Nos. W7, W9/10) or two phosphor bands (others). No wmk

W7	W **1**	3d	lilac	10	15	☐ ☐
W8		4d	blue	10	15	☐ ☐
W9		4d	sepia	15	15	☐ ☐
W10		4d	vermilion	15	15	☐ ☐
W11		5d	blue	15	15	☐ ☐
W12	W **3**	1s 6d	blue	3·50	3·50	☐ ☐

Presentation Pack (comprises Nos. W4, W6/7, W9/11)	4·00	☐

W **4** With 'p'   W **5** Without 'p'

Decimal Currency

1971–92 Type W 4. No wmk

(a) Printed in photogravure with phosphor bands

W13	2½p	magenta (1 centre band)	20	20	☐ ☐
W14	3p	ultramarine (2 bands)	25	20	☐ ☐
W15	3p	ultramarine (1 centre band)	25	25	☐ ☐
W16	3½p	olive-grey (2 bands)	20	30	☐ ☐
W17	3½p	olive-grey (1 centre band)	20	30	☐ ☐
W18	4½p	grey-blue (2 bands)	30	30	☐ ☐
W19	5p	violet (2 bands)	1·25	1·25	☐ ☐
W20	5½p	violet (2 bands)	25	30	☐ ☐
W21	5½p	violet (1 centre band)	25	30	☐ ☐
W22	6½p	blue (1 centre band)	20	25	☐ ☐
W23	7p	brown (1 centre band)	25	25	☐ ☐
W24	7½p	chestnut (2 bands)	1·75	1·75	☐ ☐
W25	8p	rosine (2 bands)	30	35	☐ ☐
W26	8½p	yellow-green (2 bands)	30	35	☐ ☐
W27	9p	violet (2 bands)	40	40	☐ ☐
W28	10p	orange-brown (2 bands)	40	40	☐ ☐
W29	10p	orange-brown (1 centre band)	40	40	☐ ☐
W30	10½p	blue (2 bands)	45	45	☐ ☐
W31	11p	scarlet (2 bands)	45	45	☐ ☐

(b) Printed in photogravure on phosphorised paper

W32	12p	yellow-green	50	50	☐ ☐
W33	13½p	purple-brown	60	70	☐ ☐
W34	15p	ultramarine	60	70	☐ ☐

(c) Printed in lithography. Perf 14 (11½p, 12½p, 14p (No. W39), 15½p. 16p, 18p (No. W46), 19½p, 20½p, 22p (No. W54), 26p (No. W61), 28p (No. W63)) or 15 × 14 (others)

W35	11½p	drab (1 side band)	90	80	☐ ☐
W36	12p	bright emerald (1 side band)	2·00	2·00	☐ ☐
W37	12½p	light emerald (1 side band)	70	70	☐ ☐
		a. Perf 15 × 14	4·75	4·25	☐ ☐
W38	13p	pale chestnut (1 side band)	60	60	☐ ☐
W39	14p	grey-blue (phosphorised paper)	70	70	☐ ☐
W40	14p	deep blue (1 centre band)	75	75	☐ ☐
W41	15p	bright blue (1 centre band)	80	75	☐ ☐
W42	15½p	pale violet (phosphorised paper)	75	75	☐ ☐
W43	16p	drab (phosphorised paper)	1·75	1·75	☐ ☐
		a. Perf 15 × 14	1·75	1·75	☐ ☐
W44	17p	grey-blue (phosphorised paper)	70	80	☐ ☐
W45	17p	deep blue (1 centre band)	90	80	☐ ☐
W46	18p	deep violet (phosphorised paper)	1·00	95	☐ ☐
W47	18p	olive-grey (phosphorised paper)	95	90	☐ ☐
W48	18p	bright green (1 centre band)	75	75	☐ ☐
		b. Perf 14	7·50	7·50	☐ ☐

W49	18p	bright green (1 side band)	2·00	2·00	☐	☐
W50	19p	bright orange-red (phosphorised paper)	1·00	80	☐	☐
W51	9½p	olive-grey (phosphorised paper)	1·75	2·00	☐	☐
W52	20p	brownish black (phosphorised paper)	90	90	☐	☐
W53	20½p	ultramarine (phosphorised paper)	3·75	3·75	☐	☐
W54	22p	blue (phosphorised paper)	1·10	1·10	☐	☐
W55	22p	yellow-green (phosphorised paper)	95	1·10	☐	☐
W56	22p	bright orange-red (phosphorised paper)	1·00	1·10	☐	☐
W57	23p	bright green (phosphorised paper)	1·00	1·10	☐	☐
W58	24p	Indian red (phosphorised paper)	1·25	1·25	☐	☐
W59	24p	chestnut (phosphorised paper)	75	75	☐	
	b.	Perf 14	7·50	7·50	☐	
W60	24p	chestnut (2 bands)	1·25	1·50	☐	
W61	26p	rosine (phosphorised paper)	1·10	1·10	☐	☐
	a.	Perf 15 × 14	5·75	6·00	☐	☐
W62	26p	drap (phosphorised paper)	1·75	1·75	☐	☐
W63	28p	deep violet-blue (phosphorised paper)	1·50	1·50	☐	☐
	a.	Perf 15 × 14	1·50	1·50	☐	☐
W64	28p	deep bluish grey (phosphorised paper)	1·50	1·50	☐	☐
W65	31p	bright purple (phosphorised paper)	1·75	1·75	☐	☐
W66	32p	greenish blue (phosphorised paper)	1·75	1·75	☐	☐
W67	34p	deep bluish grey (phosphorised paper)	1·75	1·75	☐	☐
W68	37p	rosine (phosphorised paper)	2·25	2·25	☐	☐
W69	39p	bright mauve (phosphorised paper)	2·25	2·25	☐	☐

Nos. W49 and W60 were only issued in stamp booklets. The former exists with the phosphor band at the left or right of the stamp.

Presentation Pack (P.O. Pack No. 28) (contains
2½p (W13), 3p (W14), 5p (W19), 7½p (W24)) **3·50** ☐

Presentation Pack (P.O. Pack No. 63) (contains
3p (W15), 3½p (W16), 5½p (W20), 8p (W25),
later with 4½p (W18) added) **2·50** ☐

Presentation Pack (P.O. Pack No. 86) (contains
6½p (W22), 8½p (W26), 10p (W28),
11p (W31)) **2·00** ☐

Presentation Pack (P.O. Pack No. 129c) (contains
7p (W23), 9p (W27), 10½p (W30), 11½p (W35),
12p (W32), 13½p (W33), 14p (W39), 15p (W34),
18p (W46), 22p (W54)) **9·00** ☐

Presentation Pack (P.O. Pack No. 3) (contains
10p (W29), 12½p (W37), 16p (W43),
20½p (W53), 26p (W61), 28p (W63)) **20·00** ☐

Presentation Pack (P.O. Pack No. 7) (contains
10p (W29), 13p (W38), 16p (W43a),
17p (W44), 22p (W55), 26p (W61), 28p (W63),
31p (W65)) **17·00** ☐

Presentation Pack (P.O. Pack No. 11) (contains 12p
(W36), 13p (W38), 17p (W44), 18p (W47), 22p
(W55), 26p (W61a), 28p (W63a), 31p (W65)) **18·00** ☐

For combined packs containing values from all three Regions see under Northern Ireland.

1993 (7 Dec.)–**96** Printed in lithography by Questa. Perf 15 × 14 (with one elliptical hole on each vertical side)

W70	W **4**	19p bistre (1 centre band)	80	70	☐	☐
W71		19p bistre (1 side band)	3·75	4·00	☐	☐
W72		20p bright green (1 centre band)	1·75	2·00	☐	☐
W73		25p red (2 bands)	1·25	1·00	☐	☐
W74		26p red-brown (2 bands)	2·00	2·25	☐	☐
W75		30p deep olive-grey (2 bands)	1·25	1·25	☐	☐
W76		37p bright mauve (2 bands)	2·75	3·00	☐	☐
W77		41p grey-brown (2 bands)	2·00	2·00	☐	☐
W78		63p light emerald (2 bands)	4·50	4·75	☐	☐

No. W71 was only issued in stamp booklets.

For combined presentation packs for all three Regions see under Northern Ireland.

1997 (1 July)–**98** Printed in photogravure by Walsall (20p, 26p (No. W80a), 63p), Harrison or Walsall (26p (No. W80), 37p) Perf 14 (No. W79a) or 15 × 14 (both with one elliptical hole on each vertical side)

W79	W **5**	20p bright green (1 centre band)	80	80	☐	☐
W79a		20p bright green (1 side band)	3·00	3·00	☐	☐
W80		26p chestnut (2 bands)	1·00	1·00	☐	☐
	a.	Perf 14	3·00	3·00	☐	☐
W81		37p bright mauve (2 bands)	2·75	2·75	☐	☐
W82		63p light emerald (2 bands)	5·00	5·00	☐	☐

Presentation Pack (P.O. Pack No. 39)
(Nos. W79 and W80/2) **17·00** ☐

Nos. W79a and W80a were only issued in stamp booklets.

W **6** Leek   W **7** Welsh Dragon   W **8** Daffodil   W **9** Prince of Wales Feathers

1999 (8 June)–**2002** Printed in photogravure by De La Rue (68p), Walsall or De La Rue (1st), (2nd), (No.W83) or Walsall (others). One phosphor band (2nd) or two phosphor bands (others). Perf 14 (No. W83a) or 15 × 14 (others) (both with one elliptical hole on each vertical side)

W83	W **6**	(2nd) orange-brown, yellow-orange and black (1 centre band)	60	50	☐	☐
W83a		(2nd) orange-brown, yellow-orange and black (1 side band)	4·00	4·00	☐	☐
W84	W **7**	(1st) blue-green, greenish yellow, silver and black	1·00	1·00	☐	☐
W85	W **8**	(E) greenish blue, deep greenish blue and grey-black	1·75	1·75	☐	☐
W86	W **9**	64p violet, gold, silver and black	9·00	9·00	☐	☐
W87		65p violet, gold, silver and black	3·25	3·25	☐	☐

W88	68p violet, gold, silver and black	3·25	3·25	☐	☐	

Presentation Pack (P.O. Pack No. 46)
(contains 2nd, 1st, E, 64p)
(Nos. W83, W84/6) 14·00 ☐

Presentation Pack (P.O. Pack No. 51) (contains
65p) (No. W87)) 12·00 ☐

Presentation Pack (P.O. Pack No. 56) (contains
2nd, 1st, E, 65p) (Nos. W83,
W84/5, W87) 15·00 ☐

PHQ Cards (Nos. W83, W84/6)	8·00	14·00	☐	

Nos. W83, W84 and W85 were initially sold at 19p, 26p and 30p, the latter representing the basic European airmail rate.

No. W83a was only issued in stamp booklets.

For combined presentation packs for all four Regions, see under England.

W 10

2000 (15 Feb.) Type W **4** redrawn with '1af/st' face value as Type W **10**. Two phosphor bands. Perf 14 (with one elliptical hole on each vertical side)

W97 W **10**	(1st) bright orange-red	3·00	2·75	☐	☐

No. W97 was only issued in stamp booklets.

2003 (14 Oct.)–**02**. As Nos. W83, W84/5 and W88, but with white borders. One centre phosphor band (2nd) or two phosphor bands (others). Perf 15 × 14 (with one elliptical hole on each vertical side)

(a) Printed in photogravure by Walsall or De La Rue (42p) or De La Rue (others)

W98 W **6**	(2nd) orange-brown, deep orange-brown and black	80	75	☐	☐
W99 W **7**	(1st) blue-green, greenish yellow, silver and black	80	75	☐	☐
W100 W **8**	(E) greenish blue, deep greenish blue and grey-black	2·50	2·50	☐	☐
W101	40p greenish blue, deep greenish blue and grey-black	1·50	1·50	☐	☐
W102	42p greenish blue, deep greenish blue and grey-black	1·50	1·50	☐	☐
W103	44p greenish blue, deep greenish blue and grey-black	1·50	1·50	☐	☐
W104	48p greenish blue, deep greenish blue and grey-black	90	90	☐	☐
W105	50p greenish blue, deep greenish blue and grey-black	1·00	1·00	☐	☐
W105a	50p greenish blue, deep greenish blue and grey-black	1·25	1·25	☐	☐
W106 W **9**	68p violet, gold, silver and black	2·00	2·00	☐	☐
W107	72p violet, gold, silver and black	2·00	2·00	☐	☐
W108	78p violet, gold, silver				

	and black	1·40	1·30	☐	☐
W109	81p violet, gold, silver and black	1·75	1·75	☐	☐
W109a	81p violet, gold, silver and black	2·00	2·00	☐	☐

(b) Printed in lithography by Enschedé

W120 W **7**	(1st) blue-green, greenish yellow, silver and black	7·50	7·50	☐	

Presentation Pack (P.O. Pack No. 65)
(Nos. W98/100, W105) 7·00 ☐

PHQ Cards (set of 4) (Nos. W98/100, W106)	2·00	6·00	☐	☐

Nos. W98/100 were initially sold at 20p, 28p and 38p, the latter representing the basic European airmail rate.

No. W108 was only issued in £7.66 stamp booklets. Stamps as W120 but self-adhesive were issued on 1 March 2007 in sheets of 20 with *se-tenant* labels. These sheets were printed in lithography and perforated 15 × 14 without the elliptical holes. The labels show either Welsh scenes or personal photographs.

Stamps as Nos. EN18, NI95, S131 and W120 but self-adhesive were issued on 29 September 2008 in sheets of 20 containing five of each design with *se-tenant* labels.

Opening of New Welsh Assembly Building, Cardiff

2006 (1 Mar.) Sheet 123 × 70 mm. Printed in photogravure by De La Rue. One centre phosphor band (2nd) or two phosphor bands (others). Perf 15 × 14 (with one elliptical hole on each vertical side

MSW121 Nos. W98, W99 × 2 and W106 × 2	5·00	5·00	☐	☐
First Day Cover		6·00		☐

50th Anniv of the Country Definitives

2008 (29 Sept.) As Nos. W1, W3 and W5 (definitives of 1958) but inscribed 1st and printed in lithography by De La Rue. Two phosphor bands. Perf 15 × 14½ (with one elliptical hole on each vertical side)

W122 W **1**	(1st) deep lilac	1·25	1·25	☐	☐
W123 W **3**	(1st) green	1·25	1·25	☐	☐
W124 W **2**	(1st) deep claret	1·25	1·25	☐	☐

Nos. W122/4 come from £9.72 stamp booklets.

W 11

2009 (26 FEB.). Sheet 123×70 mm. Printed in lithography by De La Rue. Two phosphor bands. Perf 15×14 (with one elliptical hole on each vertical side (1st) or 14½×14 (81p).

MSW125	(1st) Red dragon; (1st) No. W120; 81p St. David; 81p National Assembly for Wales, Cardiff	5·25	5·25	☐	☐
First Day Cover		7·00		☐
Presentation Pack		6·25		☐
PHQ Cards (set of 5)	2·25	10·00	☐	☐

The five PHQ cards show the four individual stamps and the complete miniature sheet.

ISLE OF MAN

CHANNEL ISLANDS

Regional Issues

| 1 | 2 | 3 |

1958–67 Wmk 179. Perf 15 × 14

1	1	2½d red	50	1·25	☐	☐
2	2	3d lilac	50	20	☐	☐
		p. One centre phosphor band	20	50	☐	☐
3		4d blue	1·50	1·50	☐	☐
		p. Two phosphor bands	20	30	☐	☐

1968–69 One centre phosphor band (Nos. 5/6) or two phosphor bands (others). No wmk

4	2	4d blue	25	30	☐	☐
5		4d sepia	25	30	☐	☐
6		4d vermilion	45	75	☐	☐
7		5d blue	45	75	☐	☐

Decimal Currency

1971 (7 July) One centre phosphor band (2½p) or two phosphor bands (others). No wmk

8	3	2½p magenta	20	15	☐	☐
9		3p ultramarine	20	15	☐	☐
10		5p violet	80	80	☐	☐
11		7½p chestnut	90	90	☐	☐
Presentation Pack			3·25		☐	

For comprehensive listings of the Independent Administration issues of the Isle of Man, see Stanley Gibbons *Collect Channel Islands and Isle of Man Stamps.*

1 General Issue

| C **1** Gathering Vraic | C **2** Islanders gathering Vraic |

Third Anniversary of Liberation

1948 (10 May) Wmk Type 127. Perf 15 × 14

C1	C **1**	1d red	25	30	☐	☐
C2	C **2**	2½d blue	25	30	☐	☐
First Day Cover				35·00		☐

2 Guernsey

(a) War Occupation Issues

Stamps issued under British authority during the German Occupation.

| 1 | 2 | 3 |

1941–44 Rouletted. (a) White paper. No wmk

1d	1	½d green	4·00	2·00	☐	☐
2		1d red	3·25	2·00	☐	☐
3a		2½d blue	10·00	7·00	☐	☐

(b) Bluish French bank-note paper. Wmk loops

4	1	½d green	30·00	22·00	☐	☐
5		1d red	16·00	22·00	☐	☐

(b) Regional Issues

1958–67 Wmk 179. Perf 15 × 14

6	2	2½d red	35	40	☐	☐
7	3	3d lilac	30	30	☐	☐
		p. One centre phosphor band	15	20	☐	☐
8		4d blue	25	30	☐	☐
		p. Two phosphor bands	15	20	☐	☐

1968–69 One centre phosphor band (Nos. 10/11) or two phosphor bands (others). No wmk

9	3	4d blue	10	20	☐	☐
10		4d sepia	10	15	☐	☐
11		4d vermilion	20	25	☐	☐
12		5d blue	20	30	☐	☐

For comprehensive listings of the Independent Postal Administration issues of Guernsey, see Stanley Gibbons *Collect Channel Islands and Isle of Man Stamps.*

3 Jersey

(a) War Occupation Issues

Stamps issued under British authority during the German Occupation.

1

2 Old Jersey Farm   **3** Portelet Bay

4 Corbière Lighthouse   **5** Elizabeth Castle

6 Mont Orgueil Castle   **7** Gathering Vraic (seaweed)

1941–42 White paper. No wmk Perf 11

1	**1**	½d green	8·00	6·00	☐	☐
2		1d red	8·00	5·00	☐	☐

1943 No wmk Perf 13½

3	**2**	½d green	12·00	12·00	☐	☐
4	**3**	1d red	3·00	50	☐	☐
5	**4**	1½d brown	8·00	5·75	☐	☐
6	**5**	2d orange	7·50	2·00	☐	☐
7a	**6**	2½d blue	1·00	1·75	☐	☐
8	**7**	3d violet	3·00	2·75	☐	☐
Set of 6			30·00	21·00	☐	☐

(b) Regional Issues

8   **9**

1958–67 Wmk 179. Perf 15 × 14

9	**8**	2½d red	30	45	☐	☐
10	**9**	3d lilac	30	25	☐	☐
		p. One centre phosphor band	15	15	☐	☐
11		4d blue	25	30	☐	☐
		p. Two phosphor bands	15	25	☐	☐

1968–69 One centre phosphor band (4d values) or two phosphor bands (5d). No wmk

12	**9**	4d sepia	15	25	☐	☐
13		4d vermilion	15	25	☐	☐
14		5d blue	15	50	☐	☐

For comprehensive listings of the Independent Postal Adminstration issues of Jersey, see Stanley Gibbons *Collect Channel Islands and Isle of Man Stamps*.

REGIONAL FIRST DAY COVERS

PRICES for First Day Covers listed below are for stamps, as indicated, used on illustrated envelopes and postmarked with operational cancellations (before 1964) or with special First Day of Issue cancellations (1964 onwards). First Day postmarks of 8 June 1964 and 7 February 1966 were of the machine cancellation 'envelope' type.

£sd Issues
18 Aug. 1958

Guernsey 3d (No. 7)	20·00	☐
Isle of Man 3d (No. 2)	32·00	☐
Jersey 3d (No. 10)	20·00	☐
Northern Ireland 3d (No. NI1)	30·00	☐
Scotland 3d (No. S1)	17·00	☐
Wales 3d (No. W1)	12·00	☐

29 Sept. 1958

Northern Ireland 6d, 1s 3d (Nos. NI3, NI5)	35·00	☐
Scotland 6d, 1s 3d (Nos. S3, S5)	25·00	☐
Wales 6d, 1s 3d (Nos. W3, W5)	25·00	☐

8 June 1964

Guernsey 2½d (No. 6)	30·00	☐
Isle of Man 2½d (No. 1)	45·00	☐
Jersey 2½d (No. 9)	30·00	☐

7 Feb. 1966

Guernsey 4d (No. 8)	8·00	☐
Isle of Man 4d (No. 3)	15·00	☐
Jersey 4d (No. 11)	10·00	☐
Northern Ireland 4d (No. NI2)	7·00	☐
Scotland 4d (No. S2)	7·00	☐
Wales 4d (No. W2)	7·00	☐

1 March 1967

Northern Ireland 9d, 1s 6d (Nos. NI4, NI6)	4·00	☐
Scotland 9d, 1s 6d (Nos. S4, S6)	6·00	☐
Wales 9d, 1s 6d (Nos. W4, W6)	4·00	☐

4 Sept. 1968

Guernsey 4d, 5d (Nos. 10, 12)	3·00	☐
Isle of Man 4d, 5d (Nos. 5, 7)	4·00	☐
Jersey 4d, 5d (Nos. 12, 14)	3·00	☐
Northern Ireland 4d, 5d (Nos. NI8, NI10)	3·00	☐
Scotland 4d, 5d (Nos. S9, S11) .	3·00	☐
Wales 4d, 5d (Nos. W9, W11)	3·00	☐

Decimal Issues

7 July 1971

Isle of Man 2½p, 3p, 5p, 7½p (Nos. 8/11)	3·00	☐
Northern Ireland 2½p, 3p, 5p, 7½p (Nos. NI12/13, NI18, NI23) .	3·50	☐
Scotland 2½p, 3p, 5p, 7½p (Nos. S14/15, S20, S25)	3·00	☐
Wales 2½p, 3p, 5p, 7½p (Nos.W13/14, W19, W24)	3·00	☐

23 Jan. 1974

Northern Ireland 3p, 3½p, 5½p, 8p (Nos. NI14/15, NI19, NI24)	2·40	☐

Scotland 3p, 3½p, 5½p, 8p
(Nos. S16/17, S21, S26) 2·50 ☐
Wales 3p, 3½p, 5½p, 8p
(Nos. W15/16, W20, W25) 2·50 ☐

6 Nov. 1974
Northern Ireland 4½p (No. NI17) 1·50 ☐
Scotland 4½p (No. S19) 1·50 ☐
Wales 4½p (No. W18) 1·50 ☐

14 Jan. 1976
Northern Ireland 6½p, 8½p
(Nos. NI21, NI25) 1·50 ☐
Scotland 6½p, 8½p (Nos. S23, S27) 1·50 ☐
Wales 6½p, 8½p (Nos. W22, W26) 1·50 ☐

20 Oct. 1976
Northern Ireland 10p, 11p
(Nos. NI27, NI30) 1·75 ☐
Scotland 10p, 11p (Nos. S29, S32) 1·50 ☐
Wales 10p, 11p (Nos. W28, W31) 1·50 ☐

18 Jan. 1978
Northern Ireland 7p, 9p, 10½p
(Nos. NI22, NI26, NI29) 1·75 ☐
Scotland 7p, 9p, 10½p
(Nos. S24, S28, S31) 1·75 ☐
Wales 7p, 9p, 10½p
(Nos. W23, W27, W30) 1·75 ☐

23 July 1980
Northern Ireland 12p, 13½p, 15p
(Nos. NI31/3) 3·00 ☐
Scotland 12p, 13½p, 15p (Nos. S33/5) 2·75 ☐
Wales 12p, 13½p, 15p (Nos. W32/4) 3·00 ☐

8 April 1981
Northern Ireland 11½p, 14p, 18p, 22p
(Nos. NI34, NI38, NI45, NI53) 2·50 ☐
Scotland 11½p, 14p, 18p, 22p
(Nos. S36, S40, S44, S47) 2·50 ☐
Wales 11½p, 14p, 18p, 22p
(Nos. W35, W39, W46, W54) 2·50 ☐

24 Feb. 1982
Northern Ireland 12½p, 15½p, 19½p,
26p (Nos. NI36, NI41, NI50, NI60) 4·00 ☐
Scotland 12½p, 15½p, 19½p, 26p
(Nos. S38, S41, S45, S49) 3·50 ☐
Wales 12½p, 15½p, 19½p, 26p
(Nos. W37, W42, W51, W61) 3·50 ☐

27 April 1983
Northern Ireland 16p, 20½p, 28p
(Nos. NI42, NI52, NI62) 4·00 ☐
Scotland 16p, 20½p, 28p
(Nos. S42, S46, S50) 4·00 ☐
Wales 16p, 20½p, 28p
(Nos. W43, W53, W63) 3·50 ☐

23 Oct. 1984
Northern Ireland 13p, 17p, 22p, 31p
(Nos. NI37, NI43, NI54, NI64) 4·75 ☐
Scotland 13p, 17p, 22p, 31p
(Nos. S39, S43, S48, S51) 4·00 ☐
Wales 13p, 17p, 22p, 31p
(Nos. W38, W44, W55, W65) 4·25 ☐

7 Jan. 1986
Northern Ireland 12p (No. NI35) 2·00 ☐
Scotland 12p (No. S37) 2·00 ☐

Wales 12p (No. W36) 2·00 ☐

6 Jan. 1987
Northern Ireland 18p (No. NI46) 2·00 ☐
Scotland 18p (No. S59) 1·80 ☐
Wales 18p (No. W47) 2·00 ☐

8 Nov. 1988
Northern Ireland 14p, 19p, 23p,
32p (Nos. NI39, NI49, NI56, NI65) 4·25 ☐
Scotland 14p, 19p, 23p, 32p
(Nos. S54, S62, S67, S77) 4·25 ☐
Wales 14p, 19p, 23p, 32p
(Nos. W40, W50, W57, W66) 4·50 ☐

28 Nov. 1989
Northern Ireland 15p, 20p, 24p, 34p
(Nos. NI40, NI51, NI57, NI66) 5·00 ☐
Scotland 15p, 20p, 24p, 34p
(Nos. S56, S64, S69, S78) 5·00 ☐
Wales 15p, 20p, 24p, 34p
(Nos. W41, W52, W58, W67) 5·00 ☐

4 Dec. 1990
Northern Ireland 17p, 22p, 26p, 37p
(Nos. NI44, NI55, NI61, NI67) 5·00 ☐
Scotland 17p, 22p, 26p, 37p
(Nos. S58, S66, S73, S79) 5·00 ☐
Wales 17p, 22p, 26p, 37p
(Nos.W45, W56, W62, W68) 5·00 ☐

3 Dec. 1991
Northern Ireland 18p, 24p, 28p, 39p
(Nos. NI47, NI58, NI63, NI68) 5·50 ☐
Scotland 18p, 24p, 28p, 39p
(Nos. S60, S70, S75, S80) 5·50 ☐
Wales 18p, 24p, 28p, 39p
(Nos. W48, W59, W64, W69) 5·50 ☐

7 Dec. 1993
Northern Ireland 19p, 25p, 30p, 41p
(Nos. NI69, NI72, NI74, NI76) 6·00 ☐
Scotland 19p, 25p, 30p, 41p
(Nos. S81, S84, S86, S88) 6·00 ☐
Wales 19p, 25p, 30p, 41p
(Nos. W70, W73, W75, W77) 6·00 ☐

23 July 1996
Northern Ireland 20p (1 centre band),
26p, 37p, 63p (Nos. NI71, NI73, NI75,
NI77) 8·75 ☐
Scotland 20p (1 centre band), 26p, 37p,
63p (Nos. S83, S85, S87, S89) 8·75 ☐
Wales 20p, 26p, 37p, 63p (Nos. W72,
W74, W76, W78) 7·00 ☐

1 July 1997
Wales 20p (1 centre band), 26p, 37p,
63p (Nos. W79 and W80/2) 6·00 ☐

8 June 1999
Northern Ireland 38p, 64p
(Nos. NI83, NI86) 4·00 ☐
Scotland 2nd, 1st, E, 64p (Nos S94/7) 6·00 ☐
Wales 2nd, 1st, E, 64p (Nos. W83,
W84/6) 6·00 ☐

25 Apr. 2000
Northern Ireland 1st, 40p, 65p
(Nos. NI84, NI87, NI88b) 7·00 ☐
Scotland 65p (No. S98) 3·00 ☐

Wales 65p (No. W87)	3·00	☐

6 Mar. 2001

Northern Ireland 2nd, 1st, E, 65p		
(Nos. NI89/92)	4·50	☐

23 Apr. 2001

England 2nd, 1st, E, 65p (Nos. EN1/4)	3·25	☐

4 July 2002

England 68p (No. EN5)	3·50	☐
Northern Ireland 68p (No. NI93)	2·50	☐
Scotland 68p (No. S99)	1·75	☐
Wales 68p (No. W88)	1·75	☐

14 Oct. 2003

England 2nd, 1st, E, 68p		
(Nos. EN6/8, EN14)	3·25	☐
Northern Ireland 2nd, 1st, E, 68p		
(Nos. NI94/6, NI100)	3·25	☐
Scotland 2nd, 1st, E, 68p		
(Nos. S109/11, S117)	3·25	☐
Wales 2nd, 1st, E, 68p		
(Nos. W98/100, W106)	3·25	☐

11 May 2004

England 40p (No. EN9)	2·75	☐
Northern Ireland 40p (No. NI97)	2·75	☐
Scotland 40p (No. S112)	2·75	☐
Wales 40p (No. W101)	2·75	☐

5 Apr. 2005

England 42p (No. EN10)	1·40	☐
Northern Ireland 42p (No. NI98)	1·40	☐
Scotland 42p (No. S113)	1·40	☐
Wales 42p (No. W102)	1·40	☐

28 Mar. 2006

England 44p, 72p (Nos. EN11, EN15)	2·75	☐
Northern Ireland 44p, 72p		
(Nos. NI99, NI101)	2·75	☐
Scotland 44p, 72p (Nos. S114, S118)	2·75	☐
Wales 44p, 72p (Nos. W103, W107)	2·75	☐

27 Mar. 2007

England 48p, 78p (Nos. EN12, EN16)	4·00	☐
Northern Ireland 48p, 78p		
(Nos. NI104, NI106)	4·00	☐
Scotland 48p, 78p (Nos. S115, S119)	4·00	☐
Wales 48p, 78p (Nos. W104, W108)	3·50	☐

31 Mar. 2009

England 56p, 90p (Nos. EN13a,		
EN17a)	4·75	☐
Northern Ireland 56p, 90p		
(Nos. NI105a, NI107a)	4·75	☐
Scotland 56p, 90p (Nos. S116a, S120a)	4·75	☐
Wales 56p, 90p (Nos. W105a, W109a)	4·75	☐

1 Apr. 2008

England 50p, 81p		
(Nos. EN13, EN17)	4·00	☐
Northern Ireland 50p, 81p		
(Nos. NI105, NI107)	4·00	☐
Scotland 50p, 81p (Nos. S116, S120)	4·00	☐
Wales 50p, 81p (Nos. W105, W109)	4·00	☐

POSTAGE DUE STAMPS

PERFORATION. All postage due stamps to No. D101 are perf 14 × 15.

D **1**   D **2**

1914–22 Wmk Type 100 (Royal Cypher ('Simple')) sideways

D1	D **1**	½d green	50	25	☐	☐
D2		1d red	50	25	☐	☐
D3		1½d brown	48·00	20·00	☐	☐
D4		2d black	50	25	☐	☐
D5		3d violet	5·00	75	☐	☐
D6wi		4d green	40·00	5·00	☐	☐
D7		5d brown	7·00	3·50	☐	☐
D8		1s blue	40·00	5·00	☐	☐
Set of 8			£120	32·00	☐	☐

1924–31 Wmk Type 111 (Block G v R) sideways

D10	D **1**	½d green	1·25	75	☐	☐
D11		1d red	60	25	☐	☐
D12		1½d brown	47·00	22·00	☐	☐
D13		2d black	1·00	25	☐	☐
D14		3d violet	1·50	25	☐	☐
D15		4d green	15·00	4·25	☐	☐
D16		5d brown	65·00	45·00	☐	☐
D17		1s blue	8·50	50	☐	☐
D18	D **2**	2s 6d purple/yellow	85·00	1·75	☐	☐
Set of 9			£200	60·00	☐	☐

1936–37 Wmk Type 125 (E 8 R) sideways

D19	D **1**	½d green	12·00	10·50	☐	☐
D20		1d red	2·00	1·75	☐	☐
D21		2d black	12·00	12·00	☐	☐
D22		3d violet	2·00	2·00	☐	☐
D23		4d green	50·00	34·00	☐	☐
D24a		5d brown	33·00	28·00	☐	☐
D25		1s blue	16·00	8·50	☐	☐
D26	D **2**	2s 6d purple/yellow	£325	12·00	☐	☐
Set of 8			£450	90·00	☐	☐

1937–38 Wmk Type 127 (G vi R) sideways

D27	D **1**	½d green	13·00	3·75	☐	☐
D28		1d red	3·00	50	☐	☐
D29		2d black	2·75	30	☐	☐
D30		3d violet	10·50	30	☐	☐
D31		4d green	£110	10·00	☐	☐
D32		5d brown	16·50	75	☐	☐
D33		1s blue	78·00	75	☐	☐
D34	D **2**	2s 6d purple/yellow	85·00	1·25	☐	☐
Set of 8			£260	18·00	☐	☐

1951–52 Colours changed and new value (1½d) Wmk Type 127 (G vi R) sideways

D35	D **1**	½d orange	3·50	3·50	☐	☐
D36		1d blue	1·50	75	☐	☐
D37		1½d green	2·00	2·00	☐	☐
D38		4d blue	50·00	22·00	☐	☐
D39		1s brown	28·00	5·25	☐	☐
Set of 5			75·00	28·00	☐	☐

1954–55 Wmk Type 153 (Mult Tudor Crown and E 2 R) sideways

D40	D **1**	½d orange	7·00	5·25	☐	☐
D41		2d black	26·00	23·00	☐	☐
D42		3d violet	75·00	60·00	☐	☐
D43		4d blue	26·00	32·00	☐	☐
D44		5d brown	20·00	20·00	☐	☐
D45	D **2**	2s 6d purple/yellow	£150	5·75	☐	☐
Set of 6			£250	£120	☐	☐

1955–57 Wmk Type 165 (Mult St Edward's Crown and E 2 R) sideways

D46	D **1**	½d orange	2·75	3·25	☐	☐
D47		1d blue	5·00	1·50	☐	☐
D48		1½d green	8·50	7·00	☐	☐
D49		2d black	45·00	3·50	☐	☐
D50		3d violet	6·00	1·50	☐	☐
D51		4d blue	25·00	6·00	☐	☐
D52		5d brown	26·00	20·00	☐	☐
D53		1s brown	65·00	2·25	☐	☐
D54	D **2**	2s 6d purple/yellow	£200	8·25	☐	☐
D55		5s red/yellow	£150	32·00	☐	☐
Set of 10			£425	65·00	☐	☐

1959–63 Wmk Type 179 (Mult St Edward's Crown) sideways

D56	D **1**	½d orange	15	1·25	☐	☐
D57		1d blue	15	50	☐	☐
D58		1½d green	2·50	2·50	☐	☐
D59		2d black	1·10	50	☐	☐
D60		3d violet	30	30	☐	☐
D61		4d blue	30	30	☐	☐
D62		5d brown	45	60	☐	☐
D63		6d purple	50	30	☐	☐
D64		1s brown	90	30	☐	☐
D65	D **2**	2s 6d purple/yellow	3·00	50	☐	☐
D66		5s red/yellow	8·25	1·00	☐	☐
D67		10s blue/yellow	11·50	5·75	☐	☐
D68		£1 black/yellow	45·00	8·25	☐	☐
Set of 13			70·00	20·00	☐	☐

1968–69 Design size 22½ × 19 mm. No wmk

D69	D **1**	2d black	75	1·00	☐	☐
D70		3d violet	1·00	1·00	☐	☐
D71		4d blue	1·00	1·00	☐	☐
D72		5d orange-brown	8·00	11·00	☐	☐
D73		6d purple	2·25	1·75	☐	☐
D74		1s brown	4·00	2·50	☐	☐
Set of 6			17·00	20·00	☐	☐

1968–69 Design size 21½ × 17½ mm. No wmk

D75	D **1**	4d blue	7·00	6·75	☐	☐
D76		8d red	50	1·00	☐	☐

D **3**   D **4**

Decimal Currency

1970–77 No wmk

D77	D **3**	½p turquoise-blue	15	2·50	☐	☐
D78		1p reddish purple	15	15	☐	☐
D79		2p myrtle-green	20	15	☐	☐
D80		3p ultramarine	20	15	☐	☐
D81		4p yellow-brown	25	15	☐	☐
D82		5p violet	25	15	☐	☐
D83		7p red-brown	35	1·00	☐	☐

D84	D **4**	10p red	30	30	☐	☐
D85		11p green	50	1·00	☐	☐
D86		20p brown	60	25	☐	☐
D87		50p ultramarine	2·00	1·25	☐	☐
D88		£1 black	4·00	1·00	☐	☐
D89		£5 orange-yellow and black	36·00	1·50	☐	☐
Set of 13			40·00	7·75	☐	☐

Presentation Pack (P.O. Pack No. 36)
(Nos. D77/82, D84, D86/8)   20·00   ☐

Presentation Pack (P.O. Pack No. 93)
(Nos. D77/88)   10·00   ☐

D **5**   D **6**   D **7**

1982 No wmk

D90	D **5**	1p lake	10	30	☐	☐
D91		2p bright blue	30	30	☐	☐
D92		3p deep mauve	15	30	☐	☐
D93		4p deep blue	15	25	☐	☐
D94		5p sepia	20	25	☐	☐
D95	D **6**	10p light brown	30	40	☐	☐
D96		20p olive-green	50	60	☐	☐
D97		25p deep greenish blue	80	90	☐	☐
D98		50p grey-black	1·75	1·75	☐	☐
D99		£1 red	3·25	1·25	☐	☐
D100		£2 turquoise-blue	7·00	4·25	☐	☐
D101		£5 dull orange	14·00	2·25	☐	☐
Set of 12			24·00	10·00	☐	☐
Set of 12 Gutter Pairs			48·00			
Presentation Pack			48·00		☐	

1994 (15 Feb.) Perf 15 × 14 (with one elliptical hole on each vertical side)

D102	D **7**	1p red, yellow and black	10	75	☐	☐
D103		2p magenta, purple and black	10	75	☐	☐
D104		5p yellow, red-brown and black	15	50	☐	☐
D105		10p yellow, emerald and black	30	75	☐	☐
D106		20p blue-green, violet and black	75	1·50	☐	☐
D107		25p cerise, rosine and black	1·50	2·00	☐	☐
D108		£1 violet, magenta and black	7·00	10·00	☐	☐
D109		£1.20 greenish blue, blue-green and black	8·00	12·00	☐	☐
D110		£5 greenish black, blue-green and black	30·00	20·00	☐	☐
Set of 9			45·00	45·00	☐	☐
First Day Cover				22·00		☐
Presentation Pack			60·00		☐	

ROYAL MAIL POSTAGE LABELS

OFFICIAL STAMPS

These imperforate labels were issued as an experiment by the Post Office. Special microprocessor-controlled machines were installed at post offices in Cambridge, London, Shirley (Southampton) and Windsor to provide an after-hours sales service to the public. The machines printed and dispensed the labels according to the coins inserted and the buttons operated by the customer. Values were initially available in ½p steps to 16p and in addition, the labels were sold at philatelic counters in two packs containing either 3 values (3½, 12½, 16p) or 32 values (½p to 16p).

From 28 August 1984 the machines were adjusted to provide values up to 17p. After 31 December 1984 labels including ½p values were withdrawn. The machines were taken out of service on 30 April 1985.

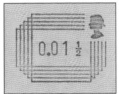

Machine postage-paid impression in red on phosphorised paper with grey-green background design. No watermark. Imperforate.

1984 (1 May–28 Aug.)

Set of 32 (½p to 16p)	15·00	22·00	☐	☐
Set of 3 (3½p, 12½p, 16p)	2·50	3·00	☐	☐
Set of 3 on First Day Cover (1 May)		6·50		☐
Set of 2 (16½p, 17p) (28 August)	4·00	3·00	☐	☐

Various stamps of Queen Victoria and King Edward VII overprinted in Black.

I.R.   **I. R.**   **O.W.**

OFFICIAL   **OFFICIAL**   **OFFICIAL**
(O 1)   (O 2)   (O 3)

ARMY   **ARMY**

                         GOVT
OFFICIAL   **OFFICIAL**   **PARCELS**
(O 4)   (O 5)   (O 7)

BOARD   **R.H.**   ADMIRALTY

OF

EDUCATION   **OFFICIAL**   OFFICIAL
(O 8)   (O 9)   (O 10)

1 Inland Revenue
Overprinted with Types O **1** or **2** (5s, 10s, £1)

1882–1901 Queen Victoria

O 2	**52**	½d green	70·00	28·00	☐	☐
O 5		½d blue	70·00	24·00	☐	☐
O13	**71**	½d vermilion	10·00	4·00	☐	☐
O17		½d green	15·00	10·00	☐	☐
O 3	**57**	1d lilac (Die II)	6·00	4·00	☐	☐
O 6	**64**	2½d lilac	£400	£150	☐	☐
O14	**74**	2½d purple on blue	£120	15·00	☐	☐
O 4	**43**	6d grey (Plate 18)	£450	£110	☐	☐
O18	**79**	6d purple on red	£325	90·00	☐	☐
O 7	**65**	1s green	£5000	£1500	☐	☐
O15	**82**	1s green	£750	£250	☐	☐
O19		1s green and red	£3500	£1250	☐	☐
O 9	**59**	5s red	£5000	£1600	☐	☐
O10	**60**	10s blue	£8500	£2500	☐	☐
O11	**61**	£1 brown			☐	☐
		(Wmk Crowns)	£55000	£22000	☐	☐
O12		£1 brown (Wmk Orbs)	£80000	£30000	☐	☐
O16		£1 green	£9000	£2200	☐	☐

1902–04 King Edward VII

O20	**83**	½d blue-green	24·00	3·25	☐	☐
O21		1d red	17·00	2·25	☐	☐
O22	**86**	2½d blue	£900	£250	☐	☐
O23	**83**	6d purple	£275000	£170000	☐	☐
O24	**93**	1s green and red	£3500	£700	☐	☐
O25	**95**	5s red	£14000	£8000	☐	☐
O26	**96**	10s blue	£90000	£38000	☐	☐
O27	**97**	£1 green	£55000	£22000	☐	☐

2 Office of Works

Overprinted with Type O **3**

1896–1902 Queen Victoria

O31	71	½d vermilion	£250	£110	☐	☐
O32		½d green	£350	£160	☐	☐
O33	57	1d lilac (Die II)	£400	£110	☐	☐
O34	78	5d dull purple and blue	£2800	£1000	☐	☐
O35	81	10d dull purple and red	£4800	£1500	☐	☐

1902–03 King Edward VII

O36	83	½d blue-green	£550	£160	☐	☐
O37		1d red	£550	£160	☐	☐
O38	85	2d green and red	£1600	£400	☐	☐
O39	86	2½d blue	£2800	£600	☐	☐
O40	92	10d purple and red	£30000	£6000	☐	☐

3 Army

Overprinted with Types O **4** (½d, 1d) or O **5** (2½d, 6d)

1896–1901 Queen Victoria

O41	71	½d vermilion	5·00	2·50	☐	☐
O42		½d green	5·00	10·00	☐	☐
O43	57	1d lilac (Die II)	4·00	5·00	☐	☐
O44	74	2½d purple on blue	35·00	25·00	☐	☐
O45	79	6d purple on red	80·00	45·00	☐	☐

Overprinted with Type O **4**

1902 King Edward VII

O48	83	½d blue-green	5·50	2·25	☐	☐
O49		1d red	5·50	2·25	☐	☐
O50		6d purple	£160	75·00	☐	☐

4 Government Parcels

Overprinted with Type O **7**

1883–1900 Queen Victoria

O69	57	1d lilac (Die II)	75·00	18·00	☐	☐
O61	62	1½d lilac	£325	70·00	☐	☐
O65	72	1½d purple and green	£110	15·00	☐	☐
O70	73	2d green and red	£175	30·00	☐	☐
O71	77	4½d green and red	£275	£200	☐	☐
O62	63	6d green	£2500	£1000	☐	☐
O66	79	6d purple on red	£200	50·00	☐	☐
O63	64	9d green	£2000	£800	☐	☐
O67	80	9d purple and blue	£300	75·00	☐	☐
O64	44	1s brown (Plate 13)	£1300	£225	☐	☐
O64c		1s brown (Plate 14)	£2750	£400	☐	☐
O68	82	1s green	£550	£225	☐	☐
O72		1s green and red	£500	£200	☐	☐

1902 King Edward VII

O74	83	1d red	32·00	13·00	☐	☐
O75	85	2d green and red	£150	38·00	☐	☐
O76	83	6d purple	£250	38·00	☐	☐
O77	91	9d purple and blue	£600	£160	☐	☐
O78	93	1s green and red	£1100	£275	☐	☐

5 Board of Education

Overprinted with Type O **8**

1902 Queen Victoria

O81	78	5d dull purple and blue	£3000	£850	☐	☐
O82	82	1s green and red	£7500	£4500	☐	☐

1902–04 King Edward VII

O83	83	½d blue-green	£160	38·00	☐	☐
O84		1d red	£160	38·00	☐	☐
O85	86	2½d blue	£4000	£300	☐	☐
O86	89	5d purple and blue	£22000	£6000	☐	☐
O87	93	1s green and red	£120000		☐	

6 Royal Household

Overprinted with Type O **9**

1902 King Edward VII

O91	83	½d blue-green	£375	£200	☐	☐
O92		1d red	£325	£175	☐	☐

7 Admiralty

Overprinted with Type O **10**

1903 King Edward Vii

O101	83	½d blue-green	27·00	13·00	☐	☐
O102		1d red	16·00	6·50	☐	☐
O103	84	1½d purple and green	£300	£140	☐	☐
O104	85	2d green and red	£325	£150	☐	☐
O105	86	2½d blue	£450	£140	☐	☐
O106	87	3d purple on yellow	£400	£150	☐	☐

PHILATELIC, NUMISMATIC AND PHILATELIC MEDALLIC COVERS

On 2 June 1993 Royal Mail and the Royal Mint prepared a commemorative cover to celebrate the 40th anniversary of the Coronation of Her Majesty The Queen. The cover bore the Royal Mint's Coronation Anniversary Crown and the £10 'Britannia' stamp, issued on 2 March 1993 (No. 1658).

On 1 March 1994 a similar cover was produced for the 25th Anniversary of the Investiture of HRH The Prince of Wales. The cover bore the set of five stamps issued on that date (Nos. 1810/14), showing paintings by Prince Charles, and a commemorative medal struck by the Royal Mint.

So began a series of Philatelic Numismatic Covers (PNC) and Philatelic Medallic Covers (PMC) produced by Royal Mail and the Royal Mint.

This listing comprises only those jointly produced covers sold by the Philatelic Bureau. Privately sponsored covers incorporating coins or medals including those sponsored by the Royal Mint alone, are outside its scope.

No.	Date	Issue	Stamps	Coin/Medal	Price
RMC1	2.6.93	Coronation 40th Anniv	1658	£5 Coin	28·00
RMC2	1.3.94	Prince of Wales Investiture 25th Anniv	1810/14	Medal	22·00
RMC3	27.7.94	Bank of England 300th Anniv	1666×4 +label	£2 Coin	20·00
RMC4	20.5.95	R. J. Mitchell Birth Cent	1666×4+label	Medal	20·00
RMC5	15.8.95	End of Second World War 50th Anniv	1873, 1875	£2 Coin	20·00
RMC6	29.10.95	William Wyon Birth Bicent	Y1707	Medal	20·00
RMC7	21.4.96	Queen's 70th Birthday	1666×4+label	£5 Coin	24·00
RMC8	14.5.96	European Football Championship	1925/9	£2 Coin	20·00
RMC9	1.10./3.11.96	Classic Sports Cars	1945/9	Medal	20·00
RMC10	28.1.97	King Henry VIII 450th Death Anniv	1965/71	£1 Coin	20·00
RMC11	30.6.97	Transfer of Hong Kong to Chinese Rule	1666×4+label	Hong Kong $5 Coin	20·00
RMC12	23.8.97	British Aircraft Designers	1984/8	£2 Coin	20·00
RMC13	20.11.97	Royal Golden Wedding	2011/14	£5 Coin	24·00
RMC14	24.2.98	Order of the Garter 650th Anniv	2026/30	£1 Coin	20·00
RMC15	5.7.98	NHS 50th Anniv	2046/9	50p Coin	20·00
RMC16	25.8.98	Notting Hill Carnival	2055/8	50p Coin	20·00
RMC17	14.11.98	HRH Prince of Wales 50th Birthday	1666×4+label	£5 Coin	24·00
RMC18	12.5.99	Berlin Airlift 50th Anniv	1666×4+label	Medal	20·00
RMC19	1.7.99	New Scottish Parliament Building	S94/7	£1 Coin	20·00
RMC20	1.10.99	Rugby World Cup, Wales	1664a×4+label	£2 Coin	20·00

No.	Date	Issue	Stamps	Coin/Medal	Price
RMC21	31.12.99	Millennium	**MS**2123	£5 Coin	34·00
RMC22	4.4.00	National Botanic Garden of Wales	2124×4+label	£1 Coin	20·00
RMC23	14.8.00	150 Years of Public Libraries	2116, 2121, 2100	50p Coin	20·00
RMC24	4.8.00	Queen Mother's 100th Birthday	**MS**2161	£5 Coin	24·00
RMC25	1.1.01	Archers Radio Programme 50th Anniv	2107/8, 2110	Medal	20·00
RMC26	24.5.01	RN Submarine Service Cent	2202/5	Medal	20·00
RMC27	20.6.01	Queen Victoria Death Cent	2133+label	£5 Coin	24·00
RMC28	2.10.01	Northern Ireland	NI89/92	£1 Coin	20·00
RMC29	6.02	Golden Jubilee	2253/7	£5 Coin	24·00
RMC29a	6.2.02	Golden Jubilee	2258/9	£5 Coin and £5 note	28·00
RMC30	31.5.02	World Cup Football, Japan & Korea	531st from **MS**2292	£1 Coin	20·00
RMC31	16.7.02	17th Commonwealth Games, Manchester	2299/303	43£2 Coins	30·00
RMC32	11.12.02	Queen Mother Commemoration	2280/3	£5 Coin	24·00
RMC33	25.2.03	Discovery of DNA 50th Anniv	2343/7	£2 Coin	21·00
RMC34	2.6.03	Coronation 50th Anniv	2368/77	£5 Coin	24·00
RMC35	27.8.03	Extreme Endeavours	2360/5	£1 Coin	20·00
RMC36	7.10.03	British Museum 250th Anniv	2404/9	Medal	20·00
RMC37	13.1.04	Classic Locomotives	2417/22	£2 Coin	21·00
RMC38	6.4.04	Entente Cordiale Cent	2446/7 + France 50c, 75c	£5 Coin	25·00
RMC39	13.4.04	Ocean Liners	2448/53	Medal	22·00
RMC40	25.5.04	RHS Bicentenary	2456/61	Medal	21·00
RMC41	30.11.04	Scotland Definitive	S109/10, S112/13	£1 Coin	20·00
RMC42	24.2.05	Charlotte Brontë 150th Death Anniv	2518/23	50p Coin	20·00
RMC43	1.3.05	Wales Definitive	W98/9, W101/2	£1 Coin	20·00
RMC44	21.4.05	World Heritage Sites	2532/5+Australia 2×50c. & 2×$1	50p Coin + Australia 50c.	24·00
RMC45	5.7.05	End of the War 60th Anniv	**MS**2547	Medal and £2 Coin	24·00
RMC46	18.10.05	Battle of Trafalgar Bicent	2574/9	23£5 Coins	37·00
RMC47	23.2.06	Brunel Birth Bicent	2607/12	23£2 Coins	24·00
RMC48	17.3.06	Northern Ireland Definitive	NI94/5, NI98, NI100	£1 Coin	20·00
RMC49	21.4.06	Queen's 80th Birthday	2620/7	£5 Coin	27·00
RMC50	6.6.06	World Cup Football	2628/33	Medal	22·00
RMC51	18.7.06	National Portrait Gallery 150th Anniv	2640/9	Medal	22·00
RMC52	21.9.06	Victoria Cross 150th Anniv	2657/62	2350p Coins	23·00
RMC53	16.1.07	Act of Union 300th Anniv	6×1st as 2570 but litho	£2 Coin	23·00
RMC54	13.2.07	'The Sky at Night' 50th Anniv	2709/14	Medal	22·00
RMC55	22.3.07	Abolition of the Slave Trade Bicent	2728/33	£2 Coin	23·00
RMC56	23.4.07	England Definitive	EN6/8, EN12, EN15	£1 Coin	20·00
RMC57	5.6.07	First Machin Stamps 40th Anniv	Type 1984	Medal	22·00
RMC58	3.7.07	British Motor Racing	2744/9	Medal	22·00
RMC59	26.7.07	Scouting centenary	2758/63	50p Coin	23·00
RMC60	20.11.07	Diamond Wedding	2780/6	£5 Coin	35·00
RMC61	1.4.08	Territorial Army Cent	2774/6	Medal	22·00
RMC62	13.5.08	St. Paul's Cathedral 300th Anniv	**MS**2847	Medal	22·00
RMC63	5.6.08	First Machin Coin 40th Anniv	Type 1984	Medal	22·00
RMC64	17.7.08	Farnborough 'A Celebration of Aviation'	2885/60	Medal	22·00
RMC65	24.7.08	1908 Olympic Games, London Cent	4x1st	£2 Coin	25·00
RMC66	29.9.08	Country Definitives 50th Anniv and £1 Coin 25th Anniv	**MS**NI111	£1 Coin	20·00
RMC67	6.11.08	Armistice 90th Anniv	2883/5	Medal	22·00
RMC68	13.1.09	Mini car 50th Anniv	2889×2	Meda	22·00
RMC69	22.1.09	Robert Burns 250th Birth Anniv	**MS**S137	£2 Coin	23·00
RMC70	12.2.09	Charles Darwin Birth Bicent	2898/903	£2 Coin	30·00
RMC71	2.3.09	First Concorde Test Flight 40th Anniv	2891×2	Medal	22·00
RMC72	23.4.09	Accession of Henry VIII 500th Anniv and Accession of Elizabeth I 450th Anniv	2925, 2929 2×£5	Coins	35·00
RMC73	19.5.09	Royal Botanic Gardens, Kew 250th Anniv	**MS**2941	50p Coin	23·00
RMC74	1.9.09	Fire and Rescue Service	2958/63	Medal	22·00
RMC75	18.9.09	Big Ben 150th Anniv	Type **1517**+label	Medal	22·00
RMC76	22.10.09	Countdown to London 2012 Olympic Games	2981/90	£5 Coin	26·00

TRUE STORY OF THE STAMP TRADE'S BIGGEST PROBLEM

The solution wasn't obvious, but with your help (Collectors) – would it work?

Managing Director Andrew McGavin of Universal Philatelic Auctions explains:

Twenty years ago, and I suspect the same is true today, the typical stamp dealer's biggest problem was not what sold, but what would not sell. In those days mail-bid postal auctions would parcel up their unsold lots (unsolds) and sell them on to other auctions which hopefully had different collectors in their database to whom such material would be new.

In this way they would "release" funds in order to be able to purchase new stamp collections. Other auctions not participating in this exercise would spend a significant proportion of their describing time in re-describing "unsolds" in order to re-present them as "new."

The significance of re-cycling/re-presenting material should not be underestimated – too high a proportion of unsold material stymied dealers from purchasing new stock – a problem many collectors may recognize today when re-visiting suppliers who never seem to have something new to offer: ultimately collectors stop going back to dealers who offer only stale stock.

In essence, a dealer selling the best stamps out of any collection he or she has purchased may cover costs, but the profit in any typical collection lies in slower moving stock which is more difficult and takes longer to sell.

Try as they might, there didn't seem to be a satisfactory solution, although today many dealers use eBay to clear unsold stock even at a loss.

Universal Philatelic Auctions (UPA) puzzled long over the problem, seeking to turn a "negative" into a "positive." The breakthrough came when its Director took the view that if it was not selling it must be too expensive. This soon led to the conclusion "why don't we reduce the estimate (and reserve) until sold or given away" – after all – everything must be worth something, and if not it should be given away to make way for new stock ... and so ... ten years ago ...

The Universal Unique Reducing Estimate lot system was born

In 1999 a 6,500-lot UPA auction was created. The director agonized – "would it work?" No dealer or auction, to his knowledge, had ever done this before. Would collectors hold off from bidding and wait until the next auction when the estimate was lower? – or, worse still, the following auction – when the estimate was reduced even lower? Would collectors pass up the first opportunity at new stock and wait – and, if so, for how long?

It was a tense few months, but in the end the director need not have worried. There were 650 different collectors who bid in that first auction, spending £65,000 (US $100,000+). Collectors who saw something they really wanted would bid first time. But, what of the unsold stock – did it sell? Universal had done something never seen in stamps before, or since – it actually told collectors in subsequent auctions how many times a lot had been unsold – so that collectors could work out how much it had been reduced by from the original estimate ...

... and did the unsolds sell? Collectors bid on the unsolds in following auctions – so that sometimes an unsold lot reoffered actually sold for more than available before.

And now, some ten years later, we come to today. UPA runs quarterly auctions with approximately 13,000 lots in each auction and over £400,000 (US $600,000+) of stamps from all over the world offered – including Thematics, British, US, and most countries of the world. Today UPA holds the United Kingdom record for the most stamp collectors bidding in a single auction – 1,275 different collectors – collectors who live in all corners of the world ... and it was honoured by the Gibraltar Philatelic Bureau Ltd's selection of Universal to auction its £517,795 Art and Archives auction in October 2009.

STANLEY GIBBONS
GREAT BRITAIN DEPARTMENT

LOOKING FOR THAT ELUSIVE STAMP?

Send a copy of your wants list or call:
MARK FACEY

020 7557 4424

If you are interested in receiving regular stock updates on Great Britain material, please contact us on the telephone number above or email mfacey@stanleygibbons.co.uk

View our huge range of stock at
www.stanleygibbons.com

Stanley Gibbons Limited, 399 Strand
London WC2R 0LX
Tel: +44 (0)20 7836 8444 Fax: +44 (0)20 7557 4499